Land Use Information

A Critical Survey of U.S. Statistics
Including Possibilities for Greater Uniformity

LAND USE INFORMATION

A Critical Survey of U.S. Statistics Including Possibilities for Greater Uniformity

by **Marion Clawson**
with **Charles L. Stewart**

Text prepared under the direction of a special committee organized by Resources for the Future.

RESOURCES FOR THE FUTURE, INC.

Distributed by THE JOHNS HOPKINS PRESS, Baltimore

Library of Congress Catalogue Card Number 66–14380
Price: $6.00

RESOURCES FOR THE FUTURE, INC.
1755 Massachusetts Avenue, N.W., Washington, D.C. 20036

Resources for the Future is a non-profit corporation for research and education in the development, conservation, and use of natural resources. It was established in 1952 with the co-operation of The Ford Foundation and its activities since then have been financed by grants from that Foundation. Part of the work of Resources for the Future is carried out by its resident staff, part supported by grants to universities and other non-profit organizations. Unless otherwise stated, interpretations and conclusions in RFF publications are those of the authors; this book is the outgrowth of the work of the Committee on Land Use Statistics, the names of whose members are listed on the following page. Writing and revision of the report was the responsibility of Marion Clawson, member of the RFF staff in land use and management, and chairman of the Committee; other members of the Committee should not be held responsible for statements and conclusions in this book, although they contributed actively toward its preparation. RFF takes responsibility for the selection of significant subjects for study, the competence of the researchers, and their freedom of inquiry.

Director of RFF publications, Henry Jarrett; *editor*, Vera W. Dodds; *associate editor*, Nora E. Roots.

Committee on Land Use Statistics

The Committee on Land Use Statistics consisted of the following persons, who served in individual rather than in official capacities (agency names given for identification only):

JAMES R. ANDERSON, University of Florida
PHILIP J. BARBATO, Bureau of Public Roads
NORMAN BECKMAN, Advisory Commission on Intergovernmental Relations
ROBERT H. BEST, Wye College, University of London
LAWRENCE N. BLOOMBERG, Bureau of the Budget
GEORGE F. BURKS, Forest Service, USDA
ROBERT C. COLWELL, Urban Renewal Administration and Federal Housing Administration*
W. C. DUTTON, JR., American Institute of Planners and National Capital Planning Commission†
WILLIAM T. FAY, Bureau of the Census
ROBERT N. GOLD, National Capital Planning Commission
EDWIN D. GOLDFIELD, Bureau of the Census
SHIRLEY V. GRIFFITH, Bureau of the Budget and Geometric Project of the Department of Defense‡
MORRIS E. HANSEN, Bureau of the Census
ROY D. HOCKENSMITH, Soil Conservation Service, USDA
EARL E. HOUSEMAN, Statistical Reporting Service, USDA
RICHARD IVES, Urban Renewal Administration
NORMAN E. LANDGREN, Economic Research Service, USDA
MICHAEL LASH, Bureau of Public Roads
ALLEN MANVEL, Bureau of the Census
GARLAND E. MARPLE, Bureau of Public Roads
RICHARD M. MARSHALL, Soil Conservation Service, USDA
BRUCE D. MCDOWELL, Advisory Commission on Intergovernmental Relations and Metropolitan Washington Council of Governments§
HAROLD A. MERRILL, Urban Renewal Administration

* Mr. Colwell was connected with the Urban Renewal Administration until July, 1963, when he transferred to Federal Housing Administration.

† Mr. Dutton was connected with the American Institute of Planners until September, 1963, when he transferred to the National Capital Planning Commission.

‡ Mr. Griffith was adviser on cartography of the Bureau of the Budget until December, 1964, when he joined the Geometric Project of the Department of Defense.

§ Mr. McDowell was connected with the Advisory Commission on Intergovernmental Relations until September, 1964, when he transferred to the Metropolitan Washington Council of Governments.

William C. Pendleton, University of Pittsburgh
Burk Peterson, American Institute of Planners
Jerome P. Pickard, Urban Land Institute
Albert J. Richter, Advisory Commission on Intergovernmental Relations
Jacob Silver, Bureau of Public Roads
Robert L. Williams, American Institute of Planners
Hugh H. Wooten, Economic Research Service, USDA

Foreword

Many persons and many organizations are interested in land use in the United States today. A growing population, rising real incomes per capita, and other factors have intensified the competition for the fixed area of land which our country contains. Land uses are changing in numerous and often complex ways, and further changes in the future seem certain.

In this dynamic situation, accurate, meaningful, current data on land use are essential. If public agencies and private organizations are to know what is happening, and are to make sound plans for their own future action, then reliable information is critical. But in the United States land use data have evolved gradually, piecemeal, to meet specific limited needs. They have often served those needs well. But no comprehensive system of collection, analysis, and publication of land use data has ever been put into operation. There has not even been full agreement as to land use definitions and concepts. Each specific data source has used definitions most useful for it, or most easily applied; each has tended to lump together highly varied uses which were not of prime interest to it. "One man's miscellaneous was another man's prime concern."

By and large, land use data for the United States are a hodge-podge. It is very difficult to obtain national total acreages for many land uses, on a consistent and meaningful definition. Several useful publications, notably those by the Economic Research Service of the United States Department of Agriculture, have summarized and brought into reasonable comparison such data as do exist. But the authors of these studies are fully aware of the deficiencies of the data they use. Moreover, the situation is much worse if one attempts the same data compilation and summarization on a regional, state, or smaller geographical basis. Errors which average out or are concealed in national totals may become glaring for smaller areas.

We faced this problem when we prepared our book, *Land for the Future.* Our experience there emphasized for us the great need for improved statistics on land use in the United States. Other interested persons, notably Jerome P. Pickard of the Urban Land Institute and Hugh H. Wooten of the Economic Research Service of the U.S. Department of Agriculture, urged some action to try to improve present data. As a result of informal discussions with these men and others, in the summer of 1962 we invited a number of specialists in this field to work together as an informal unofficial committee on land use statistics. That group met at approximately monthly intervals from the summer of 1962 until the winter of 1965. The group was not a constant since some who were active at the beginning gradually relinquished their participation to others from their organization; others were added, as time went on; some came to only a few Committee meetings, while others attended regularly. The Committee membership has been listed previously.

Concurrently with the studies of this Committee, the Urban Renewal Administration and the Bureau of Public Roads jointly carried on a parallel inquiry into land use statistics. The initial work in this effort was a preliminary report prepared by Barton-Aschman Associates under contract with the Urban Renewal Administration. Over fifty individuals and organizations reviewed this preliminary report. The comments and recommendations received were then taken into consideration in developing the standard system for identifying and coding land use activity. The results of the work of the two agencies is presented in the publication entitled, *Standard Land Use Coding Manual.* The men in the two agencies concerned, who were most directly responsible for that report, have also been members of this Committee. Several of the persons who reviewed their draft report have also reviewed a draft of the present report. Finally, we print as Appendix I of this book their report, unabridged. The relationship between the two inquiries is thus very close. The work of the two agencies influenced the content of this book materially, and we believe that the Committee discussions also influenced their report significantly. Nevertheless, the two inquiries are independent. This book is in no sense an official document of the two federal agencies, nor of any other public agencies.

In addition to those who participated in Committee meetings, draft manuscript material was reviewed by and comments were received from the following persons (agency connections are listed for identification only, since persons commented in an individual rather than in an official capacity):

BARTON, GLEN T. Economic Research Service, USDA
BESTOR, GEORGE C. engineer and land surveyor
CHAPIN, STUART F., JR. University of North Carolina
CRANE, DONALD A. University of Pittsburgh
DOVRING, FOLKE University of Illinois
GUTTENBERG, ALFRED Z. University of Illinois

Hand, Irving Planning Commission, Nashville & Davidson Co.
Hearle, Edward F. R. RAND Corporation
Huesmann, Fielding L. Office of Emergency Planning
Johnson, Walter K. Wisconsin Department of Resource Development
Kaufman, Stephen A. Cleveland Regional Planning Commission
Kelso, M. M. University of Arizona
Knott, Lawson B. General Services Administration
Landstrom, Karl S. Office of the Secretary, USDI
McGimsey, George B. Planning Commission, Baltimore
Ottoson, Howard W. University of Nebraska
Pushkarev, Boris Regional Plan Association, New York
Schmid, A. Allan Michigan State University and RFF
Shanklin, John F. Bureau of Outdoor Recreation, USDI
Smith, Edward J. Economic Research Service, USDA
Soltman, Theodore J. Pittsburgh Area Transportation Study
Stoddard, C. H. Bureau of Land Management
Voorhees, Alan M. Alan M. Voorhees and Associates
Yoho, James G. Duke University and RFF
Zivnuska, John A. University of California

This book consists of two main parts: the report of the Committee, and several appendices. The report was drafted initially by Marion Clawson and Charles L. Stewart, and was based largely on discussions in the Committee. Those early drafts were reviewed by the Committee, and some rather major revisions made by the same two drafters. This revised draft was then reviewed by the Committee members and also by the list of persons, previously noted, to whom it was sent for comment. On the basis of a large number of written comments, a subcommittee of the whole Committee offered a plan for revision of the manuscript. This has been followed by Marion Clawson, in preparing the manuscript which now becomes this book. Since this latter has not been reviewed again by the Committee, he alone is responsible for the statements made. In any case, the members of the Committee had participated in an individual capacity, rather than as official representatives of their organizations. Their help in the preparation of this book has been invaluable; probably no one—and certainly not the Committee chairman—could have done it without their help. They generally agree with the results reported in this book, but they have not been asked nor have they had the opportunity to endorse this manuscript specifically and in detail. This book is not an official report of any of the government agencies or private groups represented on the Committee.

The appendices, on the other hand, have been prepared by the agencies whose programs they report, and each is an approved statement of the programs and interests of the agency concerned. These appendices were prepared explicitly for this book, in light of the Committee interests and discussions. But the appendices have been neither reviewed nor approved by the Committee as a whole nor by the chairman; instead, they are in the form prepared by each agency. They are, we believe, highly valuable because of their official origin.

We wish at this time to express our particular appreciation to those reviewers of the draft manuscript who were not members of the Committee. All are busy people, and many had previously taken time to review the Barton-Aschman report to which reference has been made. Their thoughtful and valuable comments could not always be followed, partly because some proposals were contradictory with other proposals, partly because some would have led in directions the Committee preferred not to go. These reviewers should obviously not be held responsible for the content of this book.

The purposes of this book are broadly two-fold: first, to present information and ideas, and to develop a system for handling land use data; and, second, to suggest in a general way that a continuing organization is necessary. We believe that we present a system for handling data about land which is flexible enough to fit all land uses, and to be usable in all areas or parts of the United States. We believe further that this system has a basic core which will permit comparisons of data from one area or one source with another, or from one time period with another. Still further, we believe that this system will permit the maximum use for many purposes of the same basic data. For all these reasons, we think that the system is practical and widely usable. However, we recognize that many detailed, practical, operational problems will arise in its use, and that time will almost surely bring the need for modifications. Because of this, we suggest that a permanent continuing committee or organization is necessary. However, we do not spell out in detail the nature of this organization nor its operations; that, we hope to pursue in ways other than the publication of this book.

To anticipate briefly the conclusions of this study: we do not visualize a single, sharply defined, universally applied system of land use data for the United States. Our society and economy is too multi-centered and reflects too many influences for such rigidity; no level of government nor any organization is in a position to require conformity from all public agencies at all levels of government and from the numerous private groups interested in land use. On the other hand, we hope that the advantages of a larger degree of comparability will persuade many groups to adopt the general outlines of our proposals, or to adapt their present data system more nearly to that presented herein.

Lastly, as chairman of the Committee I wish here to express my very great debt to Charles L. Stewart, emeritus professor of agricultural economics, University of Illinois. For several months in 1962 and 1963, he was a consultant to and in effect a temporary staff member of Resources for the Future, and served as secretary to the Land Use Statistics Committee. It would have been impossible for me to have carried out the duties as committee chairman without his help. He assembled material, worked with committee members, wrote draft manuscript, kept committee records, and helped in numerous other ways. It was a pleasure to have worked with him. The Committee—indeed, the nation—is indebted to him for the work he did.

MARION CLAWSON

Washington, D.C.
July, 1965

Table of Contents

Land Use Information

A Critical Survey of U.S. Statistics
Including Possibilities for Greater Uniformity

CHAPTER I.

Summary and Conclusions

A modern nation requires adequate statistics about itself. These must cover all essential aspects of its economic and social life. They must be adequate in volume, accuracy, and relevance; they must be adequate for decision-making by government and private business. The existence of such statistics is one of the distinguishing characteristics of an economically advanced, as compared with an economically retarded, nation.

These statements are true about land, as about many other aspects of modern life. In the United States, this was recognized long ago for agriculture. Several important data series on land use in agriculture were begun roughly 100 years ago, and have been amplified greatly over the decades. The Census Bureau published a table showing the area of the larger cities in 1890. Some of the major data on forestry as a use of land were begun about forty years ago, although there were some important forerunners. More recently, especially since World War II, land data have assumed major importance in city planning and in highway and transport planning generally. Slum clearance, urban renewal in the older city centers, and suburban expansion around the city peripheries all require data on land. Every comprehensive city plan includes data on present land use and projections about future land use. Trip origin and destination studies, which are basic to all transportation planning, are typically linked to present and projected future land use.

In all of these, and perhaps in other major ways, data about land and its use are important. But land data in the United States have developed piecemeal, in various specialized data series, usually by different agencies, and to meet specific practical needs. Several federal agencies and a great many city and other local agencies have developed their own data about land. There has never been an over-all comprehensive approach to all land, for all uses, using one set of concepts and definitions, in the United States. In the recent studies of land use in the larger cities, each city or metropolitan planning organization has designed its own land data system. As a result, comparability between one area and another, or between one time period and another for the same area, has been severely restricted or impossible. When we consider for a moment how much human understanding arises out of comparisons between areas and time periods, it can be seen that this lack of comparability in data is extremely serious. In a way, it is comparable to the confusion that exists in any country with several gauges or widths of railway track; each may serve locally in adequate fashion, but as a system they are seriously deficient.

Part of the problem for land data has been a confusion of concepts. Ideas of sharply different kinds have often been intermingled in data series. To this has been added differences in definitions within some of the various concepts. A first task of this study was to identify the major ideas or concepts about land. We distinguish the following:

1. Location, or the relation of a specific parcel of land to the poles, the equator, and the major oceans and land masses. This is basic to all other data about land; it is the one unchangeable aspect of a piece of land. If the location of a tract of land, large or small, is properly identified, then data from any source describing that particular tract can be associated with that location. Location can be measured in different ways, some of which are briefly discussed later in the report. Due to the requirements of different public agencies or private organizations, it may be necessary to have several systems of geographic identification. However, these systems should be developed in a manner which will permit conversion of one to the other. One important aspect of location is the relation of one tract or parcel to others of similar or different kinds. Another important aspect of location is political—in which units of government is the tract located?

2. Activity on the land; for what purpose is this piece of land or tract being used? It may be used to plant and harvest crops, manufacture various articles, carry on trade, reside, play, or do any of the myriad of things one does in a complex modern society. Activity is the concept to which we give central attention in this book.

3. Natural qualities of the land, including its surface and subsurface characteristics, and its vegetative cover. There are many different qualities of land that may be described or measured, and many different grades or degrees of each quality. In a given situation, or for a given activity, some qualities or grades are critical, others are merely important, and still others are meaningless or nearly so. One could scarcely hope to measure *all* natural qualities of any piece of land, or even to understand the mass of data that would be piled up, if he somehow did measure all its qualities.

4. Improvements to and on land. Levelling, filling, drainage, and similar changes are in the land itself, and are likely to persist for long periods. Buildings are improvements on the land. There is obviously a close relation between improvements and activity. To reside on a piece of land,

one needs a house or shelter; to manufacture something requires a factory; trade requires a store; and so on. One may even use the kind of building as an aid in describing the activity. For instance, one may say that single family residence is a different activity than multi-family residence; but the obvious measure of the difference in activity is the difference in the structure. Yet there is a logical distinction between activity and improvement.

5. Intensity of land use, or amount of activity per unit of area. Even with a single kind of activity, intensity may vary enormously; single family residences on five acre tracts versus twenty story apartments, wilderness areas versus intensively used city parks, and many other contrasts could be cited. The method of measuring intensity of use must vary with the activity carried out upon the tract. A special problem arises when the intensity of use falls so low as, for all practical purposes, to be zero. It may be impossible to ascertain any activity on the land, or to classify it according to activity, then we refer to the land as idle or vacant. It has been estimated that something like 10 percent of all land in the United States is idle in any meaningful sense. Some idleness is temporary, with the future use fairly clear; an idle dwelling or an idle vacant lot in a completely residential area are examples of fairly clear future use. A certain amount of idle land, like a certain amount of unemployment, is a necessary attribute of a fluid and developing economy and society, and some idle land may have value for future use. But in other instances the idleness is longer and the future use uncertain; the extensive areas of idle land in the suburban periphery of nearly all cities is a good example of this kind of idleness in land.

6. Land tenure. Who owns the land, who uses it, and what is the relationship between them? A great many different forms of land tenure exist in the United States. The form of land tenure often affects the activity on the land, and in turn the activity may affect the kind of tenure which is most appropriate. Some forms of tenure are common in agriculture, others in urban residential areas, still others in urban commercial areas, and so on. In addition to public ownership of much land (about a third of the entire area), the public often affects the use of private land by restrictions (such as zoning) or inducements it applies to a tract.

7. Land prices, land market activity, and credit as applying to land. At what prices does land sell, how often and in what manner is it sold, and how much credit is based upon land? These are obviously important questions to an economist. The kind of activity on the land often generates income for its user and owner, and this in turn leads to values and prices. The expectations about future activities may be equally influential upon land price.

8. Interrelations in use between different tracts of land. No piece of land stands alone; perhaps none ever did, and certainly none does in a complex society and economy such as we have in the United States. The externalities of a piece of land usually affect the activity on it more than do its internalities. We typically live, work, shop, and play on different tracts of land, many of which we share with others, who in turn use still other tracts. The many and complex interrelations between different tracts of land are made possible only by methods of transportation of goods and persons and by methods of exchanging ideas. The access that a piece of land has to other tracts may affect the activity on it, and its value, more than any characteristic of the piece of land itself.

9. Interrelations between activities on the land and other economic and social activities. Since all human activity takes place somewhere, as well as at some time, one might argue that everything is land activity. However, some kinds of data reflect activities which are only loosely tied to particular pieces of land, and as a practical matter it seems better to consider these as related rather than as land activity. Much employment, output, income, investment, and other data fall in this category. It is, however, important to be able to relate such data to other data more explicitly concerned with land and activities directly on it. In order to do this, all data must be identified with specific locations in as great detail and for as small areas as possible.

Activity on Land a Common Ground for Many Interests

The Committee which compiled this report designedly represented many interests in land and its use. During Committee discussions, it became evident that one common ground for many different interests in land is the activity on the land. This concept is also basic to almost all others. For instance, the relevant natural qualities of land depend almost entirely upon the activity to be carried out upon that tract of land; improvement on land likewise depends very largely upon the kind of activity; the measure of intensity depends also upon the activity; and so on. Activity is of interest to agriculturalists, foresters, city planners, transportation specialists, and many others. These and other groups may have different interests in activity, insofar as degree of detail is concerned, especially for activities not central to their interest. Yet a large measure of common interest does exist.

In view of this centrality of activity, we describe and discuss in Chapter VII the system for identifying and coding land use activities which was developed by the Urban Renewal Administration and the Bureau of Public Roads, and which we present as Appendix I. That system uses a numbering or digit system to describe the various land uses; specific uses are mostly identified at the four-digit level of detail. For a major part of the detailed classification, it uses the same names and definitions as are used in the Standard Industrial Classification, although the report points out that the comparisons are not always perfect. That report describes how its system is flexible to meet various needs, and illustrates the application of the system to various specific situations. In Chapter VII, we discuss some of the problems that may be encountered in actual use of the system, especially for rural areas and rural land uses, and also some of the problems that may arise in correlating this system with existing land data systems. The sponsoring agencies of the URA-BPR report anticipate making needed changes following field tests of the *Manual*, but it is the most nearly comprehensive land use data system developed to date, and seems to offer a base from which further improvement will be possible. In Chapter VIII, we point out that detailed classification systems for any of the other concepts discussed in Chapter II could be developed, but that this would involve more detail than the Committee was prepared to undertake or than could readily be presented in this report.

In developing this classification of activities using land, two ideas were basic to the Committee:

1. In field enumeration or other data assembly at the basic stage, activities as observed or reported should be recorded with the maximum detail and with the minimum of preclassification or grouping. The specific crop would be noted, not that the land was in agricultural use; the specific product manufactured, not that the land was in industrial use; the specific kind of retail shop, not that the land was used for trade; the various activities on a piece of publicly owned land under multiple use management; and so on. This leads to more accurate recording of activity, and, more importantly, the data so obtained and coded may be either grouped into broader classes by any one of several grouping arrangements or used in any detail desired. In this sense, the classification system is a flexible one; its basic categories may be re-aggregated any number of times in order to fill local requirements or for special studies.

2. Data from whatever source should be recorded separately for each parcel. In this book, a parcel is defined as the smallest tract of land identifiable on the ground or by enumeration. Ideally, separately owned tracts would be recorded as separate parcels even if the activity were the same on each; tracts with different activity, even if commonly owned, would be separate parcels; and many times tracts with significant differences in natural features, even if commonly owned and used for a single activity, would be recorded as separate tracts. For instance, each residence lot would be listed as a parcel, or each kind of crop within a farm might be shown

as a separate parcel, or level bottom land might be shown separately from steeply sloping hill land though both were in the same crop on the same farm.

Here, as in all studies of land, scale or degree of detail of basic work may necessarily lead to differences in practice. For one scale, the whole of a suburban lot is classified as residential; but on a much finer scale, the vegetable garden might be shown separately. Or a whole industrial complex might be classified one way, while its parking lot would be shown separately on a more detailed scale. If data are recorded on small but positively identified parcels or tracts, they may later be combined into any kind of larger areas desired—city blocks, city census tracts, whole cities, counties, watersheds, states, or any other desired larger grouping. For one purpose, they may be grouped in one way, for other purposes in other ways. In this regard, also, the system we propose is flexible.

The Committee recognizes that these ideal specifications often cannot, or will not, be met in practice. Some modifications may be necessary because of budgetary or other limitations. But we think these suggestions are practical in the long run, in the sense that they would save money and time in the end, and can be made fully operational. We think that frequently data on land use for analytical and planning purposes can flow out of normal governmental administrative or operating functions, often with no added cost, and thus be highly practical in this sense also.

The Committee also feels that "pure line" data series are highly desirable; that is, two or more of the previously discussed concepts should not be intermingled in a single data series. One data series should deal with activities, such as housing; another, with land tenure, such as public or private ownership; still another with type of improvements, such as single family versus multiple family dwelling units; and so on—these are pure line data series, since each embodies different categories in a single dimension. A mixed classification, in contrast, would involve several concepts in a single class—for example, ownership, density, and activity are all intermingled in a single category if that category is defined as "public housing, 10–25 units." Interrelationships of different kinds of data, for the same area, are often highly important. One may wish to know agricultural activity by physical land type, or residential activity in relation to kind of housing, for instance. If each type of data is separately identified and geographically located, then it may be interrelated in the analysis stage for any desired geographical area or purpose. This does not mean, of course, that a variety of information cannot be collected in the same survey. Economy of operation is possible and desirable even if a variety of different characteristics of land are to be identified and recorded. However, the essential point is that each data series should be recorded separately in order that it include but a single concept.

In the report which follows, we have treated the other concepts about land—those in addition to activity—very briefly. It would be possible to develop a detailed classification for each of them. However, it would almost be necessary to develop a different classification of each of the other concepts for each major activity—which would lead to a great deal of detail, indeed. Later studies might appropriately develop such additional classifications.

A Practical Program for Improvement in Land Data

In what ways, and how far, might the results of this study improve land data for the United States? This is the subject of Chapter IX, but may be summarized here more briefly.

First of all, we recognize that the United States is a multi-structured society; there is no single power center, economic or political. No issue can be decided finally at one decision-making point, and everyone else commanded to accept this decision. But it is possible to lead and persuade. Standardization has taken place in a number of aspects of American life, with actual enrichment to everyone. The Standard Industrial Classification is one means of grouping or analyzing many kinds of economic data; although obligatory in many federal data activities, it is also voluntarily used by many private organizations. Standard Metropolitan Statistical Areas have been established and much data assembled for them. In the industrial field, nuts, bolts, and screws have been standardized in large measure; so have containers in many fields, including containers for agricultural commodities. It would be possible to compile a fairly long list of national standardization programs which have wide popular acceptance because they make so much data available on a comparable and useful basis. The same thing could be done for data about land. We believe that the suggestions made in this report can form the basis for a practical, largely voluntary, program of land data standardization.

A second major factor to consider in this connection is the enormous potentiality of modern data processing techniques and machinery. Detailed data on activity and for the smallest recognizable parcels can be recorded in the field or from aerial photographs. They can then be summarized in any desired way later in the office, quickly and with only moderate cost. When data were compiled "by hand," relatively gross classifications in the field and data for larger areas were necessary, otherwise the clerical work would have been prohibitive. But that day is gone. Data put on cards, tapes, or discs can be summarized into any grouping, if man will but instruct the machine as to what he wants. Moreover, data from two or more different sources, as long as parcel location is adequate, can be brought together. Data from assessors, building permits, building inspectors, appraisers, and others could all be brought into useful comparison by these methods. Data on crop use could be related to data on physical characteristics of land, or detailed forest inventories for some parcels could be related to more generalized inventories for larger areas.

Summaries of the available data can be prepared for publication, and will suffice for many users; but answers to specific questions, for specific areas, can also be obtained if the basic data have an adequate level of detail and are properly identified as to location. Historical and geographic comparisons can be made, if the basic data permit. Data about one piece of land or area can be related to adjoining or other pieces or areas. Since all of this requires relatively expensive electronic data processing equipment and well-trained operators and programmers, it is economically feasible only when the volume of data to be stored and processed is large enough. If detailed analysis of land data is necessary, electronic equipment is not only cheaper than older methods, it may be literally indispensable, since no amount of effort could yield certain analyses by the older, simpler processes. Many large cities and metropolitan areas are able to afford modern data processing equipment and manpower, especially if the same machines and workers are used for kinds of data other than those relating to land. Small cities, towns, and rural counties often cannot finance or do not have the day-to-day need for comparable equipment or personnel; in these cases, perhaps this function could be taken over by some state or regional agency or by some commercial firm on contract.

Significant progress toward a greatly improved system of data describing a piece of land will require some form of a permanent, continuing organization to work on the problem. The present Committee has been informal and unofficial, with no special budget as such and with only very modest manpower; we think its work has been productive, and that this report is evidence of that productivity. But a continuing organization, modestly formalized and with at least a little staff, is essential. Such an organization could serve at least three functions:

1. It could refine and make fully operational the ideas set forth in a general way in this report. The coding system and procedures described in the URA-BPR report need field and office testing, especially as they apply to rural land uses. The problems of reconciling this data system with others, such as the census data for farms, must be solved. Further subdivi-

sion of some categories may be desirable, and additional auxiliary codes may be necessary. Minimum standards for field survey forms, office tabulation forms, methods of parcel identification, and other practical operating problems also must be given serious consideration.

2. The classification systems and procedures for data collection would have to be updated from time to time. While there is much merit in maintaining data series in constant form, in order to make historical comparisons more accurate, yet changing times often require the changing of data series or the addition of new ones. Even if a perfect system could be devised—a remote possibility!—it would get out of date in time.

3. Advice and consultation should be available to federal agencies, to cities, to private organizations, and to any others who wish either to collect original data about land or to analyze data already collected. We have made much of the flexibility of the system we propose; but flexibility could break down into chaos, unless there were some unifying element or standardizing mechanism. One city may wish to develop one part of the activity classification in more detail, while perhaps reducing the detail in other parts. This could be done, at least to a degree, and yet have the results comparable with those of other cities also using the same basic system; but it would require careful formulation of a program. A little such advice is now available from some federal agencies; much more might be provided, preferably from a central point which would keep the comprehensiveness of the system fully in mind.

In Chapter IX, we suggest some alternatives for how such an organization might be created and operated. The chiefly interested federal agencies—those whose personnel participated in this study—would be basic; approval of the Bureau of the Budget would be essential; some means would have to be found for drawing in other levels of government and private organizations, either on the continuing organization itself, or in an advisory capacity. A federal inter-agency committee, perhaps with a larger advisory committee, might be the best answer.

If such a permanent committee or other organization were established, and if it adopted and refined the ideas of this report, in time the country would gradually build much more uniformity into its basic land data. The process would be evolutionary, and perhaps never complete; improvement is readily possible, even if perfection is unattainable. The major advantage of our proposals is the greatly improved data that will be made available for research, for planning, and for administrative decisions. As in any good business enterprise, a detailed knowledge of the business makes for sounder decisions or conclusions. The results could mean significant savings, not only to the nation but to the local community, in time, effort, and money.

Appendices Describing Agency Land Data Activities

More than half of this book is taken up with a series of appendices prepared by the federal agencies represented on the Committee on Land Use Statistics. These are authoritative statements of the activities and interests of the various agencies, prepared especially for this book. While necessarily somewhat brief, they do give a much better picture of federal land use data than is available in any other single publication. It is impossible here to summarize briefly these several appendices in any meaningful fashion; we call them to the attention of the reader.

CHAPTER II.

Some Concepts about Land and Related Matters[1]

In recent years, there has been a great upsurge of interest in land use in the United States. The obvious encroachment of suburban development upon previously rural areas, the need for slum clearance and urban redevelopment in the hearts of older cities, the steeply rising demands for outdoor recreation, the insistent farm surplus problem, and other economic and social changes of the postwar period in each case have involved land to some degree. As a result, many professional as well as non-professional groups have become increasingly interested in land use problems.

As is so often the case when a general field of subject matter becomes of great popular interest, a wide variety of ideas hovers under a common general term, such as "land use." "Conservation" and "leisure" are other broad concepts which in recent years have come into wide popular usage. Different specialists use each term in special meanings of their own, which neither other specialists nor the general public accept. Perhaps a certain degree of imprecision in terms that come to have popular acceptance must be accepted as one cost of wider public interest. But confusion and sometimes fruitless controversy arise out of loose or indiscriminate use of one term for several distinctly different ideas.

A matter of great importance to the central theme of this book, therefore, is the definition and description, as far as possible, of the major concepts or ideas that loosely lie under the broad blanket of "land use." The difficulty is not merely, or not primarily, a lack of sharp definition of the

[1] The authors acknowledge indebtedness to numerous authors, and on some recent aspects of the problem discussed, the reader may find especially helpful material in reference lists such as the following:

United States Department of Agriculture, *Urbanization and Changing Land Use: A Bibliography of Selected References, 1950–58* (Washington, 1960).

Journal of the American Institute of Planners, XXIV, 2 (1958): *Index* to authors and subjects, *City Planning*, 1925–1934; *Planners' Journal*, 1935–1943; *Journal of the American Institute of Planners*, 1944–1958.

For other published reference lists, periodical articles, monographs, and other selected materials, see the appended bibliography.

boundaries of one concept where it borders another. A greater difficulty lies in the fact that the different concepts do not employ similar bases of definition or similar ways of grouping the complex facts of life so that one is simply not directly comparable with another. An analogy may be helpful. As one walks along a country road and sees an apple orchard, the individual trees clearly fall in rows at right angles to the road; there may be some interlacing of branches so that in a particular case it is not easy to see where one row ends and another begins. But, as one looks forward or backward, across the orchard at an angle to the road, the same trees seem to fall into quite different rows; or as one walks around the corner in the road and looks at the same orchard from a completely different direction, a wholly new pattern of rows emerges. The basic element (the group of trees) is the same, as are also the separate items (the individual trees), but the arrangement into patterns changes completely, giving an apparently different aspect to the same scene. This homely analogy has its counterpart in the world of ideas, except that the latter are infinitely more complex and variable, and that often it is not merely a matter of looking at the same basic items from differing perspectives, but rather of including some differences in items included within purview also.

In this chapter, we try to distinguish several broad ranges of concepts relating to land, and more or less to define and describe each. Although these concepts seem varied and distinct to us, we grant that someone else might divide the whole field differently, perhaps with equal logic. We point out that there are not sharp clean lines between each, or within each. The world of ideas, like human history, is a seamless web; one can often fruitfully set out a range of ideas or an approach to life, but any such attempt is likely to get fuzzy around the fringes. We think it essential to distinguish between these various ideas, although we grant that for practical purposes one might deliberately set up a definition or an inquiry which runs across several. We shall return to this matter at the end of this chapter. Reference is made again to the several appendices of this book, where the interests and viewpoints of various federal agencies are expressed.

A Few Preliminary Considerations

Before we try to outline the significant concepts relating to land, however, it seems desirable to try to clear up a few definitional matters.

First of all, what do we mean by land? There are situations where it is difficult to determine if a particular area is land or water—swamps, tidal flats, marshes, etc. Frequently there is no clear line, but a gradation between clearly land and clearly water areas, a line which may shift back and forth depending upon precipitation and runoff in a particular season. Moreover, swamps or marshes may be drained or filled, or flat, low-lying areas flooded, thus changing the character of the area. A different kind of problem arises in determining the minimum area that should be recognized separately as a water body. For some purposes, water bodies of less than forty acres and/or less than one-eighth mile wide are considered as land areas.[2] Larger water bodies are then defined as inland waters. However, for many purposes the minimum unit of water that should be recognized may be much smaller than this. There are over 1 million farm ponds in the United States, nearly all constructed within the past thirty years; these are mostly less than ten acres in size. But, under almost any classification or mapping of land use, some bodies of water will be simply too small to be noted—a tiny pond, to be measured in a few square yards or square feet, or a tiny brook that perhaps can be stepped across. In general, it seems desirable to use very inclusive definitions of "land"; if data are available for all areas, some may be excluded as not relevant for a particular purpose. But if a narrow or restrictive definition is used, it will be impossible to obtain data on some areas, except by a new inquiry. The specific definition of land may have to vary somewhat from one part of the United States to another. In any case, "land" includes not only soil but all the other attributes such as climate, topography, and the like.

Secondly, "land," however defined, always has site or locational attributes. This subject is so important that we devote all of Chapter III to it; however, it must be emphasized at this point that all discussion about concepts relating to land in this chapter assume that the location of the land under consideration has been defined adequately for the purpose at hand.

Thirdly, any data relating to land, but especially data on land use, necessarily refer to a defined point in time. The simplest situation is to record present activity or present improvements on land, or whatever other concept is being applied—"present" being defined as the moment the observer is there or that the aerial photograph was taken or that any other observation is made. Sometimes the point of time must relate to some defined recent date, as when an agricultural census ascertains the use of cropland during the growing season just closed. There is great value in historical comparisons of data relating to land, but this can best be accomplished by comparison of observations taken at two defined points in time, each for the same area and each so clearly identified as to location that no confusion will arise. An attempt to record past changes in land use, except by such clear identification of the situation at specified points in time, will almost certainly lead to confusion.

[2] See *Statistical Appendix*, various *Annual Reports* of the Director, Bureau of Land Management, for this and related definitions.

Land Using Activities

The first concept is that of man's activities on, under, or over the land or, inclusively, activities making use of land. Some land is plowed, seeded, cultivated, and harvested to wheat or some other crop; in common parlance, the land is used for agriculture. Certain properties of the land, such as the nutrients in the soil, have entered directly into this productive process. Other land is the site of a shopping center or of an urban home; we say it is used for trade or for residential purposes. A different set of land properties has been brought to bear. In each case, a productive use has been made of the land; in each case, production is not really complete unless or until the goods or services produced are or can be consumed. The classification of man's activities, or land uses in this sense, may be simple, with only a few, broadly defined classes, or it may be highly detailed and specific; there may be broad classes, with subclasses, each of which may be subdivided, and these further subdivided, etc. This is a matter which we shall get into in considerable detail in Chapter VII and in Appendix I, where a proposed classification is set out. There is nothing sacrosanct about any grouping of activities; if the job so requires, the subclasses of one grouping might be recombined into a very different series of classifications. However, there are certain activities that, for one purpose or another, are most often used. Agriculture, residential, recreation, manufacturing, forestry, and retail trade are a few examples of major classifications that are widely accepted and used. Hence, there may be good reason for continuing these major classes in any classification scheme.

This relatively simple-appearing idea of classifying land according to man's activities on it encounters many complications in practice. For one thing, in whatever manner the activities may be grouped or defined, a great deal of land—perhaps the overwhelming part of it—is not used for one activity alone, but for several, usually in different proportions. Shall the classification be based upon the dominant use only, or shall the classification be a complex one that takes into account subsidiary as well as dominant uses? The combinations are many indeed. Moreover, the uses which some observers would classify as secondary may seem dominant to others with different interests.

The problem is further complicated by the three-dimensional character of man's activities, especially in modern times. The most obvious activities are on the surface of the land, yet often subsurface and above-ground activities may be highly important. Mining and extraction of oil and other minerals is a highly important activity in many areas. But many other activities take place below the normal ground surface. Almost all urban buildings have basements or other areas below normal ground surface, sometimes relatively great distances below, and with highly important activities. Some abandoned shaft mines have been converted into repositories for records. Moreover, water, sewer, telephone, electric power, and other lines are typically below ground surface in many cities; these create great values in the land which they serve, and certainly are one form of man's activities that make use of land. At the same time, we increasingly carry on activities in the air above land. Airplane flight is a common activity; air space around airports comes to have great value and activity.

Activities below, on, and above surface cannot be completely independent. They may supplement each other, one giving value to the others; or they may conflict, one interfering with the others. The basement garage may give major value to the office building. Again, the terminal maneuvering of jet and other planes may seriously reduce the attractiveness of the surface use of surrounding land.

Still another type of complication arises, in practice, because activities using land are not all equally apparent. Some are obvious to any observer, but others can often be ascertained only by careful inquiry by someone who knows what to look for. Different observers would probably agree as to the obvious uses—a particular field is growing corn, for instance. But some activities require judgment of the observer, and here there might well be differences of opinion—is a particular piece of forest land also being used for recreational activity?

Perhaps a more basic criticism of classifying land according to its utilization by man's activities is that this classifies the observable results and not the basic causal factors. It might be argued that the classifier is, or should be, more interested in those characteristics of land which lead to specific activities, or which might do so, than in the activities themselves. The latter are certainly influenced if not determined by a host of forces not localized to the land itself, and they change over time. Moreover, there may even be some irrationality in the activities currently under way on a specific piece of land, or at least some lag in adjustment to present conditions. Certainly, the classification of land according to the activities on, under, or over it presents some logical untidiness.

Yet, there is immense interest in data describing man's activities in the use of land. In Chapter VI, where we describe several of the more important data collection and analysis programs relating to land, it will be seen that most of these relate to activities on the land. Every city or metropolitan plan, as far as we know, includes land "uses" or activities as one major element, sometimes as the basic factor. The national agricultural programs have focused upon land "use" or activity. Numerous other examples could be given. Concern over man's activities under, on, or above the land and more or less directly tied to specific pieces of land, is very great indeed.

Data on such activities are numerous and in demand, and are likely to become more so. This Committee considers such data highly important and believes that efforts to improve their usefulness are worthwhile; but even if its consensus were different, we do not see now one could reject or ignore current demands for better data on activities involving land.

Natural Qualities of Land

A different approach is to consider the natural qualities of the land, which to some degree are interrelated with current activities on the land, but to varying degrees may be apparently unrelated. It can be argued that the natural qualities of the land are more permanent and more likely to be pervasive over long periods of time, and thus somehow more basic than data on current land uses. On the other hand, the natural qualities of land are many, indeed almost infinite if one includes variations in magnitudes as well as differences in character. Some of these are more important or even crucial at a given time or in a given situation; others are unimportant or meaningless in that situation or time but may become highly important under other circumstances. One can scarcely describe "all" natural qualities of land; he can neither understand nor measure them, nor grasp their significance. Some selection is necessary, and this is very likely to be conditioned by present or possible future activities on the land. Thus, in practice, data regarding natural qualities of land and data regarding activities on, under, or above the land are not nearly so sharply differentiated as one might at first think would be the case.

The natural qualities of the land can be divided in turn into two broad classes: innate, or largely independent of man; and man-originating or man-influenced. The innate qualities of a land unit are many; some of the most important are its position on the earth's surface—a matter which we consider in some detail in Chapter III—and its geology, topography, soils, climate, and other related information. Each of these broad kinds of information can be divided into numerous subdivisions, and for each of the latter data could be obtained in varying degrees of detail and accuracy. Both "detail" and "accuracy" are always relative. The interrelations among these various kinds of information may be as important as the facts about each separately. For instance, the land classification system of the Soil Conservation Service interrelates slope and soil characteristics, as well as other information. To be usable as a basis for decisions about activities, detailed data on natural qualities of land often must be grouped or otherwise interpreted. This grouping or interpretation of such data greatly increases its value, yet it does represent a modification of this approach in the direction of the activity-oriented approach.

In many circumstances, the vegetative cover of the land is a part of its natural qualities, in spite of its dependence upon man's activities. Most of the eastern half of the United States was originally forested, for example, and there is a strong tendency for forests to become re-established on these lands. At any given time, the present forest, if any, is partly a product of man's past activities, and partly a product of the natural characteristics of the area. The species present, the density of the stand, the vigor of growth, the volume and quality of the standing trees, and many other factors are a result of important natural qualities of a site. They are not fixed, but can be changed, at least within limits. Time is required for change, however, and often, also, particular courses of action by man.

Somewhat similar comments might be made for the extensive grazing lands of the West, which normally produce grasses, shrubs, and other vegetation usable by domestic livestock. The present vegetation is an important natural feature of such land; so is the climax or ultimately attainable vegetative cover. The relation between man's activities and the kind of vegetation is also highly important.

In practice, data about land have often confused activity and vegetative cover. All land covered with trees, or likely to become so, has sometimes been classified as forest; the accuracy of this classification depends on one's definition of forests. But certainly not all such land is used for forestry, in an activity sense of the word, or in the sense of purposeful activity directed toward a desired end. On the other hand, land now devoid of trees may have recently been harvested or burned over, and may become re-established naturally or may be replanted.

All of this is to say that there is often a close relationship between natural qualities of land and the activities making use of the land, but that this relationship is neither fixed nor invariable. This is true even for activities closely oriented to the natural qualities of land, such as forestry, and it is the more so when the chief determinant of activity is site or location and not other natural qualities of the land. A city may spring up at an important seacoast nodal location, in spite of no natural harbor and in spite of poor building sites, simply because there is an important economic function to be performed and no physically better site is conveniently located. Similarly, a local park may be developed on a site that park planners would consider far from ideal, simply because people demand conveniently located recreation areas, and no physically better area is available.

Some natural qualities of land, at least at present and for the foreseeable future, are in part the results of man's past or present activity which are so deeply imbedded in the land as to be virtually indistinguishable from it. For instance, some sites have great historical significance—a great battle, a peace treaty, a birthplace, the seat of government, etc. There may be little about the site today to distinguish it, yet its history makes men willing to consider a particular piece of land as having an innate character which gives it value. Other spots may have great natural beauty, which man seeks to preserve—the Hudson Palisades, Yellowstone National Park, etc.; or man himself may have created beauty which is now an intimate part of the natural landscape—numerous areas in Washington, D.C., would fall into this latter classification. The dividing line between these man-originating natural qualities of land and man-created improvements to land, which we discuss in the next section, is not clear and sharp.

Several sources of information about natural qualities of land exist. Geologic surveys, topographic surveys, soil surveys, land classifications, forest inventories, range management surveys, and numerous other more specialized kinds of inquiries yield information about the natural qualities of land. Although in various parts of this country there are large accumulations of this kind of information, much more is needed. There is or should be a close interrelation between data on natural qualities of the land and data on current activities on the land; and the former should help to guide future activities. At the same time, there is, conceptually at least, a clear distinction between activities and natural qualities which should be maintained.

Improvements to Land

Any consideration of land use rather quickly gets into the matter of improvements to land. Land in a completely "natural" or unimproved state has very limited value to modern man, and, in fact, little if any such land still exists in the United States. Even a trail through an established wilderness area is a form of improvement. Our urban lands have intensive improvements, our rural lands less so, yet each has been materially modified for man's use.

In considering improvements, it is helpful to separate those to the land as such, which tend to become incorporated *in* the land, and those which are *on* the land. In each case, capital, or the accumulated result of past labor, has been invested in the land, although the amount and kind of capital and labor so invested may differ. In each case, the investments, once made, cannot easily be converted into income except by continued use of the land for the purpose for which the improvements were made. However, the length of time for which improvements remain useful differs greatly, from relatively a few years until virtually forever (as measured by human lifetimes).

Many improvements may be made to the land as such. These include levelling or smoothing, which change, more or less permanently, the microrelief of the area; drainage, which to the extent it is successful, changes the whole water regimen on the land; construction of roadbeds and dams, especially when these mean largely permanent re-arrangements of earth materials or of stream movement; and others. Even some kinds of farming practices, such as irrigation, desalinization and liming, may change the basic structure of the soil itself, more or less permanently. Irrigation of a raw desert soil will likely lead to a whole new microbiology within that soil, with a new nitrogen cycle, and many other changes.

In the United States, the mere act of farming itself has produced major improvements in many soils, as well as having "unimproved" or positively damaged others by erosion and other processes. In the major transformations of American agriculture of the past half-century, it is altogether possible that the quality of land, or its "improvement" in any economic sense, has been greatly changed. However, we lack really adequate information on this point.

Other improvements exist on the land. The prime example is structures of all kinds. These may range from the simplest and crudest of sheds to the tallest and most complex of city skyscrapers, with numerous specialized intermediate types. But there are many other kinds of improvements essentially on the land—water and sewer lines, electric power lines, even cadastral survey lines which are reflected in rural fence lines and other structures. Some improvements may be below normal ground surface, as in the case of underground garages or underground storage of natural gas.

Improvements exist in varying degrees of permanence, and it is impossible to draw a sharp line between those *on* the land and those *in* it. A roadway is a permanent feature on or in the land as long as it is maintained; if neglected, time might turn it, at least in part, to another use. Normal maintenance tends to perpetuate many improvements. In the case of buildings, economic obsolescence is more likely to bring them down than is sheer physical decay. Moreover, the fact that both maintenance and replacement tend to occur piecemeal tends to keep a whole area in permanent use and improvement. It is true that urban renewal of recent decades has brought about a wholesale shift in use of certain areas, but more commonly the decisions are made incrementally.

There is, in practice, a rather close connection between activity on land and improvements. If one sets out to make a land use survey in some city, for instance, he is likely to establish as one land use class, "single family dwellings"; but this in turn is dependent upon a particular type of improvement on the land. Or one may delineate commercial areas separately, and these, too, have improvements of identifiable types. If one really measures the activity directly, then one will surely find a degree of improvement which supports it and which is supported in turn by it; often, one notes the kind of improvement and infers that the use accords with it. For many kinds of usage, activity and improvements are directly related in other cases, different activities are possible with similar improvements, or different improvements are made to provide for the same activities.

As a matter of current practice, inventories of activities and of improvements are often intermingled—a single inventory often gets information on both subjects. As inferred above, there is good reason why the two descriptions must be considered very closely together. Yet we also think it essential to keep the two separate, and to recognize that activity and improvements are not invariably and uniquely interrelated—either can change without an equal initial change in the other.

Intensity of Land Use

A consideration of improvements on or to land leads rather directly into the matter of intensity of land use. Land is improved in order to be used more fully, or more intensively; and more intensive use usually requires improvements in order to be effective. However, intensity and improvements are not invariably and directly correlated, and in any event intensity is a degree of use, whereas improvements are a form of investment in land.

Intensity may be measured in many ways, and in fact takes many forms, depending upon the activity or activities on the land. In the case of highly improved urban land, it might be measured by the ratio of total floor area to land surface area, by the ratio of clerical employees per unit of floor area, by the volume of retail sales per unit of floor area, or in other ways. In the case of residential housing, it might be measured by the proportion of the land area covered by buildings or dwelling units per acre, by the number of persons per room, by the square feet of floor space per person. In the case of agriculture, it might be measured by the intensity of the crop rotation (defined in different ways), by the amount of fertilizer or other current input per acre, or in still other ways. For forestry, it might be by the length of the cutting cycle, by the amount of reseeding or replanting, or by the kind and amount of stand improvement. For recreational use of land, the number of visits or visitor days per acre might be the best measure. The measure of intensity must be adapted to the activity, and should be one which is susceptible of ready ascertainment; moreover, it should be adapted to the subsequent use planned for that measure.

In general, intensity of land use can be measured. It consists of either (1) greater annual inputs of labor, capital, other materials, and management per unit of area, or (2) great usage or output of product or services per unit of land surface. These two are rather closely related, and hence measurement of one is to a large extent measurement of the other; but there are differences between them which may be significant in particular instances.

In any event, intensity of land use extends over a wide range for each major activity—a range so wide as to be at times almost a difference in kind as well as degree. Land may be used as the site for housing, ranging all the way from two-acre or larger lots to an intensity of several dozen families per acre, as in the case of very high-rise apartments. Land may be used for recreation in ways that involve less than one visitor day per 1,000 acres annually (as in the case of wilderness areas) to ways which involve several thousand visitor days per acre annually (as in the case of urban playgrounds and heavily used local parks). Similar examples could be given for each major activity on land. In each of these there is a continuum of intensity of use, from the most extensive to the most intensive. For convenience of economic analysis or for other reasons, one may wish to establish grades or groupings of intensity, such as "light," "moderate," and "very heavy," or others; but such terms are meaningful only if defined in quantitative and objective terms.

Vacancy and Idleness as Land Use Concepts

Conceptually, activity involving land or land use is distinct from the intensity with which the land is used. In fact, however, some land is used at such a low degree of intensity that one cannot say with any assurance that it is used at all, or cannot know for what purpose it is used. We might, in fact, say that its use was "none." A field on a farm may be left out of crop for a year, growing up to weeds; a building may stand idle, its future use uncertain. Some land, such as some western deserts and high mountain areas, may never have had any obvious use in the past. Large areas around most cities have ceased to be used for agriculture, hopefully to be used for industry, trade, or residential uses at some future date. What is the present use of these lands? One may say, all are "used" for watersheds, since some precipitation falls on them and some runoff occurs, but this certainly strains the meaning of "use." Or one can say that each has scenic value, since some people cannot avoid seeing each; but this, too, seems strained. Or one can resort to the ancient chestnut: are they there to hold the rest of the world together, or to hold it apart?

Although idleness or vacancy is not a "use" in the same sense as agriculture, residence, trade, or industry, yet any practical attempt to measure activity on land or land use which seeks to account for all land area must take account of idle or unused land. There is no problem in land use data which is more difficult or slippery (nor—it may be added—upon which the Committee spent more time in discussion and on which reviewers of the draft of this book expressed more widely divergent views).

J. R. Anderson, a member of the Committee, has pointed significantly to problems identifying and classifying *idle, other,* or *miscellaneous* land.[3] Using 1960 data he estimated that over 10 percent of the land area of conterminous United States, or 280 million acres, was "idle." This acreage he distributed, in millions of acres, as follows: cropland, 20; pastureland, 50; unreserved non-commercial forestland, 138; non-stocked commercial forestland, 42; unused land in farms, not classified as cropland, pastureland or forestland, 20; unused land in urban-fringe areas, 10.

Anderson points out that "frequently this idle or other territory is the very type about which the student of land utilization would like to have more detailed information and which needs the most attention focused upon it in the study of land-use problems and in the formulation of policies relating to the development of resources." He explains that "the condition of idleness can best be stated in terms of an area's last, or most obvious, productive use. A subsequent return to economic productivity may be within the present category of use, although frequently a state of idleness may merely represent a transition period during which a change from one major use to another is occurring." He notes the need for objectivity in identifying land uses, pointing out that otherwise the separation of idle land from other types will not serve a useful purpose. A major conclusion of this point of view is that there should be a designation of idle cropland, idle pastureland, idle forestland, and idle urbanland, where the future use of the land seems fairly clear. Idle bodies of water also exist. In addition, the probable future use of some idle land is so unclear that a general or miscellaneous idle category may be necessary.

Idleness of land arises from many causes, and the length of the idle period is highly variable. Some temporarily idle land areas or facilities provide for new or peak period demands; hotel rooms, office space, vacant lots in suburban residential areas, unused capacity in parks, and other idle areas fall into this category. Some amount of seasonally idle area or facilities for these reasons may be highly productive, in the sense that it facilitates accommodation to peak demands or to new uses. But other land is held out of use primarily for speculative reasons; much suburban idle land is held in the hopes that some day it will come into active demand and that its

[3] James R. Anderson, "The Dilemma of Idle Land in Mapping Land Use," *The Professional Geographer*, XIV, 3 (May, 1962). See also his article in the same journal, XIII, 6 (November, 1961), entitled "Toward More Effective Methods of Obtaining Land Use Data in Geographic Research."

very idleness or ready availability will be an asset. Some land is idle because of reduced economic demand for its products; this largely accounts for much of the idle agricultural land. In these latter cases, it is hard to argue that land idleness is productive; the reasons for its idleness and its extent each suggest that idleness here rises largely from lack of opportunity for productive use. Idleness at any given time may be part of a longer cycle of activity, as when recently harvested forest land is not yet back into production, or when grazing land is recuperating from previous over-use, etc. Because of these various reasons for idleness, it is usually not sufficient merely to classify land as idle. Additional information about it is necessary.

The extent of idle land in a country is partly a function of the total demand for land for all purposes, partly a function of the economic and social organization of a nation which either facilitates or retards transfers of land from one use to another, and partly the function of other factors. In the United States, although demands for the products have increased, developing technology has often permitted these demands to be met from a smaller area of land than in the past; this has been the case in agriculture, for example. In other cases, social and economic organizational characteristics have made it possible for land to lie idle for many years, while shifting from an earlier to an ultimate use. This seems to be the case in many suburban areas. Were the requirements for land, in relation to the available area, much more stringent the nation undoubtedly could find ways of greatly reducing the area of idle land. Pressures of demand for land have not forced us to do so yet.

Land Tenure

Another concept relating to land is that of tenure, or the ownership and control of land. Many studies have been concerned with land ownership, for several reasons. The landowner always exercises some control over the activities, the improvements, and the intensity of land use; he has or retains some of the decision-making or entrepreneurial functions about land. Moreover, from a welfare point of view, society may wish to know who owns land, who controls its activities, and who enjoys the fruits of its use. However, tenure is much broader than ownership, for it includes all forms of tenancy and leasing, and in some instances may include the relationship of the labor force to land. In the case of a tenant, the bundle of rights to land is split between the owner and the tenant; the latter, within limits set by his lease, takes over some of the decision-making role, as to activity, improvements, and intensity, and he obtains some of the fruits of the land use. Subleasing sometimes puts a "sandwich" lease between the subleasehold and the leased fee, but this is less a rural than an urban feature. Very long-term leases are often suited to subleasing.

An activity using land may depend in part upon the personal characteristics of the owner, and to a lesser extent of the tenant, as well as upon the characteristics of the land itself and of the larger economy in which the land is used. For instance, the income position of the landowner, and consequently his tax position, will greatly influence if not determine the rate of interest which is relevant to his economic decisions. Thus, a man in a high income bracket, eager for capital gains rather than current income, may rationally hold idle suburban land speculatively on the basis of an anticipated ultimate sale price that would yield a 2 percent annual interest rate; whereas a young farmer, seriously short of capital, might with equal rationality plan his farming activities on the same land on the basis of an annual interest return of 10 percent. Obviously, the balance between current and future income would be drastically different in these two cases. Rational choices in use of land and its improvements in other cases will depend upon the personal characteristics of the land occupier. A middle to high income family owning its own home, with reasonable security of continued occupancy, may make one set of decisions about improvements, maintenance, and the like; a low income family, renting in a slum area, paying an excessive rent for the quarters obtained, with little security of future occupancy, may with equal rationality make very different decisions on the same issues.

Tenure data may apply to the surface or to the subsurface of the land. In the United States, in most but not all cases, the owner of the land surface also owns the subsurface mineral rights. However, the federal government and some large private owners possess subsurface rights to minerals on millions of acres of land, the surface of which is owned by others. However, even when ownership is in the same hands, title is often separated by leasing oil or other mineral development rights to specialists who neither want nor require full title in order to exploit the land for the product in which they are interested.

Thus far, Americans outside of cities have not established many instances of separate title to land surface and air space above it. The long-standing doctrine of fee simple ownership gave the surface owner title from the center of the earth to the top of the sky, but this was before the day of airplanes, rockets, and air pollution. While not often formally separating title to air space from land surface, there are many instances in which somewhat the same result has been achieved by setting limits to building heights, by requiring building setbacks, or by limiting activities near airports. Again, by the use of pylons, huge buildings have been built above railroad yards in air spaces to which rights have been acquired on long-term leases.

Land tenure is certainly different from activities on land, from improvements to land, or from intensity of land use; yet there is often a close interrelation between these concepts and that of land tenure. Agencies conducting economic or other studies may wish to obtain information on land tenure at the same time that they obtain information on land activity. The Census of Agriculture, for instance, has obtained information on farm size, acreage in various crops, and other land items, while at the same time getting considerable information on land ownership and farm tenure. Many surveys of housing have obtained some information on land and improvement ownership, as well as upon activity on the land. For instance, one class of land "use" is sometimes "owner-occupied single family house"; this single class includes an activity, a kind of improvement, and a type of tenure, all in one.

A special part of the tenure field relates to the public limitations on activities on land. This includes zoning, subdivision, setback, pollution control, or any other regulation which in any way limits the activities that the landowner or occupier may carry on. In some cases, these may be so few or so general as to make little or no difference. By far the greater part of the total land area of the United States has no such limitations, or they are in such general terms (such as general prohibitions in law against damaging one's neighbor), as effectively not to make any real difference in activity on land. In many urban situations, on the other hand, such limitations are both numerous and significant in their effect. One kind of land information is the mapping or otherwise describing of such enforceable public or private limitations on private land use. There are also at times private contractual limitations on land use, such as covenants running with the land.

Land Prices, Land Market Activity, and Credit

Any economic analysis or inquiry concerning land, that uses data about activities on the land, its improvements, its intensity of use, and its tenure, will almost certainly be concerned also with the selling price of land, the nature of the market for land, and credit based on land or its improvements. Such matters are not "land use" except in a very broad and loose use of this term, yet they are closely related to the concepts we have previously discussed.

To the economist, price of any resource measures the result of a number of complex and interacting forces. On the one hand, there are the various demand factors; on the other, the supply prospects. Like any capital good, land takes its value largely from the anticipated stream of income, discounted back to a present worth. Unlike many other capital items, land cannot be reproduced, hence, reproduction cost does not set a ceiling to land price. Many units of land can be improved and the possibility of improving other land may tend to set a ceiling price for a particular tract. In the discounting-to-present-value process, the current income from land is only part of the story; expectations as to future annual income may be equally important, or more so. In addition to the estimates of the future income receipts, before and after taxes, the interest rate used for discounting is critical. As we have noted earlier, this rate may rationally vary greatly, depending upon the personal income and tax situation of the persons bidding for the land.

The use potential of the land, and/or its improvements, and other factors may strongly influence its present price; but the improvements in turn may influence the uses that are made of the land. If land prices are bid up on the assumption (rightly or wrongly) of a "higher and better" use of a different kind, this can exclude the possibility of the land being used for an activity which at best can produce only a low income. In cases such as this, it is not merely the higher price, but also the uncertainty of continued use, which tends to restrict the present use of the land. Suburban land, speculatively held, is typically no longer farmed nor operated for forestry; it could be argued that these operations would return some net income and hence lower the holding costs for the (hoped for) later conversion to urban use. However, the uncertainty of continuance is a major obstacle to such less intensive land use.

Land is a resource which often moves slowly through a market; its price is often a function of the length of time employed in bringing seller and buyer together. There is frequently a vast difference between price at forced sale, price between willing seller and willing buyer, and price at what may be described as "forced purchase." Land with one kind of improvement may require several times as long, ordinarily, to find a buyer as land in another category. The market for land, like the market for any commodity or service traded in by various persons, exhibits its own peculiarities, which in turn sometimes affect activities on the land.

Closely related to this matter of the market, as an institution, is the matter of credit based upon land as security, or credit for the purpose of purchasing or improving land. In the United States, by and large, we have rather highly developed land credit institutions involving mortgages and legal procedures associated therewith. This is in contrast to parts of some Latin American and other less economically developed countries where there is almost no credit system based upon land, nor do the necessary legal procedures for writing and enforcing mortgages exist. Credit based upon land or for land purposes is not equally cheaply and easily available within the United States to all potential borrowers. The characteristics of the credit structure relating to land are important economic facts relating to activities on the land.

Interrelations of Land Use between Areas

Thus far in this chapter we have more or less implicitly spoken as if each tract or parcel of land stood alone, whether one considered activities on it, its natural features, improvements, intensity, tenure, or price and credit. Yet, in fact, especially in this complex modern economy but even in primitive ones, there are relationships between different tracts or parcels of land, which are sometimes close and intimate, sometimes less so. These interrelationships extend between lands used for the same purposes; such tracts compete for the same ultimate market. Farms in different parts of the United States, or in different parts of the world, producing the same farm commodity sold in the same markets, are in competition with each other. Likewise, land used for different shopping districts may be competing for some of the same customers. The intensity of land use, the value of the land, the kind of improvements most economical on it, and even the matter of whether it can be used for this purpose at all, depend in part upon the characteristics of the competing land.

Less competitive and more complementary is the relationship which exists between different tracts of land used for different activities. In the modern American city, a man lives on one piece of land, works on another, shops at a third (or more), plays on still others, and travels over many other pieces of land in moving from one to the other. Of some, he and his family have exclusive use, if they wish; in many more, he shares use with others, often with large numbers of other people. These relationships are often highly complex, yet it is the intricate interweaving of land uses on many separate tracts which gives value to each, and which is basic to the whole economy and culture.

Many kinds of land use depend heavily upon externalities. This is especially so for most urban land uses; the use and value of a tract is influenced more by what other persons do to their surrounding tracts than is the use and value influenced by what the man can do on his own tract. Environmental health planning is a recognized professional field. If the residential neighborhood is deteriorating seriously, it does the individual home owner little good to maintain his property; but if the neighborhood is well maintained, the value of his property is largely supported even if he neglects to maintain his improvements. The same is true of business districts. It is for these reasons that some of the public controls over private land use, such as zoning, are instituted and enforced; the general public good exceeds any inconvenience to the individual. But externalities apply in rural areas also, especially in water disposal but also in such matters as weed control. Some of the earliest and most severe efforts at public regulation of rural private land use arose in weed control, since one man's neglect often nullified the efforts of his neighbors.

The interrelationship matter reaches its highest importance in the consideration of transportation. Transportation facilities exist and operate to move goods or people between one location and another; the capacity of such facilities and their location depends upon the total pattern of economic and social activities in the larger area that includes origins and destinations. At the same time, the existence or creation of transportation facilities greatly affects the activities possible.

A special kind of information about relationships between one tract of land and another is concerned with the access of a tract of land to various kinds of transportation facilities. Access may be direct, as when a tract fronts on a highway or has a railway spur; or it may be nearby, as when a tract is located near an interchange onto a major limited-access highway. Access may be measured by distance from one tract to others; but sometimes time ordinarily spent in travel is more meaningful than is physical distance. If adequate information is obtained as to the physical location of each tract of land, including tracts used for transportation purposes, then it is possible to indicate the physical and economic access of any area with respect to any other areas.

Land Using Activities in Relation to Data on Other Inclusive Social Developments

However widely one might define the term "land use," there are some activities with a geographic dimension that would still fall outside of the definition. We have in mind employment, agricultural and industrial output, living conditions or standards, social stress, education, health, and other aspects of economic or social life. Any human activity which results in data on any one of these aspects of life takes place in some geographical setting or in some spot, and to this extent is related to land. On the other hand, if an already loose and wide series of concepts regarding land are to have any boundary at all, then at some point one must say: Here we no longer find land use and related concepts, but rather other human activities with interrelation to land. There can hardly be a clean, sharp line in any case, and different students may well draw the line in different places.

In devising an ideal or an improved system of land use statistics, however, one should surely keep in mind the desirability of interrelating land use data (no matter how the latter may be defined) with data on other aspects of life, both economic and social. This seems to require some minimum correspondence of geographic areas, and some minimum agreement of concepts.

What Do We Mean by "Land Use"?

In this chapter we have explored a number of concepts or approaches that are or may be included under the general title of "land use," at least as this is widely, and often loosely, used. In view of this extended discussion, just what does the Committee on Land Use Statistics mean by the term "land use"?

We would like to confine the term "land use" to mean man's activities on land which are directly related to the land. Quite possibly some title such as "human use of land" or "human activities on land" would be better. In any case, this idea deals as much with people as with land; it is the *use* dimension which should be emphasized. Thus, while natural qualities of land, improvements, tenure, intensity of use, and other factors are related, they are not part of the central core. Activities not closely connected with land may markedly influence the more specific land-using activities.

But the Committee recognizes that a term of so wide usage as "land use" inevitably lacks a sharply standardized definition and that it is impossible to re-define it in some specialized way. As generally used, the term includes far more than activities; some or all of the related concepts we have discussed in this chapter are included at times. The only practical answer now, in our judgment, is to use additional and more specialized terms, so as to make as clear as possible exactly which concept is in mind. "Activities using land" is less appealing, perhaps somewhat awkward, but conveys in some contexts a clearer meaning than "land use," as the latter is commonly used.

While we think there is much to be gained by separately identifying and individually maintaining the concepts previously discussed, this of course does not mean that a variety of information cannot be collected in the same survey; economy of operations could often be achieved in this way. For statistical and administrative efficiency, it might be desirable to obtain data on land-using activities, on improvements, and on landownership, all on one questionnaire or by one interview. Once the data are collected, if the individual concepts are maintained separately, the basic data can be aggregated into any combination of categories required for analytical, planning, or administrative purposes. From the point of economic rationale, an analysis might include the same range of subjects, or some other grouping. We need not keep data on land-using activities pure and undefiled from contact with other data about the same land; but there is much to be gained by separating the various concepts and then synthesizing them, rather than indiscriminately intermingling them. At the minimum, one should realize what he is doing, and why. If each kind of data is adequately identified as to location, then various kinds of data can be fruitfully interrelated in any desired analysis.

CHAPTER III.

Land Location and Parcel Identification

Ricardo and other early economists stressed the immutable and permanent characteristics of land. Today, we realize that the character of land may be changed by man in ways and to a degree which Ricardo never dreamed of, because the technological capacities of the present are beyond those of his day. By excavation and fill, water areas may be made into land, and vice versa; by drainage or irrigation or both, arid areas can be made to produce crops as if they were humid; by treatments which modify the internal structure of the soil, infertile land can be made productive; and in many other ways, some of the basic characteristics of a piece of land may be modified greatly. This is in addition, of course, to structural improvements on the land.

Yet it still remains true that many of the characteristics of land are as immutable and permanent as ever. Above all, the *physical location* of a piece of the earth's surface cannot be modified by man. Its position in relation to the equator, the poles, and the oceans, and all that depends upon these major location characteristics, is as fixed as ever. In particular, basic climate and geologic history are beyond man's power to alter. By transportation and communication technology, man can materially affect the relation of one piece of land to another, yet the location of each on the earth's surface is unchangeable.

Location is critical to any data regarding land. One must know the boundaries or geographic location of every area to which land data are applied, whether it be a nation, a state, a county, a city, a farm, or a smaller parcel.[1]

Location is relative, and must be judged in terms of the scale of the study and its purposes. For the novelist, a location in North America or Europe

[1] For the social and economic consequences of uncertain property boundaries and other uncertainties as to land records, especially in the earlier settled States of the Union, see Francis J. Marschner, *Boundaries and Records—Eastern Territory of Early Settlement with Historical Notes on the Cadaster* (Washington: U.S. Department of Agriculture, Agricultural Research Service, 1960).

may be an adequate identification; for the housewife, "some place downtown." But even for land measurement and statistical purposes of data relating to land, where vastly greater precision is needed, location is still relative. For some purposes, county totals may be adequate, while for others, data are needed for much smaller areas. The scale of study should be sufficient, at the minimum, to insure that the location of the land is properly identified with the general area for which data are desired; more commonly, many subdivisions and interrelations require more precise location within the general area.

The problem of geographic identification is especially critical if one attempts to relate one set of data to another. In Chapter II, we considered such concepts as land-using activities, natural qualities of land, improvements, intensity of use, and tenure. Frequently, data on each of these will come from different sources, often obtained in highly dissimilar ways. Such data can be interrelated and integrated only to the extent that it can be ascertained that the same areas are included in each; otherwise, quite inaccurate conclusions might be drawn.

At several places in this book, reference will be made to "parcels" of land; hence, a brief definition of "parcel" is essential. A parcel is the smallest unit or tract of land identifiable with the techniques used in a particular study. Separately-owned tracts within a single activity group, such as individual home owners in a residential neighborhood, would ordinarily be parcels. But different activities within a single ownership, such as fields with different crops within one farm, would also ordinarily be parcels. The parking lot, office headquarters, tank storage area, and actual refinery structures might well be shown as separate parcels for a petroleum refinery. The detail, or "grain," of a particular study would largely determine how small a difference would be considered sufficient to distinguish one parcel from another.

If an inquiry is concerned with activities on land, or land use, then obviously parcels must be identified on a small enough scale to measure differences in land use. However, even here there will be difficult problems of subsidiary uses within a larger parcel, such as parking lots within a trade or industrial enterprise. If the inquiry is also concerned with tenure, the parcels must be small enough to identify differences in tenure—and so on, for physical qualities of the land, improvements, and other factors. Moreover, as we shall show in later discussion, there are great practical advantages to recording and processing data for the smallest identifiable parcels of land. For now, it is sufficient to say that, if the basic data are identified and recorded by small geographic units, they then can be grouped and re-grouped into any larger unit desired.

Basic data about land will usually be obtained from aerial photographs, or from field inspection or observation, or from interview with land users or owners. Accurate and easily usable base maps are essential for any approach. Sometimes parcel boundaries and identities will be obvious—a fence line, a difference in observable activity, etc.; in other cases, a more detailed inquiry may be necessary in order to ascertain or verify differences in parcels. Again, the scale of the inquiry and the purposes of the data are likely to be determinative. However, the presumption should always be for smaller rather than larger parcels, for reasons stated above. Small parcels can always be grouped to obtain large ones; large parcels cannot be subdivided into small ones without additional field work and office tabulation, if this is even possible.

In any program of data collection, processing, and analysis, specifying the location of each area is absolutely basic. Such specification might be made by any one of several systems, or by more than one system. In any event, accuracy of location is always a relative matter, never absolute. Accuracy should be geared to the values involved, which in turn depends largely upon land use, actual or potential. The locational description of prime commercial land in large cities may require identification to fractions of a foot; the location of low-grade grazing or forest land may be identified in terms of quarter miles. Yet each would be proportionately equally accurate, if the value of use is the standard.

Systems of Parcel Identification

Several systems of land parcel identification exist in the United States, but as yet, none has been extended to the whole national area in adequate detail to serve as a single method of identifying all parcels of land.

Land identification may take place at more than one level of sophistication. The professional worker, whether engineer or land planner, can well use a grid system based upon latitude and longitude. He can easily translate any data he may acquire in the field onto office records and from them to maps, and back again. For him, this type of grid system, even if not marked out on the land, is realistic and understandable. For the analysis of economic and social problems, on the other hand, it is necessary to relate data about land to political and economic units, such as states, counties, cities, metropolitan areas and the like. At the level of field enumeration, it is essential to have a system for describing land which the respondent knows or can identify from simple maps and photos. Thus, it may often be highly desirable, if not essential, to describe the same tract of land in more than one way. Each may be equally accurate, although accuracy varies greatly within each general system. Some may be more understandable to some users than are other systems, and some may be more relevant to some problems than are others.

Location systems exist independently of maps, but most location systems are more understandable to most users if placed on a map. Maps help to locate points, not only in relation to the geographic location system being used, but also in relation to identifiable points or features on the landscape. Parcels identifiable on the ground should also be identifiable on the map used to record or analyze the data. Data about land, obtained in any way, can be and usually are recorded on maps. Grid or other location identification systems can also be shown on the same maps, thus facilitating comparison between data for different areas. There is thus a close relationship between maps and location systems, but the two are not identical.

Generally speaking, there is much to be gained by enumerating or assembling data according to location systems which are meaningful to the persons concerned. Thus, enumeration of urban housing might well be by street name and address, or enumeration of farms according to rural roads or other easily identifiable features or by cadastral survey description. Later presentation of data should also be according to units or areas that make sense to the audience. But data obtained or recorded by one system can be translated rather readily to another, in most cases. Equivalency tables can be prepared, which will show which street addresses to group into a census block, or which farm areas into a rural minor civil division, or any other grouping desired. Data by any local system can be converted into data by longitude and latitude co-ordinates. All of these conversions can be done by modern electronic data-processing equipment, if each parcel is accurately located. While there would be much to be said for a single system of geographic identification that would fit all tracts, however large or small, there are arguments against it—ready public understanding being one of the more powerful. In any case, such a system is not now in general use. Most of its advantages are obtainable through such equivalency tables and regrouping of the basic data described above. The smaller the units by which data are recorded, or the building blocks in a data program, the more accurately they can be made to fit any other geographic system of identification.

Various kinds of grid systems exist. The Coast and Geodetic Survey and the Geological Survey each has a system based on latitude and longitude. For about half of the states, there is a system of state plane co-ordinates. There is the rectangular cadastral survey system, which covers about two-thirds of the nation. There is also the new National Location Code, developed by the Bureau of the Census for the National Resource Evaluation Center, which covers the fifty states and off-shore possessions. In addition, there are many local geographic location systems, such as those for subdivisions of cities, those based on assessors' records, and the like. Many resource surveys, such as forest inventory, range survey and soil survey, have made their own maps and provided their own location system, usually working from some available base map.

There have been several proposals for formulation of a single comprehensive land parcel identification and small area classification scheme, that would cover the whole nation and be suitable for all purposes. The very fact that there are several proposals is evidence that none yet satisfies all the needs; possibly a single system is unrealistic. Or perhaps one system, such as one based on longitude and latitude, could be accepted by everyone as the *second* system, to which they would be willing to relate all data enumerated or assembled by them. This whole matter of parcel identification and data enumeration areas is one which the Committee did not find it possible to explore as thoroughly and finally as it would have liked, and might well be a subject for consideration by the permanent committee which is proposed in Chapter IX.[2]

Grid Systems and the Location of Land Area Units

If all the surface of the fifty states were laid off in squares of a mile (or some fraction of a mile) on each side, then the location of any natural or man-made feature could be pinpointed by specifying distance x and distance y from an agreed origin. This might be a corner or some other point in such a square, however large the square or wherever located.

In the thirty states in which rectangular surveying was established under the Act of April 26, 1785, or subsequently, the mile-square pattern was established in most sections of a township so as to produce quarter sections of approximately 2,640 feet on a side and quarter-quarter sections of approximately 1,320 feet on a side. Irregular sections and fractions, especially on the west and north sides of townships, are partly the results of imposing a square pattern on a round world.

Regardless of how attractive for some purposes might be grid patterns that are not square but conform to the curvature of the earth, preference for using fixed points at corners of squares will doubtless continue. From a point of origin, say, the southwest corner of such a unit in a grid system, sub-cells can be designated as so many tenths (or hundredths) of the

[2] In recent months (prior to March 1965), a number of federal, state, and local government agencies and private organizations have been exploring the possibility of uniform and standardized definitions for small geographic areas, especially for cities, to serve as the basis for tabulation and analysis of data on land use and other economic and social relationships. While there would be many advantages in uniformly defined small areas for data recording and analysis, there are also major difficulties in finding a unit which will serve all needs.

distance north and of the distance east toward the next mile line, or another grid cell's beginning, whatever the distance.

Limitations of accuracy in determining geographic location naturally reduce the practical value of blowing up maps made with a rather wide tolerance, as is a fact with most maps. Five meter accuracy as applied in a few cities of Sweden in a recent census, for example, involves a cost of collection and mapping not likely to be soon sought in most American situations.[3] In this country exceptional accuracy may continue to characterize maps for built-up centers because of the special value of such maps to fire insurance carriers in judging the fire-suppression capability that a building has and the susceptibility it has to suffering from a spread of fire among buildings.[4] Exceptional detail is found in some Coast and Geodetic Survey maps where shore properties and water craft face special hazards.

Motives for increased accuracy over wide territories have not carried us in the United States as far as those that led the British in the Napoleonic era and since to produce Ordnance Survey maps. These British maps apply to rural as well as urban areas.[5] Where the value of land has become high in rural and rural-urban fringe areas in the United States, desire for knowledge of facts about the upper horizons of the soil (for purposes of suitability for septic tank operations, for the establishment of poles, of underground installations, including foundations for structures, as well as for sound agricultural utilization) have, in some cases, seemed to warrant mapping in very great detail. Air photographs have been made feasible better understanding of the cover and of many other features that are revealed. Having all such map-form information keyed into one grid system multiplies its usefulness to those who need quick reference and an opportunity for machine operations with the data.

The maps of the United States Geological Survey at a scale of 1:250,000

[3] "The 10-meter grid system has been used in most communities of the Gävleborgs län, especially in the cities of Gävle and Hudiksvall, and in the city of Wäxiö, Kronobergs län." A letter of January, 1963, from Director Hans Wetterhall, Swedish Royal Board of Agriculture, Stockholm, emphasizes that it has not been possible to determine the locality of farms more precisely than within 1,000 meter squares.

[4] Companies insuring owners against fire loss need to take into account conditions within the structure and the relation other structures bear to it. Such companies have been principal supporters of such very detailed maps as the Sanborn Company, Pelham, New York, and some other concerns have produced. A large proportion of the cities of the United States have been covered by maps to which, at intervals, paste-ins are attached to bring each portion down to a late date.

[5] The Ordnance Survey produces maps at a scale of 6 inches to the mile covering the whole of Britain. Plans on a larger scale of 1:2500 cover the whole country except for moorland and mountainous areas. This latter series gives a detailed delineation of house plots, other properties, fields, roads, etc., defining their actual boundaries and allocating to each item a parcel number together with its acreage. Any location on a British map or plan can be described by a grid description.

re typically one degree of latitude by two degrees of longitude and bear lesignations so lettered and numbered as to tie them in with the International Map of the World. Along the Pacific Coast a zone number 10 pplies, with numbers increasing eastward to 19 in the New England states. etters are applied to each rectangle and range from NG in southern lorida, to NM in northern Maine, N always referring to rectangles north f the equator. In NK-18 as in the usual case, are 12 proportionally smaller ectangles, 18-1 standing for the Rochester (New York) rectangle, 18-4 or the Elmira area, 18-7 for Williamsport, Pennsylvania, 18-10 for Harrisurg, Pennsylvania, and on to 18-12 for the area around the City of New York.

The tie-in with the world-wide lettering and numbering system under the universal transverse mercator projection is useful for comparing maps produced not only by the United States Army Map Service, but also those produced elsewhere in this country and in other countries.

The Coast and Geodetic Survey air navigation chart coverage of the United States is complete in the 1:500,000 scale. This scale is consistent with the scale of 1:1,000,000 in the International Map of the World, long sponsored with great respectability, but still lacking completion.

While the importance of tie-in of land unit location data to dependable origins and nearby stations in a grid system is critical in areas where surveys were not of the federal rectangular type, the public domain states do not escape from a similar need. Many original survey monuments have decayed and disappeared and the stations they represented have need of being restored by survey methods. As pointed out by the Coast and Geodetic Survey, "eventually even a good survey of a limited area with only its own monuments to preserve its ground location will, by loss of original monuments and errors of replacement, become little more than a paper record, and beyond the power of a surveyor to transform into a ground pattern of monumented lines without the aid of a court decision prescribing a legal method of construing conflicting records and surveying discrepancies. Triangulation executed by the Coast and Geodetic Survey comprises a country-wide network connecting thousands of marked points whose geodetic positions are known with such accuracy and precision that any station, if its marks are destroyed, can be restored closely to the original position on the ground by surveys based on other triangulation stations whose marks have not been destroyed." Nevertheless, in rectangular survey states no location data for areas outside of cities are likely to be of greater utility than those showing subdivisions of sections, fixed by numbers, townships, and ranges.

In 1933, the Coast and Geodetic Survey developed a plane co-ordinate system for North Carolina. This was given the authority of state law a few years later. By 1963, twenty-six state systems for a nation-wide tie-in had been given similar authorization. The geodetic positions of triangulation stations within any of these states and of most other states could be transformed into plane-rectangular (X and Y) coordinates on a single grid, and surveys in all parts of the state referenced to it. It has thus become practicable for survey stations and landmarks to be accurately described by stating their coordinates referred to the common origin of the grid.

In 1944, Louisiana became the first of the public domain states to pass an act establishing the plane-co-ordinate system. Preceding her in such approval were New Jersey, 1935; Pennsylvania, 1937; New York, 1938; Maryland and North Carolina, 1939; and Massachusetts, 1941.

By using an overlay upon surveys emphasizing metes and bounds and upon surveys of other types based at angles to the meridians and base lines of the federal rectangular system, a grid pattern fitted to these meridians and base lines can be keyed in full, and provisions made for subdividing any part of the pattern to a high degree of refinement.

The place of the United States Bureau of the Census in the development of locator procedures is exemplified by analyses relating the 1960 census of population total for selected areas to the map boundaries of that area. The Geography Division of the Bureau by late 1963 had prepared reports for eight regions comprising the entire contiguous United States and all of these reports had been issued by the Office of Civilian Defense and National Resource Evaluation Center, the sponsors of this work. Areas called Standard Location Areas (SLA's) were specified small enough to contain generally no more than 10,000 people. A locator code number is presented for each SLA.

Mention was made above of a finely-meshed grid in Sweden. As of January, 1963, the 10-meter grid, while reported as applicable satisfactorily in some urban areas, giving an accuracy of location within 5 meters had apparently not been applied as a refinement of the 1,000-meter grid used in most rural areas. In most situations in the United States, even with the best of mechanical equipment for processing and manipulating information on cards and magnetic tape, the costs of using data for areas as small as 1,500 square feet could run very high. Data needed for property tax purposes in cities may involve in some cases narrow lots, some of them of no greater area than the experimental Swedish grid. The uncovering of areas that had failed to be assessed for property taxes has sometimes warranted attention to small ownership plots. Also back-of-lot uses of land, especially in areas of substandard housing, have been important in delineating districts for area redevelopment and urban renewal. Studies pointing to possibilities of providing accommodations for people who, in the event of regional emergency, may have need for housing and even for space for ccupational activity, may call for finely-meshed grid patterns. Not too rge a portion of the hemisphere would need to have suffered nuclear evastation to require host service from land unit users in other areas.

In the present treatment, the finer meshes of a grid system can be assumed o be likely, for the immediate future, to be confined to urban areas, to ocal areas of uneven topography, especially where land and water meet, nd to some areas of mineral exploitation and very intensive agriculture. 'or many situations, especially where wide stretches have similar topog-aphy, a diminutive grid would have little place for decades to come.

AND LOCATION AT DIFFERENT DEPTHS AND ELEVATIONS

The possibility of different land uses at different vertical levels has been nentioned in Chapter I. Use, tenure, or other parcels at each level must e accurately identified, just as they must be at the land surface level. The and location and parcel identification may vary from underground, to surface, to higher elevations; and parcels at one level may not coincide with parcels at another level. Identification for each level must be sufficiently accurate and detailed for the purpose for which the data are to be used. In addition, parcel location and identification at one level must be readily relatable to parcel identification and location at each other level; in this way, one can relate use or other data at one level to similar data at another level.

CODE SYSTEMS FOR RECORDING SMALL AREA LOCATIONS

Manuals on the new National Location Code had become available for all of the eight regions of contiguous United States by November, 1963. These manuals were prepared by the Bureau of the Census primarily for the Office of Civil Defense, Department of Defense, and the Office of Emergency Planning, National Resource Evaluation Center. They are published for the use of federal, state and local civil defense and emergency planning officials with responsibilities for damage assessment, resource evaluation or shelter planning. Text describing the new National Location Code (NLC) is combined in these manuals with maps showing the geographic boundaries of Standard Location Areas (SLA's) and with data listings containing their names, population in 1960, identifying codes and geographic coordinates.

The Stanford Research Institute, Palo Alto, California, developed the first National Location Code in January, 1956. The Stanford Code represented the 1950 distribution of population throughout the United States and was established in order to apply electronic computers to the problems of estimating casualties and housing losses from nuclear attack. By late 1959, it had become apparent that the Stanford Code would soon be obsolete. The identification of Standard Location Areas and the selection of appropriate geographic co-ordinates took place in the spring of 1960 following the major mapping work done by the Bureau of the Census prior to going into the field to take the 1960 Census.

Coverage in the new National Location Code has been expanded to include Alaska, Hawaii, the United States possessions of Puerto Rico, Virgin Islands, Samoa, Guam, and the Canal Zone. In the new Code, all SLA's are explicitly defined areas with rigid geographic boundaries, whereas the old Code provided a series of points throughout rural areas to which population was assigned. Again, the old Code used Standard Economic Areas in the New England States, which are groupings of whole counties. The new Code recognizes in the New England States Standard Metropolitan Statistical Areas (SMSA's) which are combinations of cities, boroughs, and towns, and do not follow county lines as in other states. The National Location Code established approximately 43,000 SLA's to provide adequate small area coverage of the United States and its outlying areas.

On the maps of the individual states found in each regional volume of the National Location Code, the appropriate data of the Army Map Service numbering system are shown. In California, for example, the westernmost AMS number is 11 and the easternmost 31, the southernmost 49, and the northernmost 67.

Each Standard Location Area in the new National Location Code is identified by an eight-digit serial number and is represented by a pair of geographic co-ordinates. In this eight-digit code the first four digits identify the region, the state, the area and the county. The last four digits of the SLA serial number identify the SLA within its county.

The absolute geographical position of each SLA is identified by both geographic (latitude and longitude) and Universal Transverse Mercator (UTM) co-ordinates. Geographic co-ordinate readings are to the nearest second and UTM co-ordinates are shown to the nearest 100 meters. For each SLA, the co-ordinate readings represent the estimated center of population.

The Army Map Service issues maps covering the United States and possessions at the following scale: 1:2,500,000; 1:500,000; 1:250,000; 1:100,000; 1:50,000; and 1:25,000. These maps show the Universal Transverse Mercator (UTM) grid system which is used by the Army and Air Force for military mapping.[6]

[6] Army Technical Manual TM 5–241 and Air Force Technical Order TO 16–1–233 may be consulted for details.

A unique numbering system is used to identify the 1:100,000, 1:50,000 and 1:25,000 scale maps. The continental United States is divided into two parts by the meridian at 90 degrees. Each part is sub-divided into areas 30 minutes of latitude in height and 30 minutes of longitude in width. Each of these areas is mapped, or will be mapped, at the scale of 1:100,000. The maps for the Western part of the United States are identified by Series Number V 602, and for the Eastern part by Series Number V 601. Numbering of the maps at 1:100,000 scale in the Western part starts at 10 on the West Coast running East through 79 at the 90th meridian; and at 35 on the South running through 80 on the North. Numbering in the Eastern part starts at 30 at the 90th meridian running East through 75 on the East Coast; and at 33 on the South running through 80 on the North.

Each 1:100,000 map is identified by an 8-digit number, the first four digits being the series number previously described. The next two digits locate the map position from West to East, and the last two digits locate the map position from South to North. Of course, the same four digits will also locate a 1:100,000 scale map in the Western half of the U.S.

The area covered by each map at scale 1:100,000 is subdivided into four equal parts which are mapped at scale 1:50,000 and are designated I, II, III, and IV, starting with the Northeast quarter and running clockwise to the Northwest quarter. Similarly, the area covered by each map at scale 1:50,000 is subdivided into four equal parts which are mapped at scale 1:25,000 and are designated NE, SE, SW and NW. Thus V 821 6265 I SE indicates a 1:25,000 scale map in the New York area which the map catalogue identifies by the name "Hicksville."

The UTM zone of each SLA, and the appropriate northing and easting in hundreds of meters is shown by mathematical conversion of the latitude and longitude readings supplied by the Bureau of the Census.

The U.S. Geological Survey also issues maps covering the U.S. and its possessions at the scales of 1:62,500 and 1:24,000. The areas covered by these maps are identical with the areas covered by the Army Map Service map system. These maps now indicate by ticks on the periphery the UTM grid coordinate lines. Older editions of such maps lacked the grid ticks.

In the Map Index for Standard Metropolitan Statistical Areas[7] one finds for each SMSA certain references to existing maps that are usefully brought together. For Altoona, Pennsylvania, for example, are shown the designations of six maps of the 1:50,000 and 1:62,500 scales and fifteen maps of the 1:25,000 and 1:24,000 scales. All of the six maps are available, but none of the fifteen had yet become available when the Index was prepared. The unavailability of so many SMSA maps and particularly of so many maps for parts of the country not included in the SMSA's is one of the more distressing aspects of the total mapping situation in the United States.

Sites refer to land area units where actions took place in the past, are occurring now, and/or are included in plans by one or more persons for a specific type of use in the future. Much that is important about a site may be hidden. A building may now be resting on a site that required extensive

[7] National Resource Evaluation Center, Technical Manual No. 133, February, 1963. This is a three-volume index.

input for excavation or for pilings. Adverse soil structural features deep underground may have threatened the construction program, but the ingenuity and exertion necessary to master the problem may be unknown to present users and others concerned with the building. In like manner, some areas on which farming operations have been proceeding for decades may have first had severe problems in respect to stones, trees, water or aridity. In some fields tile lines have been inserted, lower strata of relatively impervious accumulations broken up, depressions filled and other topographic changes effected in behalf of drainage, better use of machinery and in some cases more effective irrigation. Here, too, the untutored eye, looking for man-made structures, may see only tile outlets or parts of conducting installations, which convey none too adequate information about hidden inputs still conferring benefits.[8]

Locator items which might be relevant in a metropolitan land use study include:

1. Parcel location
   Parcel number; parcel address; legal description
   Grid co-ordinates (Parcel Centroid to nearest thousandth of a mile)
   Parcel number of other parcels comprising unit
   Tax assessor's lot-block number.
2. Political jurisdiction
   Municipality; school district; special district; township; county; state.
3. Planning statistical areas
   Census tract; census block; planning unit; residential area; community; industrial district; shopping district; urban renewal project; traffic analysis zone.

In the suggested use of parcel centroid, there is a departure suggested from the references earlier in this chapter to a corner of the parcel. Where parcels are as small as in most downtown areas, or as irregular as in some of them, and where streets do not run on cardinal directions, the arguments for centroids are strong.

The preceding may serve as an example of the types of detail coming more and more into demand in this country. Location of a part of a parcel within 5¼ feet (a thousandth of a mile) may still be regarded by some as beyond the degree of accuracy in most geographic location systems. Suitable in some situations would be a showing under parcel characteristics that would be duplicate or triplicate where special underground spatial provisions and/or special air rights structural uses exist.

[8] Inadequacy of publicly recorded information concerning underground pipes and other conducting installations and lack of attention to facts about depth and courses taken by such underground furniture explain why mechanical diggers traversing fields, lots and rights-of-way have so often made repairs necessary after interruption of essential services affecting homes, industries and offices over considerable areas.

CHAPTER IV.

The Role of Land Use Statistics in the United States Today

Statistics on land use should be utilitarian; that is, they should serve pragmatic ends. One seeks data about land use as an aid to making decisions and taking action. As far as possible, therefore, statistics should be designed to answer the kinds of questions most likely to be raised, not only today but as far into the future as needs are foreseeable. The Appendices to this book include a consideration of how several federal agencies use land use statistics, as well as how some produce them.

Statistics on land use often can, and should whenever possible, arise out of practical "operating" programs. Many kinds of public and private action both require statistics of land use and at the same time produce them. Day-to-day operations often produce land use data which can be recorded and analyzed to help produce the answers needed by the same agencies. This requires that the data be accurate, uniformly defined, properly recorded, and properly used.

There is much to be said, therefore, for having programs of land use data as an integral part of action programs. On the other hand, such operating agencies often lack expertise in data handling and, more seriously, are often too closely preoccupied with current operations to give data needs and possibilities adequate consideration. Specialized data handling organizations can often collect, tabulate, and analyze land use and other data, either to replace or to supplement the data-handling function of the operating agency. Still another role arises for the outside research or planning organization, involved in neither the administrative action nor in the basic data handling, to analyze the available data and draw conclusions about the actions or problems which underlie it. The latter type of agency, though lacking the intimate involvement in the data of the other organizations, may have an objectivity or a perspective which is possible only from such a detached position. Perhaps the best of all arrangements is one which involves cooperation among all of these groups, so that the needed data largely come from administrative action, so that the operating agency is directly committed to them, and so that the expertise of the specialized data agency is brought to bear, yet the research or planning agency is encouraged to consider and review the underlying situation.

Land use data, like other economic and social data, can be judged only in terms of their usefulness for answering questions likely to be raised. A good beginning point, therefore, is to consider, at least briefly, some of the kinds of questions that an adequate system of land use statistics might help to answer.[1] Public investment in many fields will depend in large part upon land use data of one kind or another. In urban areas, identification of blighted areas requires land use data of various kinds. Public investment programs for slum clearance, urban renewal, rehabilitation of grey areas, improvement of transportation systems, construction of public buildings, provision of social services, and many other purposes require all the more adequate land use information. The many and diverse questions in each of these fields cannot be answered by data alone, no matter how good; but defensible answers are nearly impossible without data. Provision of all manner of urban social services depends upon the kind of use now being made of land, and that likely to be made of it in the future. The same is true of any program for renewal of central business districts. Present and future tax and expenditure programs are closely related to land use. The same is true of health and sanitation codes. In all of these, and probably in many others of the manifold activities of the modern city, land use data are important, and these activities in turn have an impact upon land use.

Urban plans of all kinds, including subdivision regulations, zoning, and acquisition of tracts for public purposes, also both require usable land use data and have their impact upon land use. Most urban planning efforts begin with an intensive study of present land use and end with a projected future land use pattern. In practice, these have been highly variable, and some have probably been more efficient in meeting needs than have others. Data soundly collected on well-designed specifications would invariably be helpful. Budgets of central government loan funds and powers of insuring loans made for housing or other purposes touched with a public interest are usually limited. Selection, therefore, of parts of a hundred cities in which beneficial programs are to be regarded as eligible, and the placing of some situations on higher priority than others, put officers of the central government, as well as those of the individual cities, under the necessity of showing on what statistical grounds the delineations are made and with what consistency priorities are established as against other claimants clamoring for attention and approval.

[1] The need for data on land use is mentioned repeatedly in Werner Z. Hirsch (ed.), *Elements of Regional Accounts* (Baltimore: The Johns Hopkins Press, 1964).

Private investment in urban areas also depends upon land use data and in turn affects land use. The demand for private housing of various types, the opportunities for trade centers, the best location of industrial and other large plants—all these, and other, purposes of private investment decisions require knowledge of past and present land uses within the urban area, and also the best possible projections for future land use in the same areas.

Decisions made for or against subdivision or consolidation of land in an urban area or in the rural-urban fringe, the presence of excessive haste or delay in improving urban or rural land units, and other human interpositions may push land units into the current of development or inflict handicaps. Information about the intensities and trends in land uses within and around a growing city are needed for most effective use of private funds in providing for future needs.[2]

Transportation planning and investment, whether public or private, also uses land use data and transportation in turn affects the kinds of use made of the land. The present land use in different locations greatly affects the need to move persons and goods from one location to another; and the types and efficiency of transportation facilities available in turn affect the economic use of land at each location. For a proper understanding of what has happened and of what is likely to happen in the future, accurate and relevant land use data are highly valuable.

The various national agricultural programs, and any modifications of them, also depend upon land use data and have their effects upon land use. The area in crops, both in total and by specific crops, and the trends in such area, especially in relation to agricultural output, employment, and other measures of economic performance are important factors in the development and administration of different agricultural programs. As a matter of fact, agricultural programs to date have concentrated heavily upon land as a factor of production, especially acreages planted by growers, often to the near exclusion of concern over other factors.

Outdoor recreation is an activity coming much to the fore these days, and it depends upon land and water areas for its fulfillment. Information about past and present areas, both their extent and their use, is essential to planning to meet future needs. As a matter of fact, information about

[2] No one will contend that any current land-use picture is free from distortions brought about by more or less erratic human judgment in the use of land. Future pressures keep giving rise to series after series of superseding use dedications and tend to blot out earlier ill-timed and ill-placed uses. Private developers and other private investors are applying their intelligence and other resources to these ends, and usually are avid examiners of results of competent studies bringing the current land uses of a metropolitan or other differential area into perspective. They may thus, for example, make more enlightened decisions whether to assemble options by which to weld together smaller parcels into parcels of a size needed by a shopping district, a housing complex, an industrial establishment, etc., whether to promote a subdivision, or whether to abstain from, or go ahead with, a previously favored venture.

public areas used for recreation is rather sketchy, and information about use of private areas for the same purpose is very poor indeed. Information about outdoor recreation was greatly increased by the work of the Outdoor Recreation Resources Review Commission, and should be further increased in the future by the work of the Bureau of Outdoor Recreation. In the absence of accurate and relevant data, one must necessarily guess rather than measure. As with other possible uses of land data, the data alone do not answer the questions—that requires many judgments and decisions—but answers in the absence of data are unavoidably bad or at least not as good as they might otherwise be.

These same general points could be made regarding the use of forest land, both private and public. What are the trends in forest land area and in management of forest land? What will be the future level of productivity, under varying assumptions of future management? Will scarcity of forest products arise, or will there be a reasonable market for the entire forest output? Answers to questions such as these require much analysis and judgment, but current land use statistics are often basic.

In assessing lands and lots for property taxation one sees public personnel rating real estate with more and more persistent efforts to differentiate subunits of area according to their agronomic rating and more and more effort, especially on the outskirts of cities, to impute site values to subunits in crop or pasture uses. Questions of public policy enter into the assessment of agriculturally used land which is in the path of expansion of a nearby central city or of other urbanizing developments. Assessors responsible for locating, describing and assessing all except tax-exempt properties have to make, if not annual, then usually biennial or quadrennial reassessments of the real estate in their territory. The requirements of effective property tax administration warrant more ample and accessible land-use information than most state and county officials, to say nothing of the members of the general public, have had available to them.

Land use data are not referred to here as affording appraisers, attorneys and others concerned with public takings of private properties an escape from ascertaining as best they can the current market value of the properties or parts taken for public purposes. No judge or jury is likely to feel that general information does more than give an underpinning to the special information which every condemnation case demands. Land use data on the rate and direction of expansion of a given city can go far, however, in enabling judgment to be sound in determining whether a subject property at some distance from its corporate limits is likely to continue in the list of agricultural properties or to be taken over soon for urban uses.

Ideally, a system of land use statistics should be as usable in appraising esent public programs as in appraising very different programs, or they ould be equally usable in answering private as well as public questions. pefully, data collected today and over the years will be useful thirty, ty, or more years in the future, when a major question will be the past nds in land use. In practice, it is probably impossible to devise a system land use data of such generality and comprehensiveness that it will be ore or less equally usable for all present questions and for future ones as ll. However, a major step in this direction will have been taken if the oposals of this report are followed. To anticipate a little the later discus- on, we propose collection and tabulation of basic data in such detail, both to use of the land and as to land parcel or land unit, that the same basic ta can be used in many ways to answer many different kinds of questions. s noted above, the basic data should, as far as possible, arise out of rrent operating programs. This will go far toward insuring that the data ve usefulness, and will often mean major economies in collection, which ordinarily by far the most expensive part of any data program. But land e data should not be so defined or handled that they are useful only for e specific operating program from which they arise. While such a defini- on might appear more useful and easier to apply at the moment, the data defined would almost never be sufficiently adaptable to meet other or ture needs.

Historical comparisons of land use are often extremely important. This bviously requires data about earlier periods of time, for comparison with e present. Often it is impossible now to obtain accurate, detailed data bout some earlier time period, although sometimes this is possible. But e should recognize now that historical comparisons will be highly valuable n the future, also; therefore, we should plan to save today's data more or ess indefinitely into the future. With modern data processing, which we onsider briefly later in this chapter, data storage is much cheaper today han formerly; and present data, which will one day be data about the past, an become highly valuable with the passage of time.

Finally, data about land use should be relatable to other data about land, uch as tenure or improvement data, and to data about other economic and ocial activities, such as employment, health, and the like. Although the ocus of our concern is with land use, people everywhere are interested in nany aspects of life other than land and its use. The latter are important, out comprise only one of several important parts of total life. In collection, tabulation, analysis, and use, data about activity on land must be relatable to other data about human activities. If each is properly identified as to location, as we discussed in Chapter III, then the interrelationship is possible.

Interests in Land Use Statistics

Many persons and organizations have an interest in land use statistic the nature of these interests differs considerably. At some risk of ove simplification, the various groups and interests may be classified into fo types as follows:

1. Primary land use data recorders or handlers, who generally neith tabulate these data into summaries for their own or other use, nor a directly interested in economic and other analyses based upon their dat A prime example of this kind of interest is the county land title record (or whatever he may be called in different states). His office is responsib for recording changes in title from one owner to another. This is a extremely important function where accuracy is essential. But recorde typically do not compile statistics based upon such data. County, city, c other local government assessors in governmental jurisdictions where taxe are levied upon real estate also necessarily must obtain a large amount c information regarding land and its use. Their primary concern is wit taxable value. In many jurisdictions, few or no summaries of the data ar made beyond totalling the assessment values. Appraisers for credit institu tions, whether public or private, also collect a great deal of informatio about land use, especially on the properties appraised but sometimes als on other properties in the same localities. The units of local governmen responsible for building permits, zoning enforcement, health inspections and other aspects of current city business obtain or create data on land use These various kinds of data may have great possibilities as sources of dat on land use; with comparatively few exceptions, they have not been use in this way in the past. Moreover, it seems unlikely that in the future these primary data handlers will, on their own, exploit the data possibilities o their records. However, in larger cities or on a statewide basis, it might be possible to devise a co-operative arrangement between organizations of this type and organizations more interested in land use statistics, whereby the basic data could be summarized by useful classifications and published periodically.

2. Collectors and processors of primary data and information on land use. One major function of the agencies in this group is to collect land use data for statistical purposes. This they typically do by inspection of aerial photographs, field observation, interviews, censuses, questionnaires, or other means. Typically, they contact the landowner or land user and obtain data directly from him, although at times it is possible to collect data by direct observation (as in the case of crops). This type of work may include all land (a 1:1 sample) or it may include smaller samples of the whole population. The data collections may be periodic or episodic. With very

w exceptions, the organizations undertaking this function also tabulate d publish the results of their data collection; in fact, the method of data llection is often closely related to or governed by the later tabulation. The ensus of Agriculture and the periodic estimates of farm land use made by e Department of Agriculture are typical of this interest or function. ublications may contain a degree of analysis and interpretation, but the tter is a separate major function.

3. Analyzers and digesters of primary land use data and information. he agencies and organizations in this group typically use primary data ssembled by the preceding group. They seek to discover, measure, or luminate the economic, social, political, or other relationships among such ata, or between them and data from other sources. The methods of analysis ay vary from relatively simple to highly complex; the focus may be upon e relationships among various factors at one time in one defined geo- raphic area, or between different areas, different times, or a combination f factors, areas, and times. This type of use of land use data often proceeds o the point of drawing conclusions, presenting alternatives for social action, nd perhaps even to recommending one among a series of alternatives. Various government agencies, universities, private foundations and other groups may have this kind of interest in land use statistics. Similar use may be made by individuals or firms, especially for particular areas and times.

4. Users of data and of analyses based upon such data as guides to public and private decision-making on matters involving land. Here, the ocus is upon action, for which the data may serve as a necessary or useful base. The main interest is not in understanding for itself alone, as in the preceding case, but rather to get a sufficiently firm base for a decision. As such, those falling in this group are less concerned with data sources, processes, definitions, and generalizations than are the other groups described. Many public and private organizations can be included in this category. It includes the administrator as contrasted with the researcher, the business executive as contrasted with his analyst.

As is often the case with classifications, this one does not have sharp boundaries between classes. A county assessor may publish an annual report, showing trends in assessed land values and factors affecting such trends. Has he thereby entered the category of an analyzer and digester? Or a census-taking organization may comment briefly on the major relationships among the variables on which it has obtained information. Does this make it an analyst? There is not a sharp line between analysis, as such, and decision-making based upon land use data. Each interest merges, at the margins, with other interests.

Moreover, particular organizations or individuals do not belong in only one of these interest categories. An urban planning agency may find it necessary to collect primary land use data from landowners and users, tabulate and publish these data, to make economic and other analyses bas upon them, and, finally, to recommend a program of land use control ar development. Various other illustrations of multiple interests could be cite On the other hand, some organizations do fall completely into a sing category. A university research bureau may be only a digester and analyze for instance; it would not normally handle or process primary data, mig never conduct a field inventory or data collection, and might never b required to make an action decision about land use or control. The broa groupings of land use data interests into the four classes we have used helpful, but one should avoid assuming a nicety and rigidity which in fa does not exist.

These various roles and activities might be much more purposivel interrelated than in practice they usually have been. For instance, a cit (as a legal entity) or a metropolitan region (as a planning organization might make a land use survey, possibly as part of a comprehensive plannin effort, in which detailed data would be obtained, both as to activity or us of land and as to land parcel or areal unit. Starting with the data from thi survey as a base, all data from building permits, building inspections, ta assessments, health inspections, zoning compliance inspection, and othe operating programs of local government could be recorded for the smalles area or physical unit possible, and incorporated into the same basic dat system. By means of the electronic data processing equipment now generall available, which is discussed briefly later in this chapter and again i Chapter IX, data from one source can be related to data from another, eve when the physical units are not fully identical. By recording the variou local governmental actions currently (daily or weekly), the land use data could be kept fully up to date; very few land use changes could occur tha would not leave a trace in one of these local governmental programs. The data on land use changes would flow out of current action programs, and should be useful to the agencies concerned. But they would also be useful for general urban planning, housing planning, transportation planning, or any one of numerous other things. Such integrated data would combine the roles of data recording, data collection, data analysis, and data use. Something of this general nature is now used in such places as Portland, Oregon; Boston, Massachusetts; Santa Clara County, California; New York State; El Paso, Texas; Alexandria, Virginia; Pittsburgh, Pennsylvania; and Tulsa, Oklahoma.

Multi-centered Collection, Analysis, and Use of Land Use Data

The American culture is a multi-centered one. Our government is a federal system, with local, state, and national governments, each operating within legal powers ultimately conferred by the citizenry. Interest or pressure groups constantly seek to influence public action along lines most helpful to them. No one group is able to exert complete power. The result is nearly always a compromise of the varying influences. A generally comparable situation exists within the economic sphere. Numerous contenders try to attract the consumers' expenditures; numerous decision-points, both public and private, exist, and there is no single center of ultimate decision making. Likewise, in the social and cultural fields, many groups and many influences contend. Line-ups of persons vary from issue to issue, and from time to time. The American culture is not rigid and unchanging, but rather dynamic and fluid. Strangers with different backgrounds often find this multiplicity of influences confusing; a degree of disorder certainly does exist. Yet this very multiplicity of forces brings wealth and variety. No small part of the strength of the total American culture arises out of this richness and variety.

These comments apply also to the field of economic data generally, and more specifically to land use statistics. Many public agencies collect, analyze, and use data on land use. These agencies are to be found at federal, state, and local governmental levels. Some of their programs are described in Chapter VI, and in several appendices to this report. To understand the present programs, one must usually know how they arose. In general, each organization undertook data programs to meet some recognized need and as needs changed, so did the programs, but often with a lag. A brief history of some of the major programs is found in Chapter V. Given the inevitable reaction time of public programs, changing economic and social circumstances have often made considerable parts of some of these programs obsolete or out of date faster than modernization could bring them up to date.

The federal government has a number of programs which collect, analyze, or use land use statistics; these are found in various agencies of the Departments of Agriculture, and Commerce, and elsewhere. Some states have land use data programs also. As cities undertake the planning of their own development, they often collect data on land use. The number of these programs is considerable and their variety rather great. It is not difficult to criticize them on the grounds that the whole present system grew up piecemeal, with varying degrees of co-ordination among the parts but with no central pattern or control. It must also be recognized, however, that each program evolved to meet a recognized need, and that it was designed as well as circumstances permitted at the time. Both public and private data programs have had a clientele, at least moderately satisfied, which has enabled them to continue. Whatever its logical disarray, every part of the present systems of land use data must be considered to have now, or to have had in the past, some significant utility to some influential group.

But there is a greater interest in economic data generally than is expressed by a series of independently developed programs. In a number of phases of our economic and social life, we have voluntarily or through legislation adopted uniform programs for the greater advantage of everyone. Much standardization has been achieved in containers; in such ubiquitous construction materials as nuts and bolts and screws; and in weights and measures. It has also been applied to economic data. There is general agreement on the meaning of such terms as gross national product, national income, disposable personal income, and the like. In the handling of industry data, the standard industrial classification (SIC) has had very wide acceptance. Standard metropolitan statistical regions have been defined, and much data assembled for such areas. The list of cases in which a measure of uniformity of definition has been accepted, either voluntarily or through the legislative process, is very long.

Uniform definitions where achieved for any economic data have advantages which usually far outweigh their local disadvantages. The ability to compare different areas or regions and different time periods is very important. Understanding of a particular geographical area or particular time period is often increased greatly by comparison with other areas and other time periods. Such comparisons help to distinguish between that which is common and general, and that which is peculiar to the particular time and place. Comparative knowledge is often highly valuable. Methods of bringing out facts in local experiences can be given general application over a much wider range, perhaps becoming modified in the process.

The basic difficulty with establishing uniform definitions and concepts is to devise them with the greatest applicability to the various situations. The need is to find the broadest possible degree of commonality. This is often not easy, and may require a great deal of time and study. Situations vary from one part of the country to another, and each particular problem has its ideal data requirements. Some sacrifices of locally ideal characteristics may be necessary in order to have a program of national usefulness. Moreover, some group must pave the way for, and venture upon, the formulation of a uniform program, and that is far from easy. This book constitutes an attempt to formulate a nationally useful program of land use statistics. So far as such a program can be devised and put into practical use, great advantages will accrue for research, for planning, and for decision-making of many kinds, both public and private.

The commonality in our proposed system of land use data lies in two major characteristics: (1) detailed data on land use or activity on the land, at the enumeration and data tabulation level, with classification or grouping of uses only at the later analytical stages; and (2) data recording and processing on the smallest identifiable parcel or areal unit, so that areas may later be grouped in any desired way. The commonality lies in standardized building blocks, which provide the opportunity for use in numerous ways. The system may be described as one of standardized parts capable of an individualized output. It has great flexibility to meet present conditions and problems, and to deal with future situations as they may arise.

Given the multi-centered nature of the American culture, it is impossible—and in the minds of most of us, undesirable as well—to force any program of uniform land use data collection, analysis, and publication on all levels of government and upon all private organizations. Even if a perfect system could be devised, resistance to its forceful adoption would be very great. If a good—but not necessarily perfect—system can be devised, however, it is highly probable that many public agencies and private organizations will follow it to some extent. The advantages of generally comparable data will be so great as to warrant a degree of accommodation to such a uniform system. This has happened with many other types of economic data in the United States.

Modern Methods of Handling Data

Modern methods of handling data, primarily electronic in character, open up enormous possibilities for land use statistics which did not exist a few years ago. In devising any system of statistics, the ability to apply the system in practice is usually a major consideration. Our concept of an ideal system often must be modified to meet the limitations of process; but now the latter has changed so much, and so fast, in recent years as to open up wholly new horizons.

Modern machines can sort, group, summarize, make mathematical calculations, tabulate and store for later use masses of detailed data vastly quicker and cheaper than was possible only a few years ago. This not only makes it possible to handle far more data, and to handle it faster than before, but it permits the development of many new methods of field enumeration. Many former methods of enumeration required the enumerator to do a certain amount of classifying of data or to make calculations based on data while in the field, and often the data had to apply to large tracts or areas. Unless this was done, the office tabulation job was impossibly difficult. Now it is practical to obtain data for smaller parcels, recording what was readily observable on the ground or obtainable from the person interviewed, and leaving any summarizing or computation for later machine work. Moreover, data can be obtained for parcels as defined in one way, and later more detailed information can be obtained for a part of a component parcel with the remainder recalculated by machine. Enormous flexibility and capacity as to amounts of data, areas to which they apply, methods of summarization, and the like mark these machines.

These machines also are capable of transferring data from original cards or tabulation sheets directly to charts or maps, including precise geographic location, with much more speed than can old methods. The location characteristic of land, for example, can be measured or expressed in terms of latitude and longitude co-ordinates, in terms of cadastral surveys, or in one of several other ways, or in some combination of them. These data can be grouped for any unit of area or defined in any way. By means of equivalency tables, data originally identified by one system of location can be grouped into any one of several other systems. Newer data can be substituted for old. Moreover, it should be possible to juxtapose data from different sources or for different time periods for the same tract of land, thus facilitating comparisons of source and time. The same basic data, especially if for relatively small tracts, can be combined into numerous different groupings, thus greatly extending their value.

Modern data-processing machines have another important characteristic as far as land use statistics are concerned: data applicable to one location or stored in one place can be transferred to another point of use very quickly. Thus, it is no longer necessary that each point of data use have its own storehouse of land use data in the form of tabulations, publications, maps, etc. Instead, data obtained in one place or by one agency could be stored in a selected place, ready for use by anyone quickly and inexpensively. Data can be stored relatively inexpensively from one point in time to another; thus, data from one land use survey or other source can be preserved for later use, primarily to provide valuable historical comparisons. Land use data centers for regions or other relatively large areas are becoming much more feasible than once was the case. Data can be fed into central points, put on magnetic tapes and such for rapid manipulation, compared with older data, perhaps replacing it in some cases, and fed back to agencies or organizations in local areas or elsewhere on need. These potentialities on a truly large scale have scarcely been explored. The fact that it is possible to do these things does not prove that there is a real need to do so, or that it would be most economical to do so. Many local organizations probably would prefer to continue their own data collections, even if comparatively simple ones. But certainly new horizons have appeared.

Moreover, modern data processing can be designed to provide for later changes, as more data become available or as new concepts seem more relevant. Thus, provision can be made for change in the future, without at once trying to specify the nature of that change. We shall return, in Chapter IX, to the possibilities of such equipment and to their meaning for future land use data systems.

CHAPTER V.

Brief History of Land Use Information in the United States

Land has been a vital but changing factor in American life, from earliest colonial days down to the present. Hundreds of books and other writings have dealt with historical, political, economic, geographical, and other more or less technical aspects of land—to say nothing of hundreds of novels where land and its use was a central concern. Merely to list all such books and major reports would be a full scale research job in itself.

Our concern in this chapter is with the history of information about land, and more specifically, information about the use of land, as contrasted with other concepts which were considered in Chapter II. Even when thus delimited, there remains a very large volume of information; many writings have considered land and its use, but have not dealt so explicitly with systems of data. Our particular concern is with the latter, and even here we shall be selective, giving more attention to statistical programs and to efforts to improve them. The reader is referred to the appendices to this book. The first one deals explicitly with history, several of the others contain some historical discussion, and the last one is a selected bibliography. In Chapter VI, we shall describe the present nature of the various statistical programs.

Our treatment is topical, and only roughly chronological. Several of the subjects we consider overlapped in time, but it seemed simpler and easier to complete each more or less distinct phase before considering the next, rather than to use a strictly chronological approach. Several of the matters we treat separately were interrelated at the time, too.

An understanding of any present situation and a projection into the future of any course of action is nearly always facilitated by some knowledge of history of the subject matter under consideration. We understand better where we are if we know how we got there; and we have a better idea of where we are going if we know whence we came. This generalization applies to statistics about land. Some data about land are parts of data series that were established long ago, others are of more recent origin. The particularities of each kind of data are in large part traceable to their history. Any changes that may be inaugurated in the future are more likely to reflect past trends and present forces than to be radical departures from past experience.

The Land Ordinance of 1785, with 177 years of North American English settlement history behind it, was both a midpoint and a beginning. Whether the first settlers would have made their ventures just as they did if they had possessed as much land use information as a modern settler would demand is not for anyone to say now. They came and brought with them plans on how to hold and use the land. The kinds of land uses that seemed to be pertinent then to existence in the New World have in some ways been superseded. Some vignettes indicative of the needs and gropings for land-use information at some stages in our past are presented in Appendix A.

Early Concern with Land Taxation

In early decades of American history, most revenue for local government came from taxes based on land. Land was the chief form of tangible wealth, easily observable by any tax collector. An early and pressing concern was how to assess and tax it fairly.

The various colonies and states made many efforts to measure land, to describe its qualities, and to classify it into meaningful categories (see Appendix A for a more detailed discussion). By modern standards, these early efforts at collecting and summarizing data about land seem unsophisticated, even naïve. Broad categories of land uses or land qualities were established, with values assigned on which taxes were levied, that often had no basis except the general judgment of the men involved. But one should recognize that many of these efforts were based upon the best data existent at the time, and that the persons responsible for some of these land classifications were hard-headed by any standards. Their work provided a practical base for government of the time. It may have been rough and ready, but it worked in a pragmatic sense, and it formed the beginning from which later more detailed and more sophisticated data assemblage began.

Resources in the Federal Domain as Occasions for Land Use Data

Throughout our national history, extensive areas of federally owned land have required some attention to data concerning them. The public domain was created by land cessions from the original states, by the Louisiana Purchase, the annexation of Texas, the treaties with Mexico and England about the southwest and northwest, respectively, and by other purchases and treaties. Two-thirds of it was disposed of in a period of somewhat more than a century, in a series of the most active real estate deals in all history. In spite of an open-handed disposal policy, the federal government was forced to obtain some limited knowledge about its land; and as time went on, and some land was reserved permanently for public ownership, the need for better data became evident.

Surveying of land has been an activity which, from settlement and to some extent from pre-settlement periods, has had a relation to the description of land units, economic and, certainly, legal. Activities of public surveyors gave them as individuals considerable insight into the potentiality of unoccupied or tentatively occupied areas to which their services were applied by the colonies. The federal domain naturally claimed principal attention of surveyors and of officials of the national government and of the federal domain territories and states from the time when the race between surveyors and settlers began its primarily westerly course.[1]

Federal land surveyors were early instructed to make a record in their notes of pertinent observations within their range of view as they traversed the section boundary lines in their geometric movements through the newly laid out townships. This process was intended to make a record of land characteristics along the periphery of sections or within a section as could be seen from these peripheries. Some of the facts noted were designated on the township charts which the surveyors filed as one of the definitive products of their labors. In general, however, it remained for appraisals of Indian cession land made in connection with Indian Claims Commission suits—appraisals often covering millions of acres for an individual suit—to bring to light in the 1950's and 1960's the extent to which the land survey that followed each cession had given a basis for land classification. It is unfortunate that promptly after surveys were made both public and private uses of the classifications implicit in them were not made available more widely.[2]

In 1828, the United States Senate directed the President to require the registers and receivers of the respective land offices to make a report to the Commissioner of the General Land Office upon the quantity and quality of the land remaining unsold in their respective districts on June 30, 1828.[3]

[1] William D. Pattison, *Beginnings of the American Rectangular Land Survey System, 1784–1800*, Research Paper No. 50 (Chicago: Department of Geography, University of Chicago, December 1957).

[2] The Bureau of Land Management is required to maintain in its Washington, D.C., office a complete set of all field notes and township plats of each surveyed township in the public domain states. The field notes are filed by state in bound volumes. The township plats are filed in looseleaf form by state, township, and range. These records date back to 1800. Today, there are approximately 6000 volumes of survey notes and 135,000 township plats on file. See U.S. Department of Interior publication entitled *The Public Land Records: Footnotes to American History* (Washington, 1959).

[3] *American State Papers, Public Lands* V, Document 685.

A manifold classification was used by some directors of land offices in their reports at that time. Much land in the upper Mississippi valley was reported as of low grade because it lacked timber and easily accessible drinking water. By use of dredging equipment and tile, in less than seventy years much of the land then properly classified near bottom grade had been shifted to a first-class crop-producing status.

There arose a widespread sense of need for somewhat systematic, if not statistical, information concerning land west of the 100th meridian acquired as a result of the war with Mexico and of the treaty with Britain. The discovery of gold in California and other developments had stimulated hopes for railroad connections with the Pacific Coast. As early as 1853 surveys of possible routes for railways were initiated. It was mostly in the period 1867–1879 that several prominent figures in the United States Geological Survey produced reports designed to call attention to the potential uses of land in the West for agriculture and irrigation, timber, grazing, and mineral production.[4] Major Powell gave special emphasis to the need for liberalizing acreage restrictions in the Homestead Act of 1863 so as to adjust them better to requirements in semi-arid and arid lands of the Great Plains and in much of the Rocky Mountain region. The "voices in the wilderness" were mostly those of scientists. In 1878, the Congress asked the National Academy of Sciences to prepare such a plan for "surveying and mapping the Territories of the United States as will, in their judgments . . . secure the best results at the least possible costs."[5]

Census Data on Land Use

The Census of the United States is the oldest continuous source of data on land use and related activities available in this country; and the activities of the Bureau of the Census in providing such information today are some of the largest in this entire field. Its land use and related data programs are described in Appendix G.

[4] Ferdinand V. Hayden, 1829–1887, George M. Wheeler, 1842–1905, Clarence King, 1842–1901, and John Wesley Powell, 1834–1902, come to mind in this connection.

[5] The 1863 report by F. V. Hayden "On the Geological and Natural History of the Upper Missouri" (Expedition of 1857), in the *Transactions of the American Philosophical Society* (N.S., XII, chapter xii) went far toward enabling the public to see the possible need for man's intervention to win this part of the West. The challenge which this report and George P. Marsh's *Man and Nature* (1864) brought to many advanced thinkers found many former armed service men and others disposed to meet it. From Marsh's book entitled *The Earth as Modified by Human Action,* 1874, and Powell's 1878 report on the *Lands of the Arid Regions of the United States, with a More Detailed Account of the Lands of Utah* (House Executive Document No. 73; 45th Cong., 2d sess.) the sense of need for programs of development west of the 100th Meridian came into the thinking of many.

The setting aside of national monuments and parks operated in its earlier phases rather toward preservation than toward development. The Hot Springs area in Arkansas was set aside in 1832 and an ever-broadening program has come into effect.

The United States was the first country to initiate a regular periodic census of its population. The first census was taken in 1790 and included only four items of inquiry, all directed to population.[6] To locate and enumerate the whole population, in that early period, from an often suspicious and uncooperative citizenry, and with the transportation conditions of the day, was an extremely difficult job which took eighteen months to complete. By 1820, a few inquiries were added about manufactures; in 1840, a few additional ones about agriculture and minerals. But in this latter year there were still only eighty-two inquiries on all the questionnaires used. For these and even for much later censuses, there was no permanent organization, only one assembled for each job and dismantled soon thereafter. Thomas Jefferson, as Secretary of State, directed the first one. A permanent organization was not established until 1902.

In 1880 and 1890, a great many additional inquiries were added to all parts of the census, including agriculture. Many items, such as agricultural tenure, appeared for the first time in the 1880 Census. By this time, the use of special schedules for various kinds of information from those persons concerned was standard practice; but the tabulation and summarization of the returns was still "by hand." In 1925 there began the first of the regular five-year interval Censuses of Agriculture.

Each census has been limited by the knowledge of the farmers or others from whom information was sought, and by their willingness to respond. Although the census has legal power to compel response, this is not used except in rare cases. In the case of information about land, farmers and other land users at an earlier time were often most unsure or inaccurate in their estimates of land acreage. The knowledge and ability of the census enumerators has also always been a conditioning factor. As education has advanced in this country, the ability of both enumerators and respondents has increased. Mechanical methods of handling the voluminous data have evolved, until today extensive use is made of electronic and other modern data-handling equipment. In recent decades, use has been made and is increasing of carefully selected samples, especially for more detailed inquiries, rather than attempting a complete enumeration of all detailed items. For a long time, the Census of Agriculture was summarized only on a county basis (although the first, for 1840, provided some agricultural data by minor civil divisions), but today it is possible to get some data for smaller areas.

Information about the largest areas of land comes from the Census of

[6] Bureau of the Census, *Bureau of the Census: Fact Finder for the Nation* (Washington: U.S. Government Printing Office, 1957) presents an accurate but nontechnical account of the history and functioning of the Census. Carroll D. Wright, *The History and Growth of the United States Census*, prepared for the Senate Committee on the Census (Washington: U.S. Government Printing Office, 1900), presents a detailed account of the evolution of the Census through 1890.

Agriculture. There have been some changes in definitions of farms and in other procedural matters, which have sometimes interfered with strict comparability of one census with another. As economic and social conditions change, changes in definitions are often necessary; in the wisdom that comes with retrospection, it may now be possible to say that not all changes in farm and other definitions were wise, though they may have seemed so at the time. Information on numerous other points, including urban property, comes from other censuses and surveys taken by the Bureau. The Census Bureau has never attempted to complete accounting for all land in the nation, although it has worked from maps which permit a complete checking of all enumeration within specified boundaries. As a result, no check at the national level, except on the basis of small samples, is possible from this direction as to the extent of error in reporting acreage or in the degree of coverage, although other means are used to insure the most nearly complete coverage possible.

In spite of some weaknesses, the census, especially that on agriculture, is the best over-all source of data on land use in the United States, with the longest record of reasonable continuity of data series.

Statistics on Agricultural Production

Because of its economic and social importance in the life of the nation, agriculture became a matter of national concern at a relatively early date. Accurate data on crop acreages, livestock numbers, crop and livestock output, and other aspects of agriculture were greatly needed. The Census of Agriculture was highly valuable, but it came at intervals of ten years, and annual or more frequent estimates of current changes were needed. As a result, the Department of Agriculture began to collect such data; it has had more than 100 years of experience with this effort. Special attention is called to Appendix F, where the present scope of this program is considered more fully.

Permanent agricultural statistical programs are often traced to 1862, when Congress established the Department of Agriculture and directed the Commissioner to collect statistics. In 1863 the Department began the publication of monthly reports on crop conditions and annual reports on agricultural production. Annual estimates of acreages for several principal crops date back to 1866. Since that time, the work has been refined and detailed. Crop acreage and yield data have long been essential to economic analyses in agriculture.

Examples of useful and permanent agricultural land use statistical series published are:

- Harvested crops used for specified purposes annually. 1910–1965, BAE and SRS, USDA[7]
- Cropland used for crops annually, 1910–1965, BAE and SRS, USDA
- Principal crops annually (by individual crops), 1910–1965, BAE and SRS, USDA
- Numbers of farms and uses of land in farms for census years 1880–1920, 1924–1959, Bureau of the Census, USDC (A few items 1850–1870)
- Forest and woodland, commercial and noncommercial, 1920–1965, Forest Service, USDA
- Public-domain land areas and use, 1785–1965, GLO and BLM, U.S. Department of the Interior
- Major uses of land in farms including cropland, pasture, range, forest and special uses, 1880–1960 (five and ten year intervals), BAE and ERS, USDA

The early statistical reports which, beginning July 10, 1863, were published monthly during the summer and bimonthly during the winter, were developed from voluntary reports from crop correspondents in each county. The first reports contained data on conditions of crops and the weather. Regular monthly reports on crop conditions and annual reports on acreage, yield per acre, and production of important crops and numbers of livestock on farms were begun in 1866. In January, 1867, the first annual report on the prices of farm products was issued covering prices for 1866. It marked the real beginning of a continuous series of agricultural statistics under the direction of the Department.[8]

Judged by modern knowledge and capabilities, the early data-gathering programs of the Department of Agriculture used primitive statistical approaches, but the results seem to have had great utility at the time, in spite of errors and discrepancies. Informed people were asked to report on conditions in their locality or on their farms. The Department was limited by the funds at its disposal, by the knowledge and willingness of farmers to respond to it or to communicate with its crop reporters, by methods of transmitting information from one place to another, and by technologies for processing data. The monthly crop condition data were an attempt to forecast later crop output. Biases, in the statistical sense, arose in much

[7] Abbreviations: BAE, Bureau of Agricultural Economics; ERS, Economic Research Service; SRS, Statistical Reporting Service; GLO, General Land Office; BLM, Bureau of Land Management.

[8] U.S. Department of Agriculture, *Century of Service—the First 100 Years of the U.S. Department of Agriculture* (Washington, 1963), p. 15; U.S. Department of Agriculture, *The Agricultural Estimating and Reporting Services of the United States Department of Agriculture*, Misc. Pub. No. 703 (Washington, 1949); U.S. Department of Agriculture, *The Crop and Livestock Reporting Service of the United States*, Misc. Pub. No. 171 (Washington, 1933), p. 4.

of the data; revisions of data on crop acreage and livestock numbers were necessary after each Census of Agriculture—sometimes, quite large revisions which naturally reflected on the accuracy of the intercensal estimates. These frequent and extensive revisions of the data were often confusing to the users of these data.

Economic and statistical analysis became increasingly essential in study of the farm production problems in the early years of the twentieth century. The World War I period and subsequent years added to the demand for economic data. Land use statistics provided bases for a number of programs. Land use statistics became even more important during the years of the great depression of the 1930's and the New Deal agricultural programs. Administration of new land and farm programs relied heavily on land use data and analyses for program planning and implementation. War and postwar changes brought new demands for agricultural statistics.

The crop and livestock estimating services introduced more sophisticated statistical approaches to meet these new and more exacting demands. Statistical sampling theory was utilized to devise samples for enumeration, from which sampling bias would be eliminated and sampling error held to a known and acceptable limit. Aerial photographs provided the basis for sample selection, which had been unavailable previously. Modest but larger funds provided the basis for employing enumerators to observe and report what they saw, and to interview farmers, for the sample areas. Possibly most important of all, a more enlightened and better informed farm population was both able and willing to provide information which had been less freely or less accurately given in an earlier day.

Land use data for the United States have suffered major defects from changes in scope, definition, and area when long historical series are used. A current example is the profound disturbance to land use data series created by the admission of Alaska as a state. Through the 1954 Census of Agriculture, and later for some data series, the "United States" meant forty-eight states; now it means fifty with Alaska and Hawaii included. But Alaska is so very large that it affects the total greatly; and its land uses are so special and different from those in the contiguous forty-eight states as to influence greatly proportionate relationships.

National Forests and Forest Service Land Studies

From about 1873 one can see the beginnings of a movement toward better use of land in forests. As early as 1876 federal investigations in forestry had been started and in 1881, a Division of Forestry was established. It was in 1891, however, that newly enacted legislation enabled President Benjamin Harrison to set aside areas in the federal public domain as the first major forest reserves. It was 1905 before the efforts of President Theodore Roosevelt and Gifford Pinchot to bring about more widespread application of principles of conservation resulted, among other things, in elevating the Bureau of Forestry into the Forest Service. By 1910, the national forest system comprised about 168 million acres of formerly public domain land. Subsequently, under the Weeks Act of 1911, as amended, the federal government purchased certain lands for the purpose of protecting watersheds of navigable streams and for the production of timber. In 1954 some 6,910,000 acres of land utilization project lands were transferred to the Forest Service for administration.[9]

The Forest Service has been collecting data on land use since it was established in 1905. Most of the data gathered has been associated with management of the national forests, but the Nationwide Forest Survey authorized by the McSweeney-McNary Forest Research Act of 1928 is an example of more widespread activity. (For a more detailed statement of Forest Service land data activities, see Appendix C.)

The Nationwide Forest Service Survey has been providing up-to-date information on the use of 776 million acres of forest land or one-third of the total land area of the country. Basic forest resource facts that have been obtained by detailed studies in sample areas and sometimes in more comprehensive areas have included ownership of land and timber; character and condition of forest land; timber site classification; kind, volume, quality, and location of standing timber; amount of timber grown and amount lost due to fire and other natural causes; and amount and kind of timber cut for timber products. The facts concerning these items have been brought together by states and counties. In some instances they have been accompanied by maps on which forest and other types of land are shown.

Distinction has long been maintained between commercial and non-commercial forest land. Commercial refers primarily to timber-producing land while non-commercial generally refers to lands unsuitable for commercial timber production or to lands withdrawn for special purposes, such as national parks.

Repeat surveys have been made for most states about every eight or ten years. Surveys and re-surveys have been limited in coverage by available appropriations. Reports of any date feature the then existing situation and the trends in forest land use that had been of prime importance in the national land use picture.

Periodically, the Forest Service has made comprehensive reports on the

[9] The land utilization project lands have been administered under Title III of the Bankhead-Jones Farm Tenant Act. Nearly 90 per cent of the area administered by the Forest Service has been in national forests. It may be noted, however, that the federal government seldom has complete ownership of all the land within the exterior boundaries of the national forest, or of other units under the administration of the Forest Service.

national timber situation based largely on Forest Survey information. The reports which have been most noteworthy from the standpoint of incorporating new data and thus have been regarded as milestones in appraising forest land and timber supply situations are the so-called "Capper Report" for 1920, "Copeland Report" for 1930, the report on "Resource Conservation" for 1938, the "Reappraisal Report" for 1945, and the latest of such reports "Timber for America's Future" for 1952. A new report is scheduled for publication in 1965. The purpose has been to provide guides for policy on forest land use—both public and private—on a national, state, and local basis.

Land Reclamation as a Factor in Information about Land

In order that some land could be used for agriculture, it had to be irrigated or drained or both. In some naturally fertile but wet areas, drainage was possible by individual farmer efforts, and in some dry areas near streams, it was possible for the individual farmer to divert water for irrigation. In many instances, however, the scale of the necessary works was beyond the ability of any individual, and group efforts, through co-operatives or districts, were necessary. Some projects of each kind have been undertaken by state governments. The federal government has had a major irrigation program since 1902; on many of its projects, drainage is also necessary.

Both irrigation and drainage efforts have required a more detailed knowledge than often was necessary for agricultural use of land not requiring either of these programs. This has necessitated many engineering, soil, agronomic, economic, and other studies of the lands in question, which have often considerably enhanced our knowledge, not only of those particular lands but of all types of land. Some of these studies have been published; many have not been. No regular data series about land use have resulted from irrigation and drainage programs, however, except for the annual crop censuses of the Bureau of Reclamation on federal irrigation projects, and sometimes similar censuses on state or private projects.

Land Use Data for Zoning and for Rural Regional Planning

Zoning implies the authority to classify land according to its suitability, and to enforce the classification of permitted uses on private landowners. In practice, zoning in cities has dealt largely with the suitability of some lands for development, thus restricting industrial, commercial, or other development to those lands, and prohibiting it elsewhere. The "purity" of residential neighborhoods, from invasion by other uses, has been preserved in this way, for instance. Various kinds of zones have been established, even within residential zones, as for single family homes versus apartments, or by minimum size of dwelling lot which in turn greatly influences the kind of residential use, and so on. In practice, zoning in rural areas has been more in terms of preventing use—either use of certain kinds, or any resident use of any kind. Those applying rural zoning in a county sought to prevent farm settlement where such settlement would create unwarranted burdens for schools, roads, and local administration and would, moreover, interfere with the best use of the region as a whole, such as for forestry and recreation. The first application of the zoning method to a distinctly rural land problem (Oneida County, Wisconsin, May 16, 1933) followed by seventeen years the first urban comprehensive zoning ordinance (New York City, 1916).

For zoning to be applied intelligently by those responsible for formulating its regulations, and for it to be upheld in the courts, substantial amounts of dependable and relevant information were necessary. Moreover, once zoning restrictions were applied, they had to be enforced if they were not to become a farce; this required on-the-ground inspections, which in turn developed more information about land use. Thus, zoning has led, directly or indirectly, to substantial increases in knowledge about land and its use; however, in many instances, this knowledge has not been widely disseminated, nor well organized, nor preserved for future use.

Many of the basic, needed studies on rural lands have been made by agricultural experiment stations and other research organizations, as part of their research studies. One purpose of such studies was to improve knowledge about or understanding of rural lands, their characteristics, and their uses—knowledge which might be used in various ways, including in the teaching of college and other students. Such studies have typically been published.[10] They continue to be made. While these studies have often been highly important for the purposes for which they were undertaken, they have rarely, if ever, led to continued data series—they were one-shot affairs.

For urban zoning, the data collection and analysis process has taken a somewhat different form. There are no institutions of higher learning which perform for cities the role which the land-grant colleges perform for rural areas. With some notable exceptions, university and college people have not conducted the research and fact-finding studies which have provided much of the basis needed for urban zoning. Instead, the zoning authorities

[10] It is not practical to attempt to list all such studies; some are included in the bibliography at the end of this book, and some are in turn listed in the bibliographies included there. For a comprehensive and critical review and appraisal of the work done up to the mid-1940's, see Leonard A. Salter, Jr., *A Critical Review of Research in Land Economics* (Minneapolis: University of Minnesota Press, 1948).

or administration have had to collect their own factual material. This has been done in various ways, generally not comparable from city to city, and at varying levels of detail and accuracy. With few exceptions, the data so collected have not been published, in the way that the studies of the rural areas have been published. Like them, however, the urban studies have generally not led to systematic, continued data collection and data analysis programs. Zoning enforcement has required inspection on the ground, as has been noted, but the information obtained by such inspections has generally not been systematically recorded and used in a data-analysis sense.

When rural regional planning began or acquired greater emphasis, this too required the use of data about land and its use. The Tennessee Valley Authority found it necessary to assemble data about land in its reservoir areas, and to some extent in its whole service area. It acquired the lands flooded by the reservoirs, and sometimes considerable surrounding acreages as well; for these, naturally, careful appraisals were necessary. The river basin planning work of several federal agencies, which has evolved over the past three decades or longer, has involved extensive use of data about land and its use. Sometimes such data have been available from the Census of Agriculture or other specialized data programs, but sometimes extensive data-gathering and data-analysis programs have been undertaken as part of these river basin planning studies. In some areas, such as the Missouri Basin, the latter have been quite detailed, with detailed mapping and field study of at least some of the lands involved. Like both rural and urban zoning studies, however, these river basin or regional studies have not led to continued data series; while the results of the studies have sometimes, but not always, been published, the basic data themselves have usually not been published as such.

These zoning and rural regional planning efforts have all led to substantially increased general knowledge of the areas concerned, and each has both compiled and used much data about land. If they have not led directly into continued and published data series, they have often acquired the basic data upon which such series could be built. The necessary field work—often the most difficult and usually the most expensive part of data assembly—has usually been done. Since urban zoning, rural zoning, and rural regional planning still continue and still include data collection at the ground level, it is evident that some of the basic ingredients for comprehensive data series on land use exist in such programs.

Soil Surveys and Conservation Needs Inventories

As part of our general knowledge about land, especially its physical characteristics and their economic importance, the soil surveys and land use capability classifications which have grown out of them have been of great value. Soil surveys began before 1900. Over the years, they have been extended greatly, not only in geographic extent but in range of detail and in quantitative measurement of various characteristics, and also in their interpretation for use by farmers and others.

C. F. Marbut's study entitled *The Soils of the United States,* published as Part III of the Atlas of American Agriculture in 1935, summarized results of earlier surveys in various parts of the United States. Co-operation between state agricultural experiment stations and the Soil Survey staff of the U.S. Department of Agriculture had produced the foundations for what had been theretofore achieved and was then projected. In 1937, the first Soil Survey Manual was issued, and the U.S. Department of Agriculture's 1938 Yearbook, entitled *Soils and Men,* contained a comprehensive summary about soils in the United States and their uses. In 1943, a farmers' bulletin on classifying land for conservation farming appeared, and in 1949, there appeared in *Soil Science* a description of the federal system of soil classification as then envisaged.

In 1935, Charles E. Kellogg and J. Kenneth Ableiter developed a method of rural land classification (USDA Technical Bulletin 469, February, 1935) which was based directly upon the use of soil surveys. In McKenzie County, North Dakota, for instance, a soil survey was made; other factors were also recognized, and a classification of land for tax appraisal purposes was developed. Geographic and economic factors such as location with respect to markets are important in this classification also.

With the greatly heightened interest in soil erosion and soil conservation of the 1930's, interest in land classification, largely but not wholly based on soil surveys or at least upon soil survey concepts, grew and led to a system of land use capability classification.[11] Such factors as slope and past erosion were added to the traditional factors of soil depth, profile, and texture, to develop a general land capability classification, ranging from Class I soils suitable for a wide variety of uses without need for special conservation measures, to Class IV lands generally marginal for crop production, and on down to Class VIII lands unsuited even for grazing or forestry.[12] For a further description of the current work of the Soil Conservation Service along this general line, see Appendix D.

The period 1957–1962 was to see outstanding developments in the classifying of soil in terms of characteristics. The Soil Survey staff of the Soil Conservation Service issued a volume entitled *Soil Classification: A Com-*

[11] For a general discussion of this period and the evolution of soil conservation information, see R. Burnell Held and Marion Clawson, *Soil Conservation in Perspective* (Baltimore: The Johns Hopkins Press for Resources for the Future, Inc., 1965).

[12] A. A. Klingebiel and P. H. Montgomery, *Land-Capability Classification,* Agriculture Handbook No. 210 (Washington: U.S. Department of Agriculture, 1961).

prehensive System (Seventh Approximation), a publication many readers regard as directed to the advanced thinkers of this and other countries. In 1962 nine agencies or services of the U.S. Department of Agriculture, having constituted a Conservation Needs Committee to survey the conservation situation, issued two publications. One of these is the volume entitled *Basic Statistics of the National Inventory of Soil and Water Conservation Needs.* A brief treatment is entitled *Land Resources: Capabilities, Uses, and Conservation Needs.* A third volume will present an over-all summary and analysis of the land and water conservation situation.

These soil surveys and land use capability classification systems were neither statistical data series nor was their primary emphasis upon activity on the land, or land use as the term is used here. But they have provided valuable basic data on the physical characteristics of land, and have added greatly to our understanding of land and the factors affecting its use. In any system of land use or activity data that may be developed, these land classifications often provide a useful basis for relating land use with natural qualities of the land.

Land Use Summaries

The United States Department of Agriculture, the Bureau of the Census, and other organizations have collaborated for many years in the preparation of summaries of land use information. Some of the early efforts began roughly at the time of the first world war, when O. E. Baker began preparing maps and other summaries of available data. The USDA Yearbooks of the early 1920's presented an analysis of land use data in a fashion unknown up to that time. Following each of the agricultural censuses, for many years, graphic summaries of various aspects of land use have been prepared jointly by the Department of Agriculture and the Bureau of the Census.

Efforts to present an over-all picture or statistical summary of land use in the United States, accounting for the total area of all land, have been made for several years.[13] A basic starting point for such summaries has been the Census of Agriculture, but data have been obtained from various other sources, including the federal and state agencies responsible for public land management. The purpose of these summaries has not been to obtain new data from landowners and users, but rather to summarize for ready use and general understanding the data which exist in various places. They have been successful in this direction. They have also clearly revealed the serious

[13] The most recent one is Hugh H. Wooten, Karl Gertel, and William C. Pendleton, *Major Uses of Land and Water in the United States with Special Reference to Agriculture; Summary for 1959,* Agricultural Economics Report 13 (Washington: FED-ERS, U.S. Department of Agriculture, 1962).

discrepancies and divergences among various sources of data about land—discrepancies and divergences which in turn largely grow out of the lack of standardized definitions and statistical approaches. It has, in fact, been the experience in preparing these summaries which has underlain, in part, the present effort to devise a uniform and improved system of land use data.

Contributions of the National Resources Planning Board to Land Use Information

Major economic and social changes under way in agriculture were enormously sharpened up by the short but extremely severe economic depression immediately after the first world war, and later by the longer and more serious Great Depression of the 1930's. These events led to a heightened general interest in land and its use. The USDA Yearbook for 1923 had a series of articles by L. C. Gray, O. E. Baker, and others on various aspects of the farm land use problem—articles which were unusual for their time in breadth, perception, and insight. The continuing farm problem of the 1920's led to the calling of a national conference on land utilization in 1931, under the general auspices of the federal Department of Agriculture and the agricultural colleges. A continuing national land-use planning committee was established, staffed by federal officials and college presidents or other highly placed officials. A series of reports were prepared.[14]

With the coming of the New Deal, a national planning effort was launched by the organization which ultimately came to be known as the National Resources Planning Board. A Land Committee was established under its auspices, which largely replaced the former National Land-Use Planning Committee, with many of the same persons continuing to work on the problem. The Land Committee issued a series of reports, which are listed in the bibliography at the end of this book. Some of these reports were prepared largely or wholly within a single federal agency, others involved the co-operation of several agencies. For the most part, the reports were built on the basis of available data, although in the case of the one on soil erosion a considerable amount of original field work was reported for the first time. Most of the focus of the Land Committee was on rural land problems, but including forestry, grazing, and recreation as well as crop farming. Some attention was given to urban land problems, however. One who re-reads these reports today cannot but be impressed with the knowl-

[14] See *The Problems of "Submarginal" Areas, and Desirable Adjustments with Particular Reference to Public Acquisition of Land*, National Land-Use Planning Committee and National Advisory and Legislative Committee on Land Use (Washington: U.S. Government Printing Office, April 1933), not only for its own content but for a list of reports issued by this Committee.

edge and the insights of the men who produced these reports—many deal with problems then apparent but yet unsolved.

Some of the action programs of the New Deal more or less grew out of these reports by the Land Committee. In particular, the submarginal land purchase program clearly originated here, and was led by some of the same people, notably L. C. Gray.

This work of the Land Committee was not one of land data programs as such, but it did arouse a great deal of general public interest in land problems of all kinds, particularly those where people were more or less stranded or where land resources were used badly. These studies did reveal the shortcomings of then available information and statistics about land, and the discrepancies among different sources. Had this work continued, it is possible that a material improvement in land use statistics would have resulted from it. However, Congress terminated the NRPB in 1943.

Metropolitan Regional Planning's Dependence on Land Use Data

More or less concurrently with the development of urban land zoning, and interacting with it, has been the development of metropolitan or large city planning. A major component of such plans has always been land use, and this in turn has required the acquisition of considerable information about the land, its basic physical qualities, its present use, and its potentialities.

The first official metropolitan regional planning in America (disregarding such early plans as the bringing of Washington, D.C., into being) was carried out in Boston with the appointment of metropolitan commissions for sewerage in 1889, parks in 1893, and water in 1895. These three commissions were combined in 1919 into the Metropolitan District Commission. In 1923 in the Boston area, regional planning received recognition in the appointment of the Metropolitan Planning Division.

The Regional Plan of New York and Its Environs was undertaken under the auspices of the Russell Sage Foundation in 1924. The results were presented in graphic form, indicating the areas best suited for business, industry, recreational use and open spaces. The plan was advisory in character. It was prepared to give guidance to over 400 municipalities in three states. Its scope in time extended first for thirty-five years. A regional plan association was formed to promote the carrying out of projects and to keep the plan up to date.

A group of business and civic organizations of the regions contiguous to and including Philadelphia, Wilmington, Trenton and Camden in 1928 raised a fund to cover the cost of surveys, studies and preparation of a comprehensive regional plan. To administer the funds the Regional Planning Federation of the Philadelphia Tri-State District was incorporated in May, 1928.

From beginnings in these three centers in eastern United States, studies of land uses in the peripheries and in the built-up sections of major cities have come along with varying emphasis and in rapidly increasing numbers of regions. Information about recent or current metropolitan planning studies is found in Appendices B and H.

The trend towards 100 percent data coverage of parcels within the urban areas subjected to study has been unmistakable. Much of the information collected for a particular survey has continuing value, especially when in a form that is consistent with updating. This relates not merely to the extent of structural and other improvements, but to assessed values, tax status, records of violations of ordinances, etc.

Special mention must be made, even in a brief historical account, of the real property surveys made in a number of the larger cities during the 1930's. These grew out of a recognized need for more accurate and detailed data, to cope with the serious urban problems of the day—decadent areas, tax delinquency, idle properties, bad housing, and the like. At the same time, these surveys were possible only because of major national public works programs to provide employment for otherwise unemployed people. These various federal programs made funds available to the cities to undertake these property surveys.

The various surveys differed somewhat in their natures; some have led to continuing data series for municipal use, others have not. In general, their primary concern was with housing; a great deal of data was assembled on numbers of housing units, their condition, facilities, age, occupancy, rentals, mortgages, changes in use, and the like. Other data were assembled, in at least some surveys, about the occupants—income, race, family composition, etc. Some surveys were essentially limited to residential property, while others included all kinds of property. The data were summarized by variable units—census tracts for Philadelphia and Cleveland, blocks for Chicago. The latter is noteworthy for publishing maps and tables showing actual use of parcels of land (by sixteen broad land use categories), summarized on a block basis as to area but identifiable on the maps by much smaller parcels.

These surveys generally gave little attention to land, as such. In contrast with many detailed tabulations of data on housing characteristics, there are few or no tabulations on land area in various uses. Nevertheless, these surveys did provide a great deal of useful information closely related to land, and they were a stage in the evolution of modern data on urban land use.

There has been a very recent trend toward assembling and keeping available much of the data on rental and other income from individual parcel in a form consistent with assembling facts concerning comparable propertie as might be needed by assessors, appraisers, borrowers and lenders, an purchasers, public and private. Its growth can be traced in considerabl measure to the participation of the federal agencies in the acquisition cost of rights-of-way, in costs of studies to select areas for urban renewal, etc Federal participation in a given urban renewal project can be approved fo a stated portion of a city only as the need can be shown to be clear b comparison with similarly needy portions of other cities and in comparison with other portions of the same city.

Modern urban land use data have become of vital importance and bid fair to have outstanding growth in volume and value. The outthrust of land uses from a city into its expansion areas has brought to the fore some issues with reference to taxation and the converting of fringe land of certain descriptions into uses inconsistent with further field-crop and other food-raising operations.

Since the end of World War II, most of the larger metropolitan areas of the United States have undertaken comprehensive planning studies of which land use has nearly always been a major part. Many of these studies have been oriented toward transportation. As cities have grown in the United States, a hiatus has often developed between the problems of the economic city or congregation of cities, and the limited governmental powers of the central city, or even of any group of cities. Special function metropolitan districts have been established in several instances. Planning, including land use planning, has often been carried out on a metropolis-wide scale, even when no single unit of government possessed the power to carry out the plans.

The importance and use of statistics on land for urban areas generally and for the wide range of programs grouped under the general heading of "housing" are considered in Appendix H, which reports the interest of the Housing and Home Finance Agency in this subject. The importance of such information has increased greatly in the past decade or two, and seems likely to grow further in the years ahead. As the need for more detailed, more accurate, more relevant, and more usable data is demonstrated, it seems highly probable that the present efforts to improve such data will continue.

A great deal has been accomplished in metropolitan planning, as far as land use data are concerned, yet progress has been far from even among the various metropolitan areas. Some have relatively good data systems, with provision for updating and for preserving records about past land uses, and with flexibility to use the same basic data for different purposes and for different areal groupings. More typically, metropolitan land data systems are deficient in one or more of these desirable characteristics. The most serious weakness in their data about land, however, is that each metropolitan area has evolved its own data system without much reference to the data systems of other metropolitan areas; geographic comparability is therefore lacking. A national data series on urban land uses could not, therefore, be assembled from these various metropolitan studies. But the basic elements of adequate data systems are either available or could be obtained without much modification of present data programs; great improvement in metropolitan land use data systems is therefore within comparatively easy reach. One basic purpose of this book and of the pamphlet reprinted as Appendix I is to help in their evolution.

Transportation Planning and Land Use Data

Transportation systems use land, even when their primary medium of movement is water or air. However, their most vital effect on land is in the uses of other land which transportation makes possible or profitable. In the relationships between different areas of land, a major obstacle is distance, both physical and economic. A basic and unalterable characteristic of land is location and areal extent; it is simply impossible to have two or more tracts of land occupy one and the same spot. Transfer of goods, persons, and ideas between two or more tracts requires time and effort; to the extent that time and effort can be reduced, the different tracts can be brought into closer relationship with each other.

Historically in the United States, transportation has been a vital factor in economic development. A few of the major transportation events are noted in Appendix A. Early settlement in this country was often oriented to streams and other natural water transportation routes. Later, passable roads gradually came into being, and still later, canals and railroads were built. As new methods of transportation came into use, they opened up markets and access to and from the new areas, thus providing a major economic stimulus to the development of the newly available areas. At the same time, such new transportation routes and methods often led to the decline of the older areas; the latter simply could not face the competition from the newer and more productive areas. Agriculture began to decline, with farm abandonment, in parts of New England as early as 1830, largely because transportation routes brought products from more fertile western areas so cheaply that the older areas simply could not compete. This replacement of older by newer areas, as transportation has changed, is a phenomenon by no means confined to the past, but may be observed in many urban areas today.

These earlier transportation developments often had little formal planning and little data on land use and land potentials assembled, with still less information published and with no continuing data series arising out of them.

The railroad net for the United States was largely completed by the first world war. The basic highway network was completed then or earlier, but the enormous improvement of roads since then, has transformed that early network into a very differently functioning transportation system.

Since World War II there has been a vast increase in transportation planning, especially in and around cities. The development of a metropolitan transportation plan has sometimes been a major part of the general plan for a region. While such plans are nearly always called transportation plans, in fact they have been largely the result of state highway planning programs. The characteristics of some of these studies are discussed and reviewed by Zettel and Carll.[15]

For many years there had been a realization in the field of highway planning that travel is related to land use, or more specifically, that travel is a function of the spatial separation of activities and the intensity and characteristic of the different types of land use. However, until after World War II very little work was done to specify the nature of this functional relationship.

One of the earliest landmarks in the development of our understanding of the land use-travel relationship was the work done in the San Juan, Puerto Rico, transportation study, organized in 1948. Another phase in the development of this field was a study by Robert B. Mitchell and Chester Rapkin of the Institute for Urban Land Use and Housing Studies at Columbia University in 1950. This study was later revised and published as the book, *Urban Traffic, A Function of Land Use,* in 1954.

The next major development in this field was the work done at the Detroit Metropolitan Area Traffic Study (DATS) from 1953 to 1955. Before DATS, most studies, except for the San Juan study, either dealt only with existing traffic demands and made no forecasts, or they expanded all traffic movements uniformly according to the trend in the traffic growth rate. A few transportation studies had recognized that differential growth in land development caused differential rates of increase in traffic movements, and in these studies individual traffic "growth factors" were applied to each subarea based on estimates of the rate of land development in each subarea.

Most transportation studies that have been organized since DATS (beginning with the Chicago Area Transportation Study in 1955) have identified

[15] Richard M. Zettel and Richard R. Carll, *Summary Review of Major Metropolitan Area Transportation Studies in the United States,* prepared as information for the California Division of Highways in connection with the development of a "Prospectus for a Comprehensive Transportation Study in the San Francisco Bay Area." This is a special report by the Institute of Transportation and Traffic Engineering, University of California, Berkeley, 1962.

land use at either end of an individual's trip, e.g., a work trip from residential land use to a manufacturing land use. In addition many of the studies have made detailed land use inventories. Travel forecasts in these studies have been based, at least in part, on the analysis of existing land use-travel relationships and some type of land use activity forecast.

Section 9 of the Federal-Aid Highway Act of 1962, approved October, 1962, amended chapter 1 of title 23, United States Code by the addition of a new section 134 which reads as follows:

> It is declared to be in the national interest to encourage and promote the development of transportation systems embracing various modes of transport in a manner that will serve the States and local communities efficiently and effectively. To accomplish this objective the Secretary shall cooperate with the States, as authorized in this title, in the development of long-range highway plans and programs which are properly coordinated with plans for improvements in other affected forms of transportation and which are formulated with due consideration to their probable effect on the future development of urban areas of more than fifty thousand population. After July 1, 1965, the Secretary shall not approve under section 105 of this title any program for projects in any urban area of more than fifty thousand population unless he finds that such projects are based on a continuing comprehensive transportation planning process carried on cooperatively by States and local communities in conformance with the objectives stated in this section.

With this responsibility laid down by the 1962 Highway Act, comprehensive transportation studies sponsored by state highway departments and in co-operation with the Bureau of Public Roads can be expected to continue as well as increase in number. The planning process in these studies is closely co-ordinated with policy making and program administration and is organized with the objective of achieving agreement on action programs founded on factual information. Ten elements have been identified for which inventories and analyses are required in order to provide the necessary factual information, one of which is land use data.[16]

[16] Instructional Memorandum 50–2–63 (Washington: U.S. Department of Commerce, Bureau of Public Roads, March 27, 1963). Basic elements for which inventories and analyses are required are as follows:

1. Economic factors affecting development
2. Population
3. Land use
4. Transportation facilities including those for mass transportation
5. Travel patterns
6. Terminal and transfer facilities
7. Traffic control features
8. Zoning ordinances, subdivision regulations, building codes, etc.
9. Financial resources
10. Social and community-value factors, such as preservation of open space, parks and recreational facilities; preservation of historical sites and buildings; environmental amenities; and aesthetics.

The scope of the inventories and the extent to which the various analyses need to be carried will vary depending upon such factors as city size, age, proximity to large cities and growth potential.

The metropolitan transportation planning studies of the past have suffered from the same deficiencies as the general metropolitan planning studies, as far as data about land and its use are concerned. There has typically been a lack of flexibility to meet other needs from the same basic data; and there has also typically been inadequate or no provision for keeping up to date the information once collected. Although these problems are being considered and solved in many of the more recent studies, the lack of comparability between areas and between time periods has been serious, since it has resulted in much duplication of effort. Nevertheless, these metropolitan transportation studies have collected a great deal of information which could be made the basic building blocks for a vastly improved system of land use data. The means whereby this might be accomplished are outlined in Appendix I, the *Manual* of the Urban Renewal Administration and the Bureau of Public Roads, and is the objective of the present study.

Our Land Use Statistics Viewed in an International Perspective

The preceding vignettes from the experience in the United States illustrating need for, interest in, and piecemeal or better than piecemeal efforts to provide land use statistics leave one with a sense of curiosity as to whether our history has rated us high or low in an international comparison.

Some references to European developments west of the Iron Curtain follow.

Great Britain. Information about land uses has had much attention in Britain during most of the past century. The rise of sea power in imperial Germany was seen early by British citizens as making it important that not too little land be engaged in food production there. The annual collection of agricultural returns for the acreages of crops and grass was initiated in 1866, the same year in which annual crop data were begun in the United States. Another agricultural land use item, rough grazings, was added in 1891. The arable land acreage which was about 16.2 million acres in 1891–1895, fell to 70 percent of that amount by 1938, leaped to 111 percent of it in 1944, and in the 1960's is but slightly above the area of 70 years before.[17] Much of the land transferred to urban uses from agricultural uses

[17] R. H. Best and J. T. Coppock explain some reasons for the comparative unchangeableness (except in wartime) of rural land uses in the several regions: ". . . stability has been the characteristic feature of the eastern counties which are by nature best suited to arable farming. The middle belt has been an area of considerable fluctuation. . . . This area, particularly the heavy lands of the Midlands proper, has been most affected by mechanization in the past 20 years. The west, climatically unfavorable to arable farming but with sufficient readily cultivable soils, has shown throughout an emphasis on grass; but the nature of the soil, the maintenance of ploughing skills through the necessity to reseed grass at intervals, and the relatively large acreage of temporary or semi-permanent grass have made it possible

d been under the plow, but in wartime, the arable acreage underwent nsiderable expansion. These changes have given point to the Land ilization Survey which L. Dudley Stamp developed about 1930, and to land use studies largely centered at Wye College, University of London, der direction of Gerald Percy Wibberley.[18] Precision in the maps has en greatly aided by the availability of Ordnance Survey maps from a ntury earlier.

On the urban side, interest in Britain, as in other countries, centers on) the acreage in residential and other urban uses, and the trends it has own; and (2) the extent of public planning and its relation to the use of nd. Attempts at measuring the urban area have lagged far behind those r rural land uses. Measurement of major urban areas at regular intervals as begun under the 1947 Town and Country Planning Act. The Land tilization Survey in the 1930's had placed the total urban area of England d Wales at 2,748,000 acres. The estimate made in 1937 by the Ministry Agriculture and Forestry was 55 percent larger, and for 1950–51 Best d Coppock estimated the total urban area of England and Wales at ,601,908; and Scotland at 468,699, or a total for Great Britain of ,070,607.[19] Considering the vast expansion in urban land between the 930s and the 1950s and certain important errors in data used by the Ministry, the Land Utilization Survey figure for the early 1930's is held to e substantially correct. A 20-year increase in urban land in England and Vales is thus suggested to be about 30 percent.

Under the 1947 Act on Town and Country Planning, planning authorities England, Wales and Scotland were asked to prepare as part of their evelopment plans a comprehensive statement of existing acreages under arious forms of land use in county boroughs, large burghs, and other urban reas for which Town Maps are produced. Planning of land uses in populated places has become a prime factor in England, Wales and Scotland.

Continental European Countries. One must distinguish between naked or minimum cadasters on the one hand, and those that are clothed with land use designations and even productivity ratings on the other. Maps and istings designed to show the qualifications of a tract for high or low tax ssessments were soon found in many countries to call for land use and land

---

o increase the arable markedly in times of necessity. Thus in the west climate has been he dominant physical control, in the centre soils, while in the east climate and soil combine o maintain a large arable acreage . . . soils can reinforce or offset the effects of climate s the sandy soils of Lancashire and the clays of Essex show, and demand can be reinforced y compulsion in times of war." *The Changing Use of Land in Britain* (London: Faber and Faber, 1962), p. 95.

18 Miss A. Coleman, London University, was mentioned in 1960 as having initiated a survey similar to that of the 1930's.

19 Best and Coppock, *op. cit.*, pp. 168 and 169.

quality distinctions either incorporated in them or provided in close c junction.

Cadasters showing at least boundaries of owned parcels were of v early origin.[20] Land registers came soon to have much of their data p sented on maps. These, when highly developed, included designations land use and numerical ratings of quality by fields or subunits of the vari tracts.

Sweden and Denmark are reported to have included early use of m and of use classification markings by fields. In Sweden, the value of land survey as the foundation of the land register was early recognized a in 1628, land surveyors were given civil service status by the governme In 1691, a land survey for Swedish Pomerania was ordered. The instructi for this survey went beyond the ordinary cadaster and showed an intenti to produce an economic inventory. Land use categories, such as cropla hay meadow, pasture, swamp, stony or wasteland, heath, brushland, wo land, and forest were distinguished. The texture and productive quality the soil, the carrying capacity of the pasture, and the composition and sta of the woodland and forest were gauged and recorded. In the 160C Denmark applied similar principles in carrying through her *toende hartko* survey. The major revision of this work occupied the period 1802–184 and for about 80 percent of Denmark the maps, the field distinctions to form and land use, and the productivity ratings (1 to 24), all carefu mapped, have afforded useful guides in land tax assessments into the mid 1900's.[21]

In rural Germany, apart from the portion of Pomerania temporarily und Swedish control, and notably in Mecklenburg-Schwerin and in Prussi cadasters were early supplemented by data on land uses and by productivi ratings. In 1880, there were begun for all of Germany census statistics usi land use categories which, while involving less detail than shown in t land use and crop harvest reports for 1938, 1943, 1945 and 1946, f example, were of great pioneering value.[22] Under a statute of 1934, autho

[20] Even the origin of the word (French, cadastre; German, Kataster; Italian, catasto) so far back historically that there is difference of view as to whether it derives from Rom capitastrum (by abbreviation, catastrum) which was the head-tax register of the lat Romans, or from a Greek word meaning "down-list" or notebook. The register of land property is said to have been introduced in the early Roman period of the Kings, and t Greek-rooted title may have come West at that time. According to Th. Dreux, *Le cadast et l'impot foncier* (Paris: Librairie de renseignement Technique, 1933), Asian uses of su land registers preceded those of Europe. A register of the size, location and ownership landholdings apparently dates back to about 3,000 B.C. in Egypt.

[21] Charles L. Stewart, "Some Aspects of Land Appraisal Abroad," *Journal of the Americ Institute of Real Estate Appraisals* (renamed *The Appraisal Journal*), II, 3 (April 1934 89–193. Reference to Denmark's *toende hartkorn* system is based on Christian Rothe Beretning om den in Aaret 1844 for Kongariget indforte nye Iordsekuld faetnings: Baese og Historie, Copenhagen, 1844.

[22] Statistics for these four years were published for the British Occupation Zone, with a

zation was given for a uniform valuation system for all of Germany. This was about half completed when World War II began. Governments of occupation from Great Britain, France, and the United States gave this work encouragement. The sum total of data supporting the uniform valuation for German rural land has gone far toward creating an outstanding example of what agronomists and economists can achieve by teamwork.

The planning picture in continental European regions and cities west of the Iron Curtain affords much of interest. A few references must suffice. The Ruhr district, with its seven major river basins, is an outstanding example of regional co-operation in the use of natural resources. The Ruhr district is referred to as "one of the busiest and most crowded spots in the Western World. Within its 4,300 square miles are concentrated some 8 million people and about two-fifths of West Germany's entire industrial capacity, notably coal mining, iron and steel production, steel fabrication, and manufacture of heavy chemicals." The Genossenschaften "are the only organization in the world to have designed, built, and operated an integrated regional system of waste disposal and water supply facilities."[23]

City planning with an accent on slum clearance preceded World War II. Reconstruction of war-damaged portions of cities, a special kind of urban renewal, took the center of the stage in numerous British and continental areas following that conflict.

In Britain, much attention has been given to "exurbia," the quasi-rural domiciles of rich city folks, and to "linurbia," distant dormitory settlements along main transport routes. Planning efforts have involved restrictions far beyond the law of nuisances. Stimulated by reconstruction following war damage, by slum clearance, and by rising standards of living, Britain's cities have overshot their boundaries, and "overspill" population has been created. The favor which Ebenezer Howard showed for garden cities in the 1890's is having more than a little realization in Britain two-thirds of a century later. The new towns established in the postwar period a short distance outside of immediate metropolitan areas in Britain were slow in becoming well established. Within the last few years, however, those of the past have proved a success, administratively, socially, and, at last, financially. In 1961, the government set up a Commission for the New Towns. A second wave of such communities is in progress and apparently with

---

evident purpose of showing the extent of change and stability in the land uses and agricultural output incident to World War II. Among interesting distinctions shown the following may be illustrative: grass grown on arable land for grazing; land plowed under (green manures); uncultivated land; total arable land; gardenland, house gardenland (ornamental and small private gardens, parks, lawns), cattle pasture (a) rich and good pasture; (b) medium pastures; and (c) inferior pastures; bldgs., yards, ways r.ways; air, sport and training grounds, also church yards and public parks.

[23] Resources for the Future, Inc., *Annual Report, 1963* (Washington: Resources for the Future, Inc., 1963), p. 22.

approval from persons of many shades of opinion. Projects for new towns two to three times more distant from major cities than the earlier ones have been progressing recently.

On the Continent new centers well within the metropolitan ring have been developed in Amsterdam and The Hague to a limited degree, and more notably in Hamburg, Paris, Milan, and Rome.

Renewal of portions of core areas of cities, sometimes combining slum clearance with other objectives, while believed before World War II to be more advanced in several countries of Europe than in the United States, has generally proceeded more slowly than in the United States in the latest decade. Not only have urban renewal programs under national auspices been in effect in Great Britain, France, and Denmark, but recently have been initiated or projected in steps toward national programs in the Netherlands, Sweden, West Germany, and Italy. Urban renewal programs without benefit of national programs preceded national initiative in most of these countries, although assistance from the central governments in respect to planning, housing and road building helped to make them operative.

In urban portions of most European countries cadasters have been clothed at least scantily with information about land improvements. The French appear to have been among the more advanced in developing cadastral booklets for owners of real estate property, each such booklet serving as a kind of abstract of a tract's economic performance in recent years. In planning for consolidation of scattered holdings of rural land, nearly every country of western Europe has a record of activity.

Again, on the rural side, the surface working of minerals in strip mine operations in Britain and in western Europe has been subjected to central government control requiring re-establishment of surfaces, minimizing erosion and other disturbing effects, and facilitating normal utilization. Also wartime regulations to preserve emphasis on food production as a prime use of land have had continued emphasis, although with various modifications.

Both direct and indirect planning of land use has thus had a large place in countries of Europe. Space does not allow here an adequate treatment of this subject even for western Europe, to say nothing of other important parts of the world. Comparing the way in which land uses and information about them have progressed in the United States and in some other countries, a few points can be added.

1. Air photography and photogrammetry have done much to equalize between this country and some European countries, the fullness of coverage the accuracy of area determinations, and some other aspects of land use data. Land use data for European countries in which cadasters had been given a high degree of accuracy under supervision of central and local

governmental officers have needed less adjustment (since air photographs have supplemented their materials) than have land use data for most jurisdictions in this country.

2. Only in Germany, the United Kingdom, Sweden and one or two other European countries can one find fullness of coverage of land use items fairly comparable to that in the United States over such extensive periods of time.

3. Regional planning, assuming a region to include much more territory than a metropolitan area, has led to administrative applications in this country, mainly in the Tennessee Valley. In that valley, however, the intensive controls and applications of development capital have been concentrated in the creation of reservoirs, new waterfronts, hydro-electric and steam plants, fertilizer production and some forestry developments, but a larger proportion of the agricultural area has had its benefits restricted to less expensive electric power and test-demonstration fertilizers. A comparison can be made with Germany's Ruhr coal jurisdiction. This jurisdiction, established in 1920, has been one of Western Europe's most notable illustrations of regional planning in which a statutory body was authorized to act either by controlling and co-ordinating, or by actually carrying out plans which will serve the advance of an individual district. The Ruhr jurisdiction, besides having authority to develop a comprehensive plan, has had power to reserve and care for large open spaces, plan and construct the main roads, determine the traffic route for the future development of rail and other forms of transportation, select industrial sites, and control housing developments. Data collected by TVA for its developmental programs have likewise been less far reaching than those collected in Italy, under the Bonifica Integrale program launched in 1928.

4. Land use data have had perhaps less application in the United States in international frontier area planning than in some frontier zones in Europe, especially in the region between Belgium and the Netherlands. In the St. Lawrence River project area, and in the Niagara Frontier Regional Plan, however, the United States and Canada have worked together. The same applies to the United States and Mexico with reference to the Rio Grande valley area. Engineering types of data have not always been matched by economic analyses in these border areas.

CHAPTER VI.

Characteristics of Statistics on Land in the United States Today

In the United States today, there are a great many sources of data about land. Indeed, one is struck more by the variety and diversity of sources of such information than by their uniformity and comparability. As we have seen in Chapter V, data relating to land have been collected to meet specific needs; men and organizations responsible for data about land have been pragmatic and practical. It was natural that such data would evolve in this fashion, and much valuable data have been assembled and published over the years. As needs have changed, data have changed too, either by redefinition or by addition, sometimes quickly and sometimes after considerable delay. There has never been a data program for land in the United States which included *all* land within a single set of data, and which used a consistent and inclusive set of definitions about land. Data assembled from different sources and in different ways, when put together, have often revealed gaps and overlaps as well as inaccuracies. Had there ever been a set of sufficiently detailed and consistent definitions, and had these been used by all agencies and groups, then data from different sources could have been combined satisfactorily. One purpose of this study is to facilitate such a joining-up of data from various sources.

The purpose of this chapter is to describe briefly the present nature of the statistics on land, the evolution of which was traced in Chapter V. The reader is referred to the several appendices, where the various federal agencies have described their land data programs in more detail than is possible here. In this chapter, we shall take up data according to uses of land, thus cutting across the agency-by-agency approach of the appendices. This should set the stage for the consideration of a uniform approach to land use data, which is considered in Chapter VII and also in Appendix I.

The emphasis of this chapter is on land use, or activity on the land; some attention will be paid to the other concepts about land discussed in Chapter II, especially when relatively large amounts of data are available about them. Both limits of space and interest dictate that we shall be concerned with "major" sources of data only—admitting the difficulty of defining "major." Mostly, our attention will be focused on data series of a continuing nature. In addition to such sources, there have been a great many specific, localized studies, in which land use data are only a part, sometimes only a very small part, of the data collected in the study. Such studies are often highly valuable in adding to our general knowledge and understanding, but they are not part of a national, continuing data program; hence we omit them for the most part.

It is hard to measure the importance of different land uses today, because there is no single measure of importance. In terms of land area, grazing of native, unimproved range land is the largest single land use, taking up more than a third of the total land area (excluding Alaska); agriculture, in the sense of crop production and use of improved pastures, is next with more than a fourth of the total land area; and commercial forestry is third, with just a fourth of the total. These three major uses (major, in an area sense), or two uses if grazing is combined with agriculture, take up 90 percent of the total land area of the forty-eight states. If one considers numbers of people who actually use the land, the relationships are almost exactly the reverse: residential, trade, transportation, recreation, and other uses involving relatively few acres are engaged in by nearly everyone, while agriculture, forestry, and especially grazing involve very few people directly. It is not possible to make a direct comparison about the values of the land involved; most of the intensively used land has had large investments for roads, water supply, sewage disposal, and many other public services, either on the land or so directly serving it that the value of each tract more closely reflects invested capital than it does raw land as such. But it is probable that the raw land value of the relatively small but intensively used areas is greater than that of the much larger but more lightly used rural areas, including agriculture.

Without, we hope, implication of importance of various land uses, we shall in this chapter take up first agriculture (including grazing), then forestry, and then move into the other, smaller acreage uses. To some extent this order ranks the amount of data and the length of time various data series have been available.

There are both public and private sources of statistics about land. Our concern is with the public sources, and primarily with the federal sources. We recognize the existence of the other data, but they are harder to describe briefly and more often relate to local areas, in the case of government data other than federal, or to output, trade, or transactions more than to land use, in the case of private data. However, some reference will be made to local data.

Land use statistics have their practical values enhanced in four main ways. These values rest upon (1) the adequacy of the data in terms of detail and accuracy for the time when collected; (2) comparability with previously gathered data, so that trends can be determined with accuracy; (3) summarization not only for large areas, but for relatively small component areas as well; and (4) relatedness of the land use data to other significant data collected at the same time and cross-tabulated so as to produce a better view of the "economic relief." For land use data to be suitable to provide help in the making of decisions concerning private and public investments, there must be numerous breakdowns and correlations. In order that data of various kinds and origins be accurately relatable, each must be properly identified as to location, as we discussed in Chapter III.

The most desirable frequency of enumeration or assembly of data on land use and related matters depends on the need for data at different time periods, which in turn depends upon the use of the data. Cost and difficulty of obtaining the desired data is naturally a factor also. For instance, data on acreage of land forested and on volume of standing timber, probably by species and perhaps by size class, involve considerable expense to collect, even on a sample basis, and year-to-year changes are not likely to be large. Accordingly, surveys at intervals of every five years would probably be adequate; in practice, we have yet to achieve this, as noted in Appendix C. Or, to take another example, a Census of Agriculture, to measure the status of agriculture at any given date and to reveal broad secular changes taking place, is probably adequate every five years—which is what we have had now for forty years. But estimates of agricultural output are needed at least annually; for perishable crops, they may be needed not only seasonally but literally daily as well. The market news reporting of the U.S. Department of Agriculture covers shipments from producing areas on a daily basis during the height of the season for some perishables, and market receipts daily for a large number of markets and products. Information about the supply of a particular vegetable or fruit last week has little value in estimating today's prices, for instance.

The possibility of a continuous inventory of land according to use, roughly comparable to a continuous inventory of goods in stock by a merchandiser, exists for some kinds of land uses. A usably accurate continuous inventory requires accurate data on land use at some starting point, on additions to area in each use, on losses of area in each use, and of conversions from one use to another. These conditions may be met in many urban areas, if an accurate and detailed inventory of land use is taken for a starting point; building and remodelling permits, plus permits for demolition of buildings, plus zoning, health, or other inspection data, might well provide a continuous inventory of land use of acceptable accuracy. If there is any serious doubt as to the accuracy or completeness of the inventory at any date, then a new inventory must be taken, in whole or in part. In principle, the continuous inventory could work for forestry also, including not only area (which would not be too difficult) but timber volume (which is perhaps more important but much more difficult to keep track of). Data on growth rates, losses due to insects and disease, and some other factors may be too inaccurate, too undependable or too variable from year to year or from area to area to give the continuous inventory the desired accuracy.

Though we shall generally speak of collection of data on particular points, collection alone is not enough. Data obtained by interview or otherwise must be edited, placed upon the electronic or other data-processing equipment, summarized by areas adequate for the needs of the users, and published or otherwise made available. The original data collection and its preparation for electronic data processing usually requires careful work by competent persons; this part of the data processing job cannot be shortcut or mechanized beyond some minimum degree. In speaking of data collection in the rest of this chapter, we shall assume that the other steps are adequately taken also.

Data on Agricultural and Grazing Activities

Because the United States was once primarily an agricultural nation, because its agriculture is still important even though we have become heavily industrialized, and because agriculture depends so directly on land, some of the best and oldest data relating to land use and related items in the United States pertain to agriculture. There are two major sources of statistical and other data relating to agricultural use of land: the Census of Agriculture, and the various statistics of the United States Department of Agriculture (discussed in Appendices D, E, and F). In addition, there are a number of less important sources, or sources which do not provide continuous data series.

The Census of Agriculture has been taken at ten year intervals since 1840 and at five year intervals since 1920. For some items, information is obtained from all farm operators; for others, from a carefully selected sample of farms.[1] Data from the sample are "blown up" or expanded to provide the best estimate of the total universe. In the Census of Manufacturing and some other censuses, the "disclosure problem" is serious; that is, in order to avoid revealing data for any single enterprise, such censuses do not ordinarily publish data for any city, county, or other area with

[1] For a discussion of the methods of enumeration and sampling, of definition of terms, and related matters, see *Introduction, U.S. Census of Agriculture: 1959*, General Report, Vol. II, Statistics by Subjects (Washington: U.S. Government Printing Office, 1962). The basis of sampling is variable by size of farm and by county, but is, broadly, a 20 per cent sample.

fewer than three firms or reporting units, and this often makes county or smaller area data impossible to publish. This problem rarely arises in agriculture; its data are usually published on a county basis, and ordinarily there are far more than three farms in a county. This problem may arise for data on a minor civil division basis—data on such a basis can be obtained from the Bureau of the Census—but even here it is usually not serious. County totals and averages are adequate for a national picture and for broad regional comparisons, but less so for dealing with local land use problems.

The Census of Agriculture does have one peculiar problem arising out of land. The full acreage, output, and other data for a farm are credited to the local unit of government in which the headquarters lie. This raises no problems for the typical small or average size farm, because all or nearly all of its land will lie in one unit, even in one minor civil division. But some giant farms and ranches have their headquarters in towns and cities, with land spread over several counties or even a few states. Crediting their entire area and output to the place of their headquarters can raise some mischief-making complications, since it will lead to well over 100 percent of the total land area being in farms. While this problem does not arise often, it can be annoying in some parts of the country.

The Census of Agriculture deals with *farms*, not agricultural use of land. The definition of a "farm" has changed somewhat from census to census, but has always required that the land considered in the farm be under the control of one person or commercial organization and be used for or connected with agricultural operations. "Places of 10 or more acres in 1959 were counted as farms if the estimated sales of agricultural products for the year amounted to at least $50. Places of less than 10 acres in 1959 were counted as farms if the estimated sales of agricultural products for the year amounted to at least $250. Places not meeting the minimum estimated level of sales in 1959 were nevertheless counted as farms if they could normally be expected to produce agricultural products in sufficient quantity to meet the requirements of the definition."[2] By this standard, somewhat more than half of the forty-eight contiguous states were in farms in 1959, or slightly less than half if all fifty states are included (Alaska has a huge area, little of which is in farms). Thus, the Census of Agriculture includes most of the land not in federal ownership and not in urban uses, although considerable additional areas of nonfarm forest land are also excluded.

Data on land in farms is more than data on land used for agriculture, since substantial areas of forest land, as well as smaller areas of land used for other purposes, are in farms. Approximately 15 percent of all farm land

[2] U.S. Census of Agriculture, 1959, *op. cit.*, p. xxvi.

s in forests in 1959, according to the Census of Agriculture, and a third all commercial forest land was in farms in 1953, according to the Forest rvice. But farms do not include all land used for agriculture, if grazing of tive range is included within agriculture. A substantial area of land is azed by farm-owned livestock but not included in farm acreage statistics, cause it is neither owned nor leased by the farmer. Ranchers use extensive eas of federal land, and some state land, under a permit or license system; ıce control over the land really lies with the public agency, such land operly is excluded from Census of Agriculture statistics. Some federally-vned and state-owned land is leased to ranchers under terms such that it is · should be included in farm acreage by the Census of Agriculture, owever, since the rancher has effective control over the land use. Some ivate land is or has been used also by livestock from farms and ranchers ı a sufferance basis or in actual trespass. Some of this may yet exist in uthern forested areas. At one time it was quite common on the Great lains, where substantial areas of land were owned by nonresidents but razed by locally owned livestock, without leases. The inclusion of large reas of the latter within farms has been a major factor in increasing the otal land area within farms by more than 100 million acres in the past venty years or so. The census definitions of land use have not always been ell understood by ranchers or perhaps by its own enumerators. The rough ative grazing lands of the West would presumably fit under the heading other pasture, not cropland and not woodland," but few ranchers would hink of it in these terms. As a result, total acreage in this category in anching counties and even states in the past have fallen far below the area vhich land ownership and ranch organization studies have shown to be in anches. In the main, however, the census definitions have been applied vell.

The Census of Agriculture is taken by interview with farmers; the range ınd accuracy of data is thus limited by the knowledge, general education, ınd willingness to co-operate of farmers and of census enumerators. As we ıoted in Chapter V, these have all risen in recent decades, with the rise n general educational standards of the country. However, there still remain limitations on the number of items that can be included in census question-naires, because of the time required to answer extremely long question-naires; in part, this has been met by use of regional or special inquiries.

The 1959 Census of Agriculture obtained information on the total area of land within farms; on cropland harvested, cropland used only for pasture, cropland not harvested and not pastured (for which data on crop land in cultivated summer fallow is shown separately), and "other" cropland; on woodland pastured, woodland not pastured, and on pasture not woodland and not cropland; and on other land, such as house lots or waste land, within the farm. In some past censuses, data were also obtained on cro failure acreage, as well as for some other categories. Additional informati is obtained on land irrigated and on land drained, including crop acreag on irrigated land.

Further information is obtained on the acreage and output of all con mercially important field, vegetable, and fruit crops. These include th grains, hays and other livestock feeds, cotton, tobacco, sugar crops, an many more. For many crops, quantities sold off the farm, as well as tot quantities harvested, are reported. For corn, the acreage and value of cor cut for silage and also for corn hogged down are reported, as well a corn harvested for grain.

Some information was obtained from farmers, at the time of intervie on value of some products sold; for others, quantities sold were reporte by the farmer, and average prices were applied in the office later.[3] On th basis of these data, commercial farms were classified in 1959 accordin to type; part-time, part-retirement, and abnormal farms were grouped sep arately. In Chapter VII, we shall consider this type of farm classification i more detail, and compare it with the type of farm classification develope by the Urban Renewal Administration and the Bureau of Public Roads. I general, the type of classification represents the major source of income— dairy, cotton, poultry, etc. On the basis of farm income data, farms were als grouped according to economic class—essentially a classification on th basis of gross income.

The Census of Agriculture has also obtained information on farm build ings, farm machinery and equipment, and home improvements, and or such matters as electricity and telephone. Other information has been obtained on amounts of fertilizer used, and on expenditures for fertilizer feed, machine hire, hired labor, and other expense items. Information has also been obtained on estimated value of land and buildings in the farm, on the tenure with which the land is held—owned, leased by any one of several arrangements, partly owned and partly leased, or directed by hired man- agers. Data have been tabulated according to tenure, so that one can know land and crop acreage, numbers of farms, output and input, and many other items by type of tenure. Some information has also been obtained on the race of the farm operator, and totalled for whites and Negroes separately.

The United States Department of Agriculture collects a great deal of original data on land use and related matters, as well as making analyses using these and other data. The work of the Forest Service in assembling data about forest land, to be considered in the following section of this chapter, is not under consideration here. A great deal, but not all, of the

[3] *U.S. Census of Agriculture, 1959: Type of Farm,* Chapter XII, Vol. II, General Report, Statistics by Subjects (Washington: U.S. Government Printing Office, 1962), pp. 1245–54.

USDA land data is concerned with immediately current uses and outputs, hence timeliness of data collection and publication is critical. As we noted in Chapter V, formerly data on farm land use was collected by questionnaire from farmers who were willing to respond. While this method is still used, it is gradually being replaced by direct enumeration or observation in the field, for pre-determined sample farm areas. Biases of sampling and reporting will thus be greatly reduced, if not eliminated. Many of the data series in USDA are annual, but some are more frequent; many of the annual data series are tied to the five year Census of Agriculture. However, crop acreage and other figures reported by the latter are not invariably accepted, but are sometimes adjusted to compensate for estimated under-reporting or lack of comparability. Some of the USDA agricultural statistical work is in co-operation with state organizations, such as state departments of agriculture; some utilizes county assessor and other local records, where they exist. Like the Census of Agriculture, the USDA data are mostly on a *farm* basis, with the divergences between farms and agriculture noted above.

The timing of inquiries, the items covered, and the date of release of the data vary from crop to crop and item to item. For many crops, data are obtained on farmers' "intentions to plant," usually as of March 1; obviously, not all farmers will actually plant what they expected to plant—unfavorable weather or other factors may cause them to change their plans. But intention-to-plant estimates have been very useful. Acreages planted, livestock numbers, total acres in farms, numbers of farms, and other information is obtained, primarily by field observation and interview, in early June from the sample areas previously mentioned. These are supplemented for some crops by data on acreages planted at other seasons, when the crop is not normally planted in the spring. Monthly crop condition data are obtained for many crops; there is a high correlation between crop condition and later crop production—a correlation which increases as the season advances and the chances of disturbing elements decline. For some vegetable and fruit crops, more frequent reports, sometimes daily ones, are obtained from the principal producing areas at the height of the season; these are supplemented by market receipt data for the larger cities, on a daily basis, mostly throughout the year. Another major set of inquiries, mostly in late fall, ascertains acreages actually harvested and yields actually obtained, as well as other information. Information is obtained from various sources which makes possible estimates of crop utilization—fed on farm where grown, sold, used by industry, and the like, depending on the crop. For many vegetable and fruit crops, utilization means sold fresh, canned, frozen, dried, otherwise processed, and the like. For livestock, information is obtained not only as to numbers on farms, but as to numbers sold and livestock products produced and sold.

By various special inquiries, the USDA obtains annual or more frequent information on land prices or land values, by states; on volume of farm transfers by different methods, such as sale and foreclosure; and on cash rents per acre for rented land. By monthly or annual inquiries, other data are obtained on prices received by farmers for agricultural commodities sold, on prices paid for production and living goods purchased by farmers, on numbers of farm people, and other matters. Based upon these and other information, a number of indices are computed and published, as to prices, income, output, selected inputs, and the like.

Of special interest for our purpose is the fact that the June field inquiry obtains information on all land within the sample blocks; all land is accounted for, as an aid in getting more accurate information on the desired items. However, data on land uses other than crops—roads, farmsteads, woods, idle land, and the like—are not tabulated.

The Soil Conservation Service makes soil surveys and land capability classification surveys, as described in Appendix D. These deal primarily with the physical characteristics of the land, not directly with activities on the land, although much of the information is highly useful in interpreting actual or potential land use. These surveys typically cover an entire area, with an intensity of observation and sampling of soil profiles and other items in the field which, in the judgment of the field man, are necessary for accuracy in mapping and classification. However, for the Conservation Needs Inventory of 1958, soil and land classification was carried out for sample areas.

In addition, the USDA conducts various specialized research studies or other inquiries to obtain additional information or to explore relationships among variables. For instance, a nationwide inventory of farmland ownership was made in 1946, with later follow-up studies in some regions and states. Special studies are made of farm mechanization, farm buildings, or other special subjects, as demand seems to warrant and as funds permit.

Even this brief review of the major sources of data about land used for agriculture shows that there is a great deal of information on this subject. The activity on the land, or its use, is considered in each of the two major sources of data—activity on a business enterprise or farm basis, and also on a land tract or crop basis. The relevance of this difference in activity data may be clearer after the discussion in Chapter VII. Other data deal with the natural qualities of the land, its buildings and other improvements, its tenure, its market and prices, and other concepts of data discussed in Chapter II. Basic data are available by which to calculate indices of intensity of land use, by such items as amounts of certain inputs per acre, or of output per acre. In short, for agricultural land, some data are available on each of the concepts discussed in Chapter II.

None of this information is perfect as to accuracy, completeness of coverage, or detail; this is recognized by the agencies concerned, which are constantly improving their methodology. But, on the whole, and especially in comparison with the data for land used for most other purposes, the data on land used for agriculture are very good. In particular, data are available for many items for a far longer period than for almost any other land uses, thus permitting historical analyses.

From our viewpoint, the data about land used for agriculture have some rather serious shortcomings. First of all, the data are typically summarized by geographical areas too large for some kinds of economic analysis; the USDA data are national, regional, and state; the Census of Agriculture data are the same with the addition of county data, and unpublished data by minor civil divisions. While these data have great value for many purposes, they are inadequate for others; and the data are not available, or have not been recorded adequately, or have not been used, for smaller geographical areas nor could they readily be regrouped to meet various needs. While this deficiency is perhaps not as serious for rural land uses as it is for the more intensive urban land uses, it is a factor to consider.

Secondly, the data about agricultural use of land have been imperfectly related, one to another, in spite of great progress in this direction as a result of efforts by Census and Agriculture. Where data are available by states or counties, presumably the totals and averages are directly comparable, if the definitions of items are also comparable. But each source uses samples (two or more within Agriculture), and the samples have not been directly related, except through the larger area totals. For instance, although sample data for crop acreages will show shifts into or out of various crops, there is nothing to indicate on which class of land the changes occurred. With the declining crop acreages and rising crop yields of the past two decades, it has been generally assumed that the poorest lands were taken out of crops and the fertilizer and other inputs concentrated on the best lands; but positive evidence of this is lacking.

Thirdly, it seems fairly clear that there is a serious hiatus in land data for the broad ring (the urban-rural fringe) around cities. This land is no longer, in most cases, within farms; hence, it is not included in the Census of Agriculture nor within most USDA statistics. On the other hand, it clearly is not in residential, industrial, or other urban land uses, hence is likely to be omitted or scantily dealt with in land use surveys or other land use data arising out of city planning or other urban origins. But this is the broad zone of greatest and most important land use changes in the United

States today. This is where the concept of idle land is both so important and so difficult. The approach through farms (defined as land under individual control) also omits extensive grazing land, as we have noted; omits substantial forest land, as we shall consider in the next section; and is likely to mean the omission of small tracts or miscellaneous uses within the general zone of agriculture.

Data on Forestry as a Land Use

Available data on forestry as a land use in the United States reflect, in considerable measure, some of the special characteristics of forestry. First of all, forests in the United States have a rather unique ownership situation—a substantial area of publicly, especially federally, owned forests; a modest area of highly productive forest land in forest-industry ownership; over three million forests that are parts of farms, often only a few acres per farm, and that are relatively unproductive; and over a million acres of small forests, not parts of farms, often in poor shape and also relatively unproductive. Data must therefore be collected from several kinds of sources, as well as from many owners or managers, and there are severe limits to the kinds of information which can be obtained from some of them.

Secondly, there are major difficulties in defining in unequivocal terms what is meant by "forest" and "forestry." How small a tract of tree-covered land shall one consider as a "forest" or as a "forestry" enterprise? In practice, the Forest Service has included tracts as small as 1 acre in the eastern United States, as small as 10 acres in the West. Are the species and qualities of trees grown "commercial" or not? Standards of commercial suitability of trees have changed greatly over the past several decades, as supplies of best grade trees have diminished and as technologies have made it possible to use species and qualities of logs once considered unusable. Some forest land is reserved for special uses, such as municipal watersheds, national parks, and the like, and this has customarily been considered non-commercial forest. Much forest land is grazed seasonally. Is it forest land with incidental grazing, or grazing land with incidental forestry? These and many other definitional problems have long plagued anyone who sought to obtain forestry statistics comparable over large areas and long time periods.

Thirdly, the fact that changes occur in forests much more slowly than on land growing annual crops has greatly affected the kinds of data about forests. There is seldom a need for annual data, at least on land use and timber stands (timber production is different); data collected at intervals of five or even ten years may be quite adequate.

As a result of these peculiarities of forestry as a land use, data have been obtained mostly by sample inquiries from owners and by sample inventories on the land itself at rather irregular intervals of time. The chief source of data has been the more or less periodic forest surveys of the Forest Service, regionally and nationally. These are described in Appendix C. In making these surveys, the advice and assistance of other federal and state agencies and of private forest landowners was obtained. They have been plagued by the problems of comparability of definitions and areas mentioned above. At each survey, there is naturally a desire to collect the "best" information, given the needs of the times; however, this may well mean some departure from past practice. Recent forest surveys have contained revised figures for the preceding survey; and sometimes the revisions have been substantial.

Some limited forest information is available in the Census of Agriculture, chiefly on the area of woodland in farms. Many miscellaneous land use surveys have been made, roughly comparable to those described for agriculture—sometimes the same surveys—which have yielded information of much value locally but not data readily summarized in statistical series. The various public agencies administering forest land provide information, usually annually, regarding the forests they administer. The larger private forest owners collect data about their lands, but these are usually not publicly available. Approximately one-quarter of the nation is classed as forest land. In general, annual gross output per acre of forest land is only a fraction of annual gross output per acre of cropland, though usually it is greater than annual gross output per acre of grazing land.

The most comprehensive recent forest land statistics for the nation were obtained by the Timber Resource Review (TRR) from 1952 to 1955, and were published in 1958 as "Timber Resources for America's Future" (Forest Resource Report No. 14, Forest Service, U.S. Department of Agriculture). The results of a more recent survey are scheduled for publication in 1965. Regional offices of the Forest Service make and publish new surveys at intervals with similar kinds of information. The discussion which follows is based primarily on the TRR as exemplifying forestry statistics generally. However, the Forest Service employs an essentially biological, rather than an activity, definition of forests, although some recognition is given to activity in classifying as non-commercial forests reserved for special purposes.

The area of forest land, as defined by the Forest Service, is estimated by sample field surveys; total area is further divided according to species, whether commercial or non-commercial forest, whether reserved for special uses, etc. Data were published only by broad regional groupings—East, South, and West.

The TRR obtained and published a great deal of information about timber volumes, in total, and about areas not fully stocked. Other forest surveys have collected information about forest "sites," which basically represent differences in inherent productivity of the land for forest products. Although there is a great deal of such information, it has not been summarized into national or regional estimates of land area by site quality.

The line between natural quality of the land and improvements to it is a very hard one to draw for forest land. Much of the data on volume of timber per acre tends to measure natural land quality, certainly for the short run and to some extent for the long run; but it also measures a kind of improvement on the land. Data were included in the TRR on areas seeded or planted to commercial forest, and also on areas in need of such planting. "Timber stand improvement," which often means thinning or elimination of undesirable species, is also a form of improvement about which some information is available. For the larger forest holdings, including the publicly owned ones, the owner of the timber usually constructs the roads, hence roads through timber areas are an important kind of improvement. Information is available in public agency records on timber access roads—and on their absence—and is available for some private areas from local surveys; but this information has not been summarized into national and regional totals.

As noted above, forest land in the United States is owned by widely differing kinds of owners and in greatly different sizes of tracts. The economic possibilities of many small forest tracts are very low, and on the average such tracts are poorly managed and relatively unproductive. The forest ownership situation is therefore a major factor in the kind of forestry practiced. The TRR obtained relatively detailed information on ownership, but more recent information has not been generally available. Very little forest land in the United States is operated by tenants. In some parts of the South, pulp companies have leased land from owners, but this is not usual. Economic forestry is a long-term proposition, and generally it would be very difficult to devise and carry out a lease which would be fair to both owner and tenant, that would encourage the most productive use of the forest land. Many private firms harvest timber or otherwise use publicly owned forests under contractual or other arrangements.

The possibility of a hiatus between data on land in forestry and data on land in agriculture certainly exists, in part because data are assembled by different agencies in necessarily different ways. As we have noted, both the Census of Agriculture and most USDA data on agriculture deal with farms, on which there is a fair amount of forest. The forest surveys try to include all forests, including those on farms. It is by no means clear that the same definition is used of "woods" in the Census of Agriculture statistics as is used of "forest" in the Forest Service data. The latter includes (1) land which is at least 10 percent stocked by trees of any size and capable of producing timber or other wood products, or of exerting an influence on the climate or the water regime, (2) land from which the trees described above have been removed to less than 10 percent stocking and which have not been developed for other use; (3) afforested areas; and (4) chaparral areas. It is by no means clear that farmers have the same definition in mind, in reporting woods, or that they would draw the same line between predominantly grazing land with some trees and predominantly forest land with some grazing. To the extent that the forest surveys have different definitions of farms than has the Census of Agriculture, this would affect the area of farm forests but not the area of all forests.

It is also possible that some land may have been omitted by each, which would not show up in other land classes. How about tracts of wooded land, not part of farms as Census defines farms, and too small to be included in the forest survey, without dwellings on them? If they had a dwelling, presumably the land could be classed as residential, even if so used during only part of the year; or it might be classed as recreational, under some circumstances. Omission of these small areas would presumably not affect total acreages much, but might make it difficult to reconcile area-by-use categories with total area.

Even more than the Census of Agriculture data relating to farming, the forest surveys are aggregated for relatively large areas only. The published data in national surveys show a breakdown into three regions only; state surveys are more finely divided, but are still for relatively large areas. To obtain accurate data for smaller areas would require a more intensive and hence more expensive degree of sampling. However, unless more detailed forestry data can be made available, it will be difficult to relate data from these different sources to the same areas with any assurance.

It is not clear how close to developed urban centers the forest inventories go. In the eastern half of the United States—a naturally forested region—trees often grow unattended or in spite of considerable abuse, on vacant lands. This is the zone of relatively rapid land use change and of extensive "idle" land, previously noted. Data on agriculture usually omit such lands. Do forest inventories also? In the absence of data locatable with accuracy and detail, it is hard to say.

Data on Land Used for Mining and Mineral Extraction

Mining and mineral extraction primarily involve the subsurface resources of land. Sometimes very little of the surface is used for mineral extraction as in the case of oil wells and shaft or tunnel mining, or in natural gas storage in underground caverns. In other instances, the mining activity destroys the surface, as in the case of open-pit coal and ore mining, placer gold mining, sand and gravel extraction, or stone quarrying.[4] In most types of mineral extraction, the surface areas are not likely to be large, compared with the employment and the output. Exploration for minerals, or attempts to keep other uses off the land in the name of mineral exploration, is a form of land "use" which characterizes some federally owned land; in many instances, the legal claims or the cloud cast upon other claims to land is perhaps more important than the actual activity on the land itself.

There is very little information indeed about the acreage and location of land for mining and mineral extraction. None of the federal agencies whose activities are reported in the appendices of this book, nor any other federal, state, or private agency as far as we can learn, collects and publishes data on *land* used for mineral production. As noted below, other data on mining are available. Mining has been one of the most neglected of all land uses, as far as data are concerned. When one considers land "used" for this purpose, shall he include only the surface workings exclusive of other uses, or shall he consider also the extent of the mineral deposits which are being or may be mined? In any case, there are virtually no data on the area of land used for open-pit coal mining, oil and gas fields, sand and gravel extraction, structural clay uses, hard rock or placer mining, or indeed for any other major form of mineral extraction. There has been no systematic collection of data showing areas of land used for this general purpose. Some specialized local studies have included mining and mineral extraction as a form of land use. This is particularly the case for city and metropolitan planning studies which have included sand and gravel extraction areas. In like manner, underground cavern storage and storage capability do not appear to be systematically reported.

The United States Geological Survey, the Bureau of Mines, various state organizations, and some larger private firms have conducted surveys as to the characteristics of mineral deposits. The surface features of mineral-bearing land are usually unimportant. Data are desired on mineral content of the ore deposits, on mining and extraction costs, and on related aspects of the mineral deposit itself. These data are not easily summarized, especially in form for non-specialists. There have been many technical reports for specific areas. While the reports of public agencies are published, those of private organizations are usually unavailable. There are almost no general summaries of such local reports. Data on areal extent of mineral deposits have generally not been worked into general land use maps and statistics. The Bureau of the Census, the Bureau of Mines, and trade press

[4] James Salisbury, Jr., and Leonard A. Salter, Jr., "Subsurface Resources and Surface Land Economics," *Journal of Land and Public Utility Economics*, XVII, 3 (August 1941), 271–79, and 4 (November 1941), 385–93.

report some or all of the following items: numbers of mines, quantity of output, value of output, employment, some items of cost or input, and other economic data, some on a county basis and some by enterprises. These data, while valuable for many purposes, are often not closely identified as to location. There are virtually no data on investment.

Some forms of mineral extraction involve peculiar tenure situations, namely, extensive separation of title or leases to subsurface and surface of the land. Most oil and gas is extracted under lease, with relatively little ownership of the surface of the land. There probably are 100 million acres of publicly (federal and state) owned land under oil and gas lease to private companies, much of it not in production and not yet drilled. There are some 40 million acres of privately owned land to which the federal government still retains the mineral rights, as well as some land owned by the federal government to which former private owners still retain mineral rights. The surface rights to a great deal of land are owned by some private individuals and the subsurface mineral rights by others. There are only scattered pieces of information about this tenure situation for mineral lands.

Data on Transportation as an Activity Using Land

The importance of transportation and communication for the use and value of the land they serve has been discussed in Chapter V and need not be repeated. Every method of transportation, regardless of the medium through which it moves, uses some land—for terminals, if not for other purposes. Consideration of transportation methods should not be limited to railroads, highways, air travel, and water travel, but should include pipelines for various purposes, and the possibility of beltlines and other methods. Transportation and communication are often closely related to utilities such as power lines.

Considerable data on miles of railroad track are available from records of the Interstate Commerce Commission; on miles of highway from records of the Bureau of Public Roads; on airports and air traffic from records of the Civil Aeronautics Administration; and on water transportation from various federal sources, including the Maritime Commission.[5] In addition, data are available on many other aspects of transportation: volume of freight moved, numbers of passengers carried, investment in facilities and equipment, expenditures for various purposes, revenues, taxes, and the like. These data are very useful for many purposes; like any other social and economic data, they are not perfect, and substantial efforts have been

[5] For a discussion of these various sources and for summary data, see Bureau of the Census, *Historical Statistics of the United States, Colonial Times to 1957* (Washington: U.S. Government Printing Office, 1960).

exerted in recent years by the Association of American Railroads, the Bureau of the Census, the Bureau of the Budget, and other organizations to improve railroad freight data, and doubtless other improvements are desirable.

But, for our purposes, the significant fact is that almost none of these national sources of data contain anything about *land* as such. When we prepared our book, *Land for the Future,* we had to estimate the area in railroad and highway rights-of-way from published mileage data and from estimated average widths of rights-of-way for each type of railroad and road; and, obviously, the resulting acreage data are no more accurate than the estimates of average widths. Data on air traffic do contain data on acreages in airports.

Local land use surveys, such as metropolitan, or city general, or transportation plans, must and do consider land area used for the various forms of transportation and communication. However, there is far from a uniform method of treating these data. One may consider the means of transportation, as rail or road, with subheadings for rights-of-way, terminals, stations, parking lots, and the like; or one may reverse the order, and put certain functions, such as movement, storage, and the like first in priority, with means of movement such as rail or road in secondary position. The order in which data are considered is less important than that all necessary data be obtained on the ground and properly identified as to precise location. The scale on which one works is also highly important; for some purposes, a large industrial plant will be classified simply as industry, while for others the area of parking lots will be shown separately. This is a matter to which we shall return in Chapter VII. One broad purpose of this study is to develop a uniform method of treating data about various land uses; the opportunities for improvement are possibly nowhere greater than for transportation.

The area of land use for transportation and communication within cities is larger than many people realize. In his summaries of land planning studies for a number of American cities, Bartholomew shows that streets, alleys, and railroads alone range downward from more than a third of "occupied area" in small cities to somewhat more than a fourth in the largest cities.[6] Land is used more lavishly for all purposes in small than in large cities; as number of people increases, land is used more intensively for all purposes; but, interestingly, the proportion of land used for transportation and communication seems not to change greatly according to city size.

Our best estimate is that transportation activities in the United States

[6] Harland Bartholomew, *Land Uses in American Cities* (Cambridge: Harvard University Press, 1955).

apply to approximately 20.6 million acres of land in rural roads, to 8 million in railroad rights of way outside of corporate limits and to about 3 million acres in airports, inland waterways, etc.[7] Within urban territory there are about 1.2 million acres in streets and alleys, large acreages in port facilities, railway classification yards, terminal passenger and freight station and repair shop areas, besides rights of way and other acquired land in cities, suggesting that there has come to be at least 2 million acres in city and village transportation uses.

The right of eminent domain has enabled the designers of transportation and of some communication properties to stretch the lines about as topography, location of population centers, or other factors influencing the generation and movement of traffic and even future expectations have seemed to dictate. The land strips taken for advance-design, limited-access interstate highways have, it seems, shown about as much departure from cardinal directions as the land strips taken by railroads in the earlier days or by pipelines in more recent times. Land strips taken for land use local roads in rectangular survey states have largely straddled the outer boundary lines of the 640-acre sections, and have usually run in cardinal directions as a consequence. Except for the construction period in preparing rural roads, railroads, streets, limited-access interstate and other expressways, the number of persons needed per lineal mile or per acre of right-of-way has been small. Maintenance, policing, and other controls of these rural properties, once built, have required few workers despite the fact that, within cities, the number of persons so needed in street programs is often considerable.

There is some doubt as to how much land used for transportation is included in the usual statistics about land used for other purposes. For instance, data on forest land use are likely to include some land area in roads; forest roads range from highly improved roads for movements of large volumes of freight, downward to temporary truck roads and skid ways used for a particular timber harvest and then reverting to forest. Farms include their own roads, in some cases, which are likely to be reported as a miscellaneous farm use of land. Perhaps more important, many farmers are likely to report the gross acreage of the land as originally alienated from public ownership to form their farm, neglecting to deduct the acreage donated by them or their predecessors for the local dirt roads which so typically follow section or other cadastral survey lines. Again, the scale on which a land use inventory is made may be determinative of its classification. A suburban building lot is residential on one scale, but shows separately off-street parking area (transportation) on another scale; the parking

[7] Marion Clawson, R. Burnell Held, and Charles H. Stoddard, *Land for the Future* (Baltimore: The Johns Hopkins Press for Resources for the Future, Inc., 1960).

lot at an industrial plant or retail store shows separately on one scale but not on another, etc.

Finally, one should not underestimate the present, and even more the future, possibilities of multiple uses of land used for transportation. By far the larger part of the land reported as used for railroads and highways is in right of way, not for the actual facility moving goods and people. Wide rights of way have many advantages in protecting transportation uses from the intrusion of other uses, and vice versa. But these rights-of-way have, or might have, other uses as well. In an earlier day, a good deal of hay was cut or pasture grazed from railroad and road rights-of-way. In the future, these might be the home for some species of wildlife and for some kinds of outdoor recreation—wide highway rights-of-way might well include bicycle paths, for instance.

Data on Land in Residential Uses

Residential use of land affects everyone, since everyone lives somewhere. Residential use of land involves more than a place to eat and sleep. Many productive functions are undertaken within the home which, if done outside and by business firms, would have names other than residential—baking, cooking, laundry, sewing, repair of furniture and equipment, and many others. The range and amount of these activities has shrunken enormously over the past generation or more, yet it is still significant. Sometimes there are more directly income producing activities within the home—writing of material for sale being an obvious one which would provide little outside evidence observable by neighbors. But doctor and lawyer and other offices are sometimes housed in dwellings in residential neighborhoods. A wide variety of activities may also take place in the yards of single family dwellings; food production, recreation, and other activities may take place within the family yard which, if on specialized areas, would be classified as something other than residential. The same is true of off-street parking; part of residential on one scale, it becomes a transportation function on another scale.

Most farms in the United States include a residence on the farm; in spite of some movement to town living, most United States farmers still live on the land, or on one of the pieces of land, which they farm. Extensive farm consolidation since the war has left many farm dwellings empty or occupied by non-farmers, and many have disappeared. By and large, farm residential use of land is included with other data on agriculture—or, more precisely, other data on farms. The Census of Agriculture reports area within farms, as we have noted; in 1959, about 45 million acres were reported in "house lots, roads, wasteland, etc."; probably relatively little of this was in "house lots" and possibly much of the latter was for barns, machinery sheds, and other non-residential purposes. On a more detailed scale of inquiry than was practical in the Census, the actual area used for residential purposes on farms could be separated from other uses.

The Census of Population has obtained information on rural non-farm population, and the Census of Housing has obtained information on their dwellings comparable to the information obtained about city dwellings, described below. These data are summarized and published on a county basis; reference can be made to Appendix G for a more complete statement. But this source does not provide information on *land* used for this purpose. We do not know the area of land so used, its physical characteristics, its location with respect to roads and various public services, etc. An increasingly common and important situation of rural non-farm residence is the seasonal or part-time residence. With rising real incomes per capita, a larger proportion of the total population can afford a second or third home, for summer or winter vacations, for weekend enjoyment, or for other purposes. Difficult as it would be to establish meaningful and easily distinguishable definitions for various classes of such secondary use, it would be very interesting to know the numbers of persons, numbers of dwellings, and areas of land so involved.

Most interest on residential use of land focuses on urban housing because most people live in cities today. Various sources of private and public data are available, which deal in some way with urban residential use of land. By all odds the most important public source of data on a national scale, for residential use of land, is the Census of Housing; more detail is presented in Appendix G. Briefly, such data pertain primarily to the housing structure, its size and condition, the number of occupants and hence the degree of crowding, and to various facilities and services. These data are highly important for many purposes; they often throw considerable light on some of the concepts about land described in Chapter II. However, they do not deal directly with *land*; that is, the area of land is not shown, although many facts are available about the structures. These data are summarized and published by counties, and in less detail by cities, census tracts, and blocks. This provides a link to land area and location, although other land uses may also take place within the same area, or some land may lie idle. Large masses of data for small areas are unpublished, but can be made available for special uses.

Local transportation and general planning studies, which nearly always include a land use survey, naturally devote considerable attention to residential use of land. This use occupies a large area—often the largest single use of urban land; it also affects a great many people. Urban plans often focus on subdivision development and control. While such planning studies will invariably show residential use of land as one category, there may not always be identical definitions in cases where residences, stores, and other uses are intermingled or are on different levels of the same structure. Commonly, various subdivisions of residential activity are shown as single family separate structures, duplexes, row houses, and apartments, perhaps by size or type, and the like. There is far from uniformity among various urban planning studies. To be of maximum use for transportation planning, residential land use must be carefully integrated with population data, employment data, travel routes to work, and the like, all accurately located and subject to analysis by any area divisions desired.

Data on the physical qualities of land which is contemplated for residential development are important and increasingly are coming to be recognized as such. A great deal of the suburban development since the war has been on the basis of septic tank disposal of domestic wastes, especially for larger lots and often for more expensive homes. A great many mistakes have been made. Many areas now finding themselves with serious pollution problems are discovering the necessity of now providing expensive sewerage facilities which they had hoped to do without. Although somewhat different physical qualities are required for good subdivision land than for good farming land, the same or similar types of surveys on land and soils, and similar kinds of information, are needed. One of the growing uses of the Soil Conservation Service land capability classification, described in Appendix D, is for planning of suburban development.

Data on Commercial and Industrial Activities as Land Uses

There is a great deal of statistical information about commerce and industry in the United States. The Bureau of the Census, through its censuses of business and industry, obtains much information on numbers of establishments, sales, employment, payroll, value added by manufacture, investment, and the like; for more detail as to data obtained and areas for which summarized, see Appendix G. In addition, the Federal Reserve System, the Office of Business Economics of the Department of Commerce, the Federal Trade Commission, the Department of Agriculture, the Bureau of Labor Statistics in the Department of Labor, and other public agencies collect various amounts of information on these broad fields, as do a relatively large number of trade associations and other private organizations. Typically, these data are obtained through questionnaires sent to producers, employers, and others in the industries concerned, or from market transactions reported by them or observed by specialized market reporters. Various university and other research organizations have assembled data series or synthesized or appraised such data series as do exist. All of this has given us a volume of data for these broad fields of economic activity which is highly valuable. For reasons which become apparent below, we think it is not necessary in this book to go into detail as to the exact nature, origin, or methods of operation of any of these data series.

There is almost nothing in any of these national sources of data about commerce and industry which deals with *land* as such. How much land is used by the steel making industry, or by the retail shoe stores, or by any other group within the commercial and industrial field is unknown, nor how much land is used in total by these fields; the various sources of data on economic activities do not provide such information. Since it is not known how much land is involved, obviously the land's location, natural qualities, and relationship to other land used for other purposes is also unknown. There is some information on improvements to land, but it is more in terms of capital investment than on improvements as such. There is some limited information on buildings, including some on floor area. Within this broad group of activities using land, there are situations where buildings or other improvements cover only part of the land, with the rest used for parking lots, other surface uses, or as just open space to provide perspective and view to the buildings; there are other situations in which most or all of the land is occupied by buildings, often several stories high, with a multiplicity of specific activities in their various levels and spaces.

The various public agencies and private organizations collecting and analyzing economic data on commerce and industry seem not to have felt the need for data on land area as such. While land area, location, physical characteristics, and other factors are extremely important for the individual plant or store, the need for statistical summaries for a city or other area or for the nation have been less apparent in these national statistics.

The national data series on commerce and industry outlined above and in Appendix G have some deficiencies for comparison with accurate data on land use, even if the latter existed. The various commercial and industrial activities are usually only generally located as to county, city, or census enumeration tract; their precise geographical location is often unavailable, at least from published data. It is therefore hard to recombine such data for other geographic areas, unless the latter happen to coincide with the areas enumerated. Data are often on a business firm or establishment basis, not on a plant or store basis, hence rather large data aggregates often relate to relatively large areas and cannot be analyzed for smaller or differently determined geographic areas. The disclosure problem is often serious for census data, especially if data are desired for relatively small districts. Frequently there are fewer than three plants or stores in the area for which data are desired, hence data for such areas cannot be made available by the Bureau of the Census.

All city and metropolitan planning studies which include a land use survey consider commercial and industrial use of land. Sometimes this requires consideration of districts quite far from the city or metropolitan area, since manufacturing plants which may provide a fair amount of employment may be located well beyond the usual city boundaries. Although land use surveys get information on these uses of land, there is the greatest variety in ways of classifying such land uses. This variety in classification and in details obtained frequently destroys comparability between land use information and other information, such as to employment, output, investment, and the like, and also destroys comparability with other urban areas. A major purpose of the URA-BPR uniform land coding system reported in Appendix I is to provide greater uniformity of data definition and land classification for these very activities.

Data on Recreation as a Use of Land

Outdoor recreation is an increasingly important use of land. The numbers of people visiting publicly owned recreation areas has been increasing at a rate close to 10 percent annually since the war—or even longer, if our limited data for earlier periods is reasonably representative. This is a growth rate much higher than for other uses of land, and it shows no signs of slackening off yet. In addition, millions of families develop recreation facilities in their own backyards, or have their own cottages at lake or sea shore or in the mountains. Public interest in outdoor recreation is also rising rapidly. In the past decade, we have had a national study of outdoor recreation, under the Outdoor Recreation Resources Review Commission. Further, a number of states have voted major bond issues to expand their park systems, which is further evidence of general public support.

There are a number of difficulties in getting accurate relevant data about outdoor recreation, using any of the concepts discussed in Chapter II. Recreation may be a specific activity using land, such as camping, picnicking, or any one of several others; or it may be an attitude with which some other activity is undertaken. Thus, some men may own a tract of forest land, or a ranch, or other property, as a hobby, for recreation. This latter kind of recreation can hardly be identified as a specific use of land, certainly not by observation and often not by interview. It would perhaps be best to describe the use of such land by its more obvious activity; yet the recreational motivation of much land use cannot be ignored. Equally difficult in this definitional problem of what constitutes recreation, is the fact that recreational use, even in a strict sense of the term, is so often mingled with other land uses. A great deal of outdoor recreation is carried on within forests; this is true of the national forests, for example. Recreation is cursed with a proliferation of terms to describe its various areas—terms which often lack clear and uniform meaning. The issue is far from being merely academic or semantic; if one classifies the New York Forest Preserve in the Adirondacks as a state park, one thereby doubles the area of all state parks in the nation. Some outdoor recreation is closely allied with transportation; highway waysides or rest areas are a good example. Some is allied with education; school playgrounds, for example. Other illustrations, involving other uses, could be cited.

This problem of intermingled or dual use of land is in turn closely allied to the matter of scale of mapping or of study. The whole of the national forests are open for recreation, yet recreation as a major or dominant use is confined to relatively small areas; or the dominant use of the whole of a tract is for education, but at a different scale, part is for recreation; and so on. In this respect, recreation is somewhat like transportation, if one identifies parking areas separately from industrial, trade, or residential areas.

Data on recreational use of land are more piecemeal and scattered than data on most other uses. In part, this is because such data for public lands have nearly always arisen as an incident to administration of the various recreation areas, and have been collected by the agencies concerned to meet their own problems. There has been, and is, a notable lack of uniformity in definition of the areas themselves, of their use, and of other items. There are many sources of data about public recreation land. None is fully complete, many publish their available information in such poor form that it is virtually unusable by most people, and, until recently, there had been almost no attempt to integrate the various sources of data into summary form.[8] Major improvements have been made in very recent years, but it is still too early to say that new data series have been established.

There is very little information on privately owned lands used for recreation. In the case of property owned by one man, primarily for his own use, the previously mentioned definitional problem would be very serious. Other privately owned land is used by persons other than its owners, free or on payment of fees. While there are some scattered pieces of information about such land, there is neither a comprehensive record nor a historical data series.

The National Recreation Association, a private, non-profit organization with headquarters in New York City, makes a census of recreation land at five year intervals. In earlier years, these censuses were at two-year intervals, and still earlier were made annually. They are conducted by mailed questionnaires with follow-ups to non-respondents. A substantial proportion of

[8] Marion Clawson, *Statistics on Outdoor Recreation* (Washington: Resources for the Future, Inc., 1958).

the smaller cities do not report; it may well be that they have no parks. Under-reporting exists for cities of all sizes, but no correction is made for it in the published reports. Information is also obtained by this same organization in its recent censuses as to areas of state and federal land used for recreation. Other kinds of information are obtained also, but data are obtained on areas of land involved. Acreages and other information are presented for each reporting city.

The National Park Service for several years collected information annually about state parks, including information as to area. The published reports show area and other information for each park included in each state system. This activity has now been taken over by the Bureau of Outdoor Recreation. The various federal agencies collect and publish information about the recreation lands they administer; such information is often scanty and variable from agency to agency. These various reports are often in very poor form, consisting of a few mimeographed sheets released annually—impossible for libraries to file and save even if their value were appreciated. Over-all summaries and evaluations of these various sources of data on recreation use of land have been lacking until very recent years and still are not available on a regular, recurring basis. It is often a task merely to compile a historical series on acreage, use, investment, or other items for a particular park, region, or agency.

Information about the natural qualities of land which make it suitable for outdoor recreation has been poorly developed. One basic difficulty is a lack of full agreement on the characteristics or qualities of land which make it valuable for recreation, although a few good studies have been made for sample areas.[9] Location is often a major factor but, as we have noted elsewhere, location is primarily a relationship between one tract of land and another. There have been a good many specific studies, as when an area is proposed for inclusion in a state or national park. Some efforts have been made to classify streams and water bodies as to their suitability for recreation.[10] The outdoor Recreation Resources Review Commission made some studies of land qualities and of areas suitable for outdoor recreation.[11]

[9] Philip H. Lewis, Jr., *Recreation and Open Space in Illinois* (Urbana: Department of Landscape Architecture and Bureau of Community Planning, University of Illinois, 1961); Harold C. Jordahl, Jr., *et al.*, *Recreation in Wisconsin* (Madison: Department of Resource Development, State of Wisconsin, 1962); and DeWitt Nelson, *et al.*, *California Public Outdoor Recreation Plan*, Parts I and II (Sacramento: Documents Section, Printing Division, 1960).

[10] Frank C. Craighead, Jr., and John J. Craighead, "River Systems: Recreational Classification, Inventory and Evaluation," *Naturalist*, Journal of the Natural History Society of Minnesota, XIII, 2 (Summer 1962), pp. 2–19.

[11] Outdoor Recreation Resources Review Commission, *Outdoor Recreation for America* (Washington: U.S. Government Printing Office, 1962); see also Study Reports of the same Commission, as follows: 1. *Public Outdoor Recreation Areas—Acreage, Use, Potential;* 2. *List of Public Outdoor Recreation Areas, 1960;* 4. *Shoreline Recreation Resources of the United States;* and 8. *Potential New Sites for Outdoor Recreation in the Northeast.*

All of this growing interest is commendable, but we as yet lack systematic inventories of land classed according to its suitability for different types of outdoor recreation. Such inventories certainly would not be needed annually, yet they could not be made once-for-all, because conditions change over a period of time.

The Bureau of Outdoor Recreation, in co-operation with other federal agencies and with state agencies, has begun a comprehensive inventory, classification, and evaluation of existing outdoor recreation areas and facilities. This inventory, especially if repeated at intervals of a few years, should provide a great deal of useful information. The Land and Water Conservation Fund Act, passed in 1964, provides federal grants-in-aid to states for parks and outdoor recreation, but requires the states to produce comprehensive recreation and park plans. The latter would seem an excellent opportunity for acquisition of better, more uniform, and more readily usable data about land used for recreation.

Some data are available as to annual expenditures for capital improvements on recreation lands, in the data sources described above. There is also a good deal of data as to numbers of specific improvements, such as golf courses or campgrounds. But there is no comprehensive inventory of the *value* of existing improvements on recreation land.

Data on attendance at recreation areas are very common; but such data do not always employ comparable definitions from area to area, or even from one time to another, and their accuracy often leaves much to be desired. Numbers in attendance on a given area of land provide one measure of intensity of recreation land use. It is a matter of common knowledge that there are great differences in intensity of use within most parks, but quantitative data on this point are lacking. Data are also available for some areas on the number of recreation leaders or on other inputs into recreation management, which also provides a measure of intensity of land use.

Data on Land Used for Health, Education, and Welfare Purposes

A large part of these activities is conducted by some level of government, and thus might be included under a discussion of land used for governmental purposes; however, some are conducted by private organizations, including some by religious organizations. The latter not only have places of worship, but also schools, hospitals, and other services under this general category. There is a wide range of specific uses included in this group. Each activity is likely to use only a relatively small tract of land, and even in total it is probable that this group of uses accounts for only a modest area of land. Yet these services are often critical for the kind of living that people demand in the United States today, and hence land for these purposes in proper locations is essential. Typically, land used for these purposes is highly improved and intensively used.

No comprehensive or systematic data on this activity's use of land exist. Most metropolitan and city plans or land use surveys recognize this group of land uses, not always grouped together or separated from other uses. There is a lack of standard definitions for this group of activities. Nevertheless, their importance is so great and so generally recognized that they are shown in some way in most surveys. However, such data as exist from specific surveys have not been summarized into national totals, as far as we can learn, nor is any time series available. One cannot find out the total area of land used for school purposes, for example. In part, this lack of data about land reflects the fact that land acreage is often less important than location, investment, and use.

Data on Land Used for Governmental Purposes

Included here is the general governmental *function* only, not all governmental ownership of land. The ordinary legislative, executive, and judicial functions of national, state, and local government require relatively small but often strategic areas of land for their proper functioning. Post offices are ubiquitous, for example, and many other government activities are widespread. Defense is the largest land user among the strictly governmental functions.

The land used for governmental functions should be carefully distinguished from the land owned by some governmental unit. About one third of the entire United States is publicly owned, but most is used for forestry, grazing, recreation, or transportation (highways and streets). As noted above, much of the health, education, and welfare activity use of land is on publicly owned land. In keeping with the concepts described in Chapter II, land ownership or tenure should be kept separate from land use or activity on land. But there are governmental functions which constitute a separate kind of activity.

There is relatively little information on this activity or function—data on public landownership leave much to be desired, but in any case are not for the governmental function only. Many metropolitan and city planning studies show governmental areas separately, but not always distinguished from the health, education, and welfare activities previously discussed. However, these have not been summarized into national totals, nor do statistical data series exist. The General Services Administration compiles and publishes annual reports on federal landownership and on improvements thereon, but this is based upon ownership, not function, and includes vast areas we classify elsewhere.[12] These data are tabulated and published by states only, with no location for smaller units of area. There is nothing comparable for land owned by states and counties. Some states publish annual reports showing areas owned, but these are usually of special types of land which we have classified elsewhere, and typically do not include the general governmental function at all.

Data on Land Used for Miscellaneous Purposes

"Miscellaneous" includes such a heterogeneous and diverse group of land uses that few meaningful generalizations are possible. As far as possible, all land should be placed in some definite group according to its use or activity. Any comprehensive survey of land use should account for all tracts of land; acreage by tract use should exactly equal gross area of the unit under study. Only in this way can one be certain that all lands have been covered, but covered once only. But it must be recognized that in the United States there are a few highly unusual uses on relatively small areas which simply do not fit well into any use classification system that is not extremely long and detailed. The variety of land uses in this country constantly amazes even the specialists in this field.

Special consideration should be directed to the idle or vacant land included under "miscellaneous." The conceptual difficulties or unsatisfactoriness of establishing an idle class have been considered in Chapter II. It would be better if one could always classify land according to some discernible use, but there are circumstances when it is difficult to detect any meaningful "use" of land today—nor perhaps in the past. For some idle uses, such as a vacant dwelling, one can be fairly sure of what its normal and probable future use will be, as well as of what its past use was. But there are often instances, especially in suburban fringe areas, where it is virtually impossible to say what the use has been in the recent past, what it is today, or what it may be in the foreseeable future. Such land can best be included in a special idle or vacant subclass under the general miscellaneous category. While such land should be kept to the minimum, a survey which covers any extensive area is very likely to pick up some that falls here.

In practice, every land use survey, enumeration, and tabulation will include a "miscellaneous" category. There is grave danger, however, that "miscellaneous" will become the waste basket for errors, inconsistencies in definition or in practice, and for other irregularities. This is especially the case where data from different sources are summarized, and where differ-

[12] For instance, see *Inventory Report on Real Property Owned by the United States Throughout the World, as of June 30, 1963*, General Services Administration (Washington: U.S. Government Printing Office, 1964).

ences in definition and in concept are almost sure to exist. The discrepancies are likely to be thrown into "miscellaneous." If the latter group is broadly defined, it may well cover up many of the deficiencies and discrepancies in data, leading to a false sense of accuracy (sometimes called hyper-accuracy). In fact, one might say that the size of the "miscellaneous" category is the best single index to the rigor of the land classification, to the consistency of definition, and to the accuracy of enumeration and tabulation. The smaller it is, the better are the data, all else being equal. This is especially true when land use data are assembled by states or counties; the chance for offsetting errors is much less than on a national scale.

Accuracy of Data about Land

In the discussion of this chapter about land statistics in the United States, thus far we have said too little about accuracy at the collection level. Accuracy is always a relative matter; no matter how carefully something is measured, some small element of error remains. It is extremely difficult to estimate how accurate current data are; in retrospect, after errors are eliminated, one can form a judgment about the accuracy of some data series. One may suspect errors in current data, but proof is usually lacking.

Errors may arise in many ways. One of the most common is the lack of a single set of comprehensive definitions, whether one seeks to measure activity, natural qualities, improvements, intensity of use, or whatever. Lacking such comprehensive definitions, some land is omitted, some is counted twice or more, and some is forced into inappropriate categories like square pegs in round holes. The deficiencies are magnified when one part of the job is done by one agency and other parts by other agencies, as when one seeks to summarize data from different sources.

A closely allied kind of error is likely to creep in when a survey covers only part of the total area within defined boundaries. Some land may be omitted, other areas counted more than once, or wrong acreages used which would be impossible if enumerated or reported acreages had to sum out exactly to known totals. In an earlier day, farmers rather consistently over-estimated the acreage of their fields and crops. The New Deal agricultural programs introduced land measurement techniques which have greatly improved acreage estimates.

Much data about land use seems to have an accuracy that in fact it lacks. From published sources one can often estimate accuracy only by noting how well the entire area is accounted for; deficiencies or overlaps may be revealed. However, their absence may only mean that errors have been compensating. Data series which reveal only modest discrepancies or none at all on a national level may reveal much greater ones on a state or county level; errors here have less chance of being compensating. Percentage errors are likely to be especially large for uncommon land uses for relatively small areas. Land use inventories on a parcel basis, such as we suggest in other chapters, would either have fewer errors or make detection easier for those errors which did exist.

Perhaps the only generalization one may safely make is that, by and large, accuracy of data is constantly improving. But this general judgment does not, and perhaps cannot, rest upon any very exacting estimate of the accuracies or inaccuracies that lie imbedded in any data series.

CHAPTER VII.

Classification of Man's Activities Using Land

In Chapter II we discussed a number of concepts about land—or about land "use," to employ a widely used but thus necessarily rather imprecise term. We propose in this chapter to examine in more detail the concept of activities using land, or of land use in a narrower and stricter sense, and to review the most nearly comprehensive classification of the many kinds of activities using land which has been developed to date in the United States. We are essentially classifying man, through his activities, not the land as such; but there is a close relationship between the characteristics of the land and the activities which are carried out upon it.

This chapter is built directly upon Appendix I, which is the manual recently published by the Urban Renewal Administration and the Bureau of Public Roads under the title, *Standard Land Use Coding Manual.* As we noted briefly in the foreword, this manual grew out of extended research and discussions involving a number of specialists of various kinds; and it evolved to a considerable extent jointly with the present study by this Committee. It may fairly be said to summarize or synthesize the numerous previous attempts to develop a comprehensive scheme for classifying activities using land, especially those concerned with land uses in and around cities. Any further efforts at developing a comprehensive system of classifying activities using land, which hopefully will be widely or universally used, should build upon or refine this basic effort, not try to start anew. After some general introductory discussion, we shall review the main points of Appendix I (but the reader is urged to read it in its entirety), show how it can be used to meet different needs, and make some comments about further problems which seem still to exist in practical refinement and application of this classification to all kinds of activities using land.

In the next chapter, we shall consider briefly the various other concepts relating to land, which we described in Chapter II, and show how classifications systems could be developed for these concepts also. In the final chapter, we shall outline a program to improve statistics relating to land, including ways in which the comprehensive activity classification described in this chapter can be translated into operation.

Since every action of man takes place at some point in time and in space, one could thus conclude that everything which happens in the career of a person from the cradle to the grave involves activity on the land, or a form of land use. However, some of man's activities—agriculture, for instance—are closely related to land, while others are much less so. There is a continuum, from the very closest to the most remote relationship between man and the land which he uses; there is no sharp break, on one side of which his activity is clearly and directly land use, on the other side of which land has little or no meaning. We shall consider only those activities of man which are more or less directly related to land, with perhaps more attention to those which are closest and less attention to those which are less directly related.

In this chapter, we shall assume that the locational character of the land has been or can be adequately dealt with. That is, as pointed out in Chapter III, every piece of land has a distinctive location on the face of the earth, which is basic to any consideration of that piece of land. Any classification of use of any tract of land must properly identify the location of that parcel, both in the field enumeration and in the later office compilation. This can be done by any one of several systems of land location identification; location by one system can be translated into location by another system, through use of equivalency tables. For example, census blocks 1–19 in census tract 105 may be equivalent to transportation analysis zone number 22; or census tracts 40, 41, and 42 may be equivalent to police district 4. The problem of identifying geographic location of land is dealt with only to a limited extent in this chapter, but more fully in Appendix I. We shall, however, return to it in Chapter IX, where a program for improved land use data is set forth. Moreover, the highly significant interrelations among separate tracts of land is another facet of the locational problem. Our concern in this chapter, however, is to establish the basic information about land use on each tract. The relationships between the use made of one tract and the use made of any other tract, while often extremely important, is part of the analysis stage of any study and should not be mixed in with the collection of the basic data.

In this chapter, we shall not consider the problem of sampling versus complete enumeration, except to note that for some purposes it is essential to know exactly how every defined tract is used, and thus be able to map land use completely; while for others it may be sufficient to know how typical tracts or an average tract is used, and thus be able to compile statistics showing use of the whole of the area in a larger district. The activity classification described in this chapter is equally applicable to either purpose.

Any classification of land using activities naturally presupposes that basic data on land use are available from some source. A land use inventory can be made by any one of several methods, in varying degrees of detail and accuracy. A great deal of information can be obtained by inspection of aerial photographs; sometimes this will be adequate for a particular purpose. In some cases, observation on the ground is adequate to obtain a great deal of information; but in others, it is necessary to interview the land occupier or owner. Also, combinations of these methods may be used. In many situations, data collected for other purposes may provide the desired information about land use. The land use coding system discussed in this chapter and in Appendix I can be used with data obtained in any of these ways. An inventory, once obtained, can often be kept up to date by data from continuing governmental programs, as we explained in Chapter VI. Building permit, zoning inspection, health inspection, and other data often permit an initial inventory to be kept up to date. Since any reasonably adequate land use inventory can be recorded and analyzed by the coding system set forth in Appendix I, obviously its updating can be handled in the same way.

Characteristics of a Good Land Activity Classification

Several characteristics of a good classification of man's activities on the land may be described; in practice, it will often be necessary or convenient to deviate from these preferred or ideal characteristics, but it is nonetheless helpful to outline some of them. First of all, as far as possible the classification of activities should deal with *activities only*—a "pure line" classification, as far as possible. In Chapter II, we discussed the various concepts applicable to land; of these, activity on the land was a basic one, and one in which there is a great deal of common interest by many different groups. A classification according to activities should not, at least in theory, include references to natural qualities of the land, nor to improvements on the land, to tenure, nor to any of the other concepts discussed in Chapter II.

But a classification based on activities only is neither as easy nor as simple as it sounds. It is possible, for instance, to distinguish between residential use of land in a single-family dwelling and residential use of land in two-family dwellings, on the ground that these are significantly different activities on land; but the obvious measure of that difference in activity—if one is conceded to exist—is the kind of improvement on the land. Or, to take another case, it is possible to differentiate those recreational activities which can take place only on special kinds of sites (historical points, scenic overlooks, etc.) from other kinds of recreational activities which may take place nearly anywhere or at least under much less restrictive natural conditions; but our activity classification is thus to a degree mixed up with a classification of the natural features of the area. To take still another case, when activities such as "forestry" are classified, almost certainly some classification of the vegetative cover of the land is included. However, as far as possible, the activity classification should be kept pure.

As we note elsewhere, data on improvements to land, on land tenure, and on other concepts relating to land may be collected at the same time and by the same procedures as are data on land use or activity on land; and the same electronic or other data-processing records can readily include these additional data for each land parcel. The pure line approach for land activity requires only that intermixture of these other data with classifications of activity on land be kept to a minimum. At a later stage in analysis, data on activity may be related to or compared with data on natural qualities of land, on improvements on land, on land tenure, or on other matters. For instance, one might wish to know how improvements compared on owner-occupied and on tenant-occupied dwellings, or on single-family, owner-occupied dwellings and on multiple-family, owner-occupied dwellings. These types of comparisons could be made in the analysis stage if the basic data have been properly collected, recorded, tabulated, and analyzed; but one should not establish as a basic unit of classification "single-family, owner-occupied dwellings in good condition," or any other recording or classification unit which mixed different concepts at this level.

A second desirable characteristic of a classification of activities on land is that it be flexible, in at least two senses of the term. The classification should be usable in great detail, if desired, or, again, in rather summary form. It should also be usable in detail for some activities, in summary for others, as the needs of the user dictate. Otherwise, a rigid system will break down in use because it will either provide undesired detail or will not provide enough detail. A second kind of flexibility is the ability to recombine basic data in different ways, to meet user needs, but without modifying the activity classification as such. The former of these two kinds of flexibility has sometimes been referred to as the "accordion" idea, under which one part of the whole classification system could be played out in great detail while other parts could be compressed. But this analogy is inadequate to describe the recombination aspect of flexibility. For instance, we do not establish a category called "office buildings," yet our detailed classes could be combined to establish a category for "office buildings," however the latter might be defined. Later in this chapter and in Appendix I some specific examples of each type of flexibility are given. Other rearrangements of the basic data would be possible.

A third desirable characteristic of a comprehensive classification of activity on land is that it be based, as far as possible, upon what the field enumerator or surveyor actually sees or observes on the ground or on aerial photographs, with a minimum of classification or grouping at this point. All data about activity on land rest in the end upon some kind of observation or enumeration in the field. Some minimum amount of classification of activity is unavoidable at this stage—when the fieldman enters on his records that a particular store is a shoe repair shop, or that a particular piece of land is in wheat, he has made a minimum classification of the activity. Unless one had some slot or groove into which to fit the activity he observes or is told about, the use of each piece of land would have to be described in detail separately—an impossible task, and one that would produce useless masses of data. But the classification element should be kept to the minimum during the data collection phase, leaving broader groupings and analyses for later office operations. The cost of detailed enumeration or observation in the field or from aerial photographs, the coding of the data, and the contingency checking will often be higher than would be the enumeration of broadly grouped activities. However, the data collected will be more precise as well as more consistent, and the data collected and coded in detail will provide many more opportunities for later use by the same agency or organization that collected the data and by other organizations. In the end, data collection in detail may thus prove much more economical than data collection by broader groupings.

A corollary of the foregoing is that field enumeration or other primary data collection should be for the smallest recognizable and geographically identifiable parcel or tract or unit of land. To the extent that a separately recognizable activity exists, different parcels are involved, and should be enumerated separately. For example, ideally the different parts of a single farm would be shown separately if in wheat, cotton, woods, farmsteads, roads, etc. On the other hand, where there are large areas that contain similar activity—e.g., single family homes in suburbs—parcels ideally should be distinguished on the basis of ownership. Thus, individual lots would be shown separately, even though the whole area was in residential use.

What is defined as a "recognizable" separate parcel depends in large part upon the kinds of geographical units for which one wishes detailed data, and this in turn depends upon the data uses one has in mind. Some activities are readily observable from air photographs, and others can be obtained by ground observation; but some of necessity will require interviews with occupants or owners. The same is true of information about improvements; but most data on tenure could be obtained only by interview, although tenure parcel lines might easily be observable on the ground or from photographs. The scale on which the work was done would also affect the delineation of parcels. Ideally, the smallest unit of land with different activity, or different improvements if one were interested in improvements, or with different tenure if one were interested in tenure, and so on, would be identified as separate geographical units; but, in practice, this ideal is difficult if not sometimes impossible to achieve.

Through the use of various types of data processing equipment, data for small parcels can always be combined and summarized into larger geographic units; on the other hand, data originally collected for large geographic units can never be subdivided without additional field work which increases the expense and which may introduce new errors.

A fourth desirable characteristic of a comprehensive classification of activities on the land is that its data be readily susceptible to machine processing. The potentialities of machine processing—a subject to which we return in Chapter IX—are so very great as to have marked influence on the form of the classification itself. This means, in practice, a digit numbering system for land activities, and, as far as possible, not more than ten categories or subclasses under each more generalized classification.

Still another desirable characteristic of a classification system for activities on land is that—in modern computer terminology—it be "compatible." That is, a system adopted at one time will almost certainly require modification at some future date, as new uses of land arise or as new problems require different kinds of data. Can changes be introduced incrementally or gradually into the system, without scrapping what has been done previously and starting afresh? A system which is capable of modification and improvement without complete replacement is obviously better than one which lacks this characteristic. The system outlined in this chapter and in Appendix I does have that valuable trait.

In practice, compromises with these ideal characteristics are likely to arise in one or more of several ways. First of all many cities, metropolitan districts, states, or other political units now have some kind of land use data system, however rudimentary. The problem is likely to be one of improvement, not one of initiation. The methods by which data have been collected, tabulated, and analyzed in the past may set some limits, or seem to do so, to the ways in which data can be handled in the future. A closely related consideration is the preservation of statistical comparability with existing data series. The Census of Agriculture and the USDA statistics of farmland use and crop acreages, for instance, have great value as historical series. New data systems must consider comparability with old data systems. Although we believe that in the long run a system of land use data following the principles here described will save substantial money, any unit of government may conclude that in a specific instance it must of necessity deviate from these principles. In particular, the temptation to make summary classifications during the field collection phase will sometimes be overwhelming. We think little will be saved in this way—to classify a tract as manufacturing instead of by kind of manufacturing, or as trade instead of by kind of trade, etc. Or the classification may be applied to broad areas, rather than to separate tracts. Whatever the short run—"one shot"—savings may be, in the end costs will be higher, as the next need for land use data requires a new field enumeration. But, realistically, some units of government will compromise with the principles of land use classification outlined above, for this reason of apparent economy. Other reasons for compromise may arise in other situations also.

Partly because compromise with the ideal is inevitable, and partly because flexibility could disintegrate into chaos unless there is some restraint, a basic conclusion of this Committee, discussed more fully in Chapter IX, is that a permanent continuing organization for land use statistics should be established. Communities as well as planning programs vary considerably as to their capacity to use and manage detailed land use data. It is unrealistic, therefore, to outline a land activity classification and either expect or demand that everyone follow it exactly. A mechanism for improvement may be just as important at this stage as an outline of what is ideal.

Relationship of Activity Information to Other Data

The value of data about any activity on land is greatly increased if these data can be related in some way to other data concerning the same area. Thus, if the acreage of land in a particular use can be related to employment and other input or output data, the relationship is far more meaningful than are the acreage figures alone. If the area in residential use can be related to numbers of people resident in the total area, the result is of much more value. To take still another illustration, if land area data can be related to capital investment data, significant economic relationships may be described. In the United States, as in any economically advanced country, there are many different data series; to the extent these can be interrelated for the same tracts or areas of land, the value of each is greatly increased.

Interrelation of various kinds of data requires, above all, that each set of data apply to exactly the same tracts or areas of land. The tracts may be small—"parcels," as we use the word; or they may be much larger—census tracts, counties, etc. Data which relate to specific parcels may be unrepresentative for other parcels lying within the same larger area; hence, comparison of data about some parcels in a city or county to other data about the whole city or county might give misleading results. Interrelation of data from different sources also requires that apparently identical classes be actually identical. For instance, data on area of land used for a certain type of manufacturing must be compared with employment data for exactly the same type of manufacturing, if meaningful ratios are to result.

In this modern complex economy and society, the use and value of one tract of land often is highly dependent upon the use of other tracts of land. A dwelling has value and usefulness only because its occupant has a job; a park, no matter how attractive physically, is useful only as people residing on other tracts of land are able to use it; one manufacturing site is productive only because the products of other manufacturing sites can be processed further; and so on, for a host of economic and social interrelations. It is the externalities of each piece of land which primarily determine its value and use, more than the internalities of the same land. Accordingly, data about activity on any piece of land, no matter how detailed and accurate, can tell only part of the story about that land—and often only a minor part of that story. Hence, to the greatest possible extent, data on land activity should be developed in such a manner that it is relatable to data concerning other economic and social activities.

One specific way of classifying a great deal of economic information is represented by the Standard Industrial Classification. Although not in itself a source of data, the SIC is the basis upon which other data are collected, coded, and organized. It is concerned with economic establishments and their activities, not primarily with activity on land as such. Business and other units are classified primarily on an establishment basis—a farm, a factory, a mine, a store, which is not always the way land activity data can best be organized. In spite of some limitations for our purpose, the SIC is so widely used as a basis for organizing all sorts of other economic data that there are major advantages in classifying land on the same basis, as far as practicable. In particular, the SIC employs the principles of classifying basic units, as far as possible, and developing major classes from such detail, rather than the reverse; moreover, it has been developed on a digital basis, and hence is well adapted to machine treatment of data.

The SIC is applicable to land used for industrial and commercial purposes; it is less suitable for land used for residential and agricultural purposes, and still less suitable for some kinds of recreation and some kinds of governmental activity.

The URA-BPR system of land activity classification, presented in Appendix I, makes extensive use of the SIC classification of economic activities. For reasons explained in that appendix, apparently similar classes are not always in fact identical, hence the user of such statistics must be aware of possible discrepancies. In a great many instances, however, the SIC is fully applicable to land uses.

With adequate locational identification, land use data collected by the methods outlined in Appendix I can be related to census and other data organized on political and statistical areas such as cities, standard metropolitan areas, counties, states, and the like.

Land Use Coding Manual of URA-BPR

The URA-BPR *Standard Land Use Coding Manual,* reproduced here as Appendix I, employs many of the foregoing general ideas. The methods whereby this is done are summarized in this section and discussed in more detail in the appendix, to which the reader is referred.

"One of the most significant conclusions of [the study] . . . is that different characteristics or dimensions that describe land should *not* be combined into a single classification system if the system is to meet the objectives outlined above" (p. 3).[1] A system of categories identifying land use activities was developed, which could also be numerically coded into a four-digit system of primary description.

The coding system and categories are flexible, in both of the senses described above—they can be used in great detail or can be compressed in different parts, and their units can be recombined to meet other needs. "In developing the system of activity categories, a second major conclusion was reached, and that is that no *rigid* system for classifying land use activity is feasible for broad application to all urban areas in the United States" (p. 4). The same conclusion would probably hold for rural areas also, although the report does not state so explicitly. In a later section, we show some of the ways in which the basic data obtained by application of this system can be regrouped into different classes than are shown in the *Manual.* After discussing the needs for flexibility, the *Manual* states: "Do these types of local factors mean then that the whole idea of developing a standard system for describing land use activity in a comparable form from city to city is a lost cause? Not at all. What it does mean is that if there is to be comparability, there must be an approach to classifying land use activity that will permit *standardization in coding land use activity data and flexibility in the use of the data once it is coded*" (p. 6). This is much the same way in which the SIC is used.

A detailed four-digit system for identifying and coding land use activity is developed in the *Manual.* "Seldom will it be necessary or even desirable in any day-to-day planning operation to work with land use activity data

[1] Pages referenced in this and the following four sections apply to page numbers in the original *Manual* which is reproduced as Appendix I (pp. 269–383) in this book.

at the detailed level being recommended for data collection and coding. . . . However, if land use activity is identified and coded using the four-digit codes, the data can then be regrouped into a variety of different classification patterns to fit the needs of special studies or analyses" (p. 6).

The coding system in the *Manual* employs nine major classifications of land use, because these are considered to be the most useful to a wide range of planning studies. The categories used at the one-digit level are:

Code	*Category*
1	Residential
2 and 3	Manufacturing
4	Transportation, communication, and utilities
5	Trade
6	Services
7	Cultural, entertainment, and recreational
8	Resource production and extraction
9	Undeveloped land and water areas

The emphasis, however, is not on this classification structure, but rather on the detailed identification of activity shown at the four-digit level. Altogether there are 9 one-digit categories, 67 two-digit categories, 294 three-digit categories, and 772 four-digit categories. Codes at the two-, three-, and four-digit levels could be expanded in many instances, if necessary. The four-digit category is the most detailed, and is the level of detail recommended for coding the basic information collected through field observation or secondary sources. As one moves toward fewer digits, the categories necessarily become more generalized. While the latter are highly useful for some purposes, they do not permit the extensive degree of recombination of data which is so often desirable and hence should ordinarily not be used at the enumeration and coding levels.

An illustration may help to clarify the meaning of the four-digit categories and their grouping into more generalized classes. A beer brewery would be classified, from basic data and at the four-digit level, as 2181, "malt liquors—manufacturing." Along with other, but similar, activities, the beer brewery would be generalized into a three-digit class, 218, "beverage—manufacturing"; this in turn, along with other food manufacturing enterprises, into a two-digit class, 21, "food and kindred products—manufacturing," and these further generalized into a one-digit group, "manufacturing." Similar coding at the four-digit level of other activities would in turn lead to other generalizations at three-, two-, and one-digit levels.

In order to permit a detailed identification under one classification and a summary identification under others at the same time, only 1 to 9 subcategories were used in any subclassification. The code "zero" is used here to fill in the blank positions to the right of the code number when categories are used at the more generalized three-, two-, and one-digit levels. If there were a full 10 subgroups within every group, there would be 10 groups at the one-digit level, 100 groups at the two-digit level, 1,000 at the three-digit level, and 10,000 at the four-digit level; instead, as noted above, there are 9, 67, 294, and 772, respectively. Thus, the full theoretical possibilities of the digit system are not required to meet the subdivisions which logic and experience indicate as necessary and desirable. There are still many "empty boxes" in the system, which may or may not be used later, as the need arises.

One major innovation of this coding system is the use of auxiliary codes for land use data. In addition to the basic four-digit codes used to identify activities as such, an additional one-digit code (or conceivably two additional digits if this system is expanded) is added in order to identify "activities that are generally found separated from, but functionally and organizationally linked to other activities." Examples cited in the *Manual* include a warehouse operated by a retail concern primarily for its own use and not for public storage, a parking area operated by a manufacturing concern for use by its own employees and not for public parking, or an office performing management functions as part of a mining concern which has mines in several states. Taking the establishment approach of the SIC, the whole of an identifiable economic enterprise is identified according to its major activity; but this may include many other activities which are highly important in their own right and which would be separately identified if standing as separate enterprises. The *Manual* establishes the following auxiliary categories:

Code	*Auxiliary category*
0	Not an auxiliary
1	Central or administrative office
2	Sales office
3	Research and development
4	Warehouse and storage
5	Automobile parking
6	Motor vehicle garage (maintenance and/or storage of vehicles)
7	Steam and power plant
8 and 9	Open codes, that could be used to meet the needs of a particular situation

A public parking lot would be classified as 4600, under the general heading of transportation, communication, and utility. A parking lot limited to being used by patrons of a particular store or business firm would be classified according to the category in which that store or firm fell, but the auxiliary code 5 would identify it as a parking lot. For example, 5410-5 would be the parking lot of a grocery store.

This device of auxiliary codes opens up enormous possibilities for recording and tabulating additional data, and enormous flexibilities in use of the whole system. If each of the eight auxiliary categories shown above were applied to the 772 four-digit categories established in the *Manual,* a possible 6,176 land use situations could be described. Many of these theoretically possible combinations would never occur in practice—one cannot well conceive of an auxiliary 1 "central or administrative office" or 3 "research and development" for a four-digit coded activity such as 1210 "rooming and boarding houses," for instance. The alternative to the auxiliary system, to obtain comparable flexibility in another way, would have been to go to a five-digit system, repeating each auxiliary (0 to 7) under each four-digit category. This would have made the coding system enormously long, detailed, and cumbersome.

The *Manual* uses the SIC terminology to a large extent, especially for manufacturing, trade, and services. However, ". . . *the adoption of the same terminology does not necessarily make the land use data collected and coded under this system of categories compatible with the economic data collected using SIC specifications*" (p. 13). Most economic data using the SIC classify the activity (1) on an establishment basis and (2) on the basis of the value of the product or services offered. In contrast, the categories proposed in the *Manual,* although also using the establishment concept, classify uses according to the greatest amount of space used for the purpose. In a great many cases—perhaps the overwhelming majority—the two systems would result in the same classification for a particular establishment; but in some cases a different classification could result. If a manufacturing, trade, or other establishment is engaged in a single, four-digit activity, as described in SIC or in the *Manual,* where the same term is used in each, then there would be no question—the two would be comparable. If an establishment were engaged in more than one activity, by either system of definition, but the same activity were dominant whether one measured dominance by value of product or by land area used, there would also be no question as to comparability. It would only be where one activity would be classed as dominant on the basis of value of product and another activity would be classed as dominant on the base of land area used, that a divergence between the land coding system of the *Manual* and the coding of SIC would develop. The *Manual* necessarily cannot follow SIC for some activities, particularly some concerned with publicly owned land.

The *Manual* clearly warns the user of data to know precisely the comparability of the various items he proposes to compare—sound advice in all analysis, but especially needed where the terms are the same but their content may vary.

The *Manual* discusses the difference between its term "household unit" and the term "housing unit" as used by Census; it considers also the reasons for the large amount of detail included under manufacturing, and shows how warehousing and storage are handled under this system. The reader is referred to Appendix I for this discussion.

One especially troublesome matter in any system of land use classification is the handling of idle land or idle facilities. As we noted in Chapter II, there is in fact a good deal of land in the United States for which the only accurate answer as to present activity is "none." The land, with or without buildings, is not used at all at the moment; it is idle, in any meaningful sense. It may never have had any purposeful use or activity, as we noted, or it may be idle under such circumstances that one can assume the idleness is temporary and such that the past and probably future uses are fairly certain.

Many sources of data about land consciously or unconsciously avoid this problem of idle land. The definition of a farm used by the Bureau of the Census, for instance, will pick up idle cropland within the farm; but idle land that once was used for farming is excluded by the definition of the farm. Many inquiries or sources of data deal with activity, often getting their basic data from the persons directing that activity; if there is no activity, there may be no information. If the total acreage within a defined area is accounted for by the land use or other inquiry, then of course the idle land, if any, shows up and must be accounted for. However, as we have noted, most sources of data have a "miscellaneous" category, which in practice becomes a waste basket for errors and omissions, as well as for undefined uses or activities, such as "idle."

The *Manual* faces this problem of idle land more explicitly than does perhaps any previous attempt at a comprehensive land use classification system; however, as we shall discuss in the following section of this chapter, some further refinement may be necessary. A separate code, 9100, "identifies those parcels of land that appear to be underdeveloped or, if previously developed, are presently vacant and unused. This category includes such areas as vacant lands that were once farms located in the rural-urban fringe, as well as vacant parcels where structures have been demolished" (p. 17). Another category, 9400, identifies "only vacated *nonresidential* floor area within a structure" (p. 17). No provision is made in the *Manual* for recording vacant residential units, but this could be added within its general framework if it were desired to do so. Another special but temporary category, 95, deals with land where construction is under way; as soon as ultimate use is known, the classification should be changed to reflect the actual or clearly intended use. As we shall point out later in this chapter, this treatment of idle land may not be sufficient to deal with all idle land within farms, with unused desert and swamp areas, and perhaps with other situations. However, it is a constructive approach to a very difficult problem, and additions, if needed, can be worked into the general framework established in the *Manual.*

The reader is particularly referred to Appendix I, to see how the *Manual* is intended to be applied. Several illustrations deal with the identification of parcels, the handling of uses on second and higher floors of structures, the use of auxiliary codes, and other matters, at the field or enumeration level. These illustrations, while comparatively brief and not covering all the many kinds of situations which will be encountered in actual practice, do demonstrate how the system can be used—and above all, how flexible and versatile it is. Other illustrations consider specifically how the basic system can be used to deal flexibly with various needs or situations on the land. In particular, it is shown how the same basic data obtained from a single field survey or enumeration can be made to serve several different land planning needs. Although these, too, are rather brief, and by no means cover all the possibilities for rearrangement of the same basic data, they are very suggestive as to the various kinds of uses that can be made from a given set of basic data.

More than half of the whole *Manual* is given over to a detailed listing of the one-, two-, three-, and four-digit categories. Even so, the latter are not specifically defined, although footnotes have been used where the meanings do not seem obvious. The relationship between the codes established in the *Manual* and the SIC are shown also. It is impossible to summarize these detailed codes and classes in any meaningful way, and the reader must turn to Appendix I.

The *Manual* concludes with three short appendices: (1) a proposed coding system for identifying ownership (which puts all private ownership into a single category); (2) a proposed coding system for identifying types of farms and farm uses; and (3) a proposed coding system for identifying types of structures that would contain household units. Each of these is quite brief, considering the scope of the subject matter covered. For agriculture, a "farm use" code is proposed; as proposed, this has three digits, but presumably it could be expanded in more detail within the same general framework if necessary. This code would be supplementary to the main activity code; under the latter, farms would be identified by type. Under the "farm use" code, specific crops and other activities on land *within* the farm would be identified. The *Manual* includes an illustration of how the farm use code could be used in conjunction with the major land use activity codes. We comment further upon this approach in a later section of this chapter. It represents a new approach to agricultural land use, one which will be unfamiliar to most students of agriculture, and hence perhaps resisted at first contact by specialists from this field. But it is, or can be made, a highly flexible and versatile tool for dealing with a broad range of difficult problems.

Regrouping of Basic Data for Other Purposes

We have emphasized the flexibility inherent in detailed uniform coding of land use or activity on the land; this may now be illustrated with a few examples that may make these possibilities clearer. The four-digit categories in the *Manual* are building blocks, which might be combined in many different ways; the 772 four-digit categories listed, plus others that might be added later, can be combined into an infinite number of patterns. However, logic, purpose, and usefulness will make far fewer, but still a considerable number of groups sensible. We shall use three illustrations: forestry, recreation, and urban land uses.

There is considerable interest in forests and in forestry as a land use. When one specifies forests or forestry, to some extent he is classifying according to vegetative type on the land, or, in some sense, according to the natural qualities of the tracts in question. A growing forest represents a capital investment also. There are many purposes in forestry: watershed management, scenic values, recreation, and others as well as the production of commercial products such as sawlogs and pulpwood. Thus, one person might define forestry or forests in one way, another might define it in another way; or the same person might logically use different definitions for different purposes.

The *Manual* has a three-digit group 831, "commercial forestry production," with a footnote indicating that this includes land *not* on farms and ranches; this is subdivided into eight four-digit groups, according to the purpose of production—predominantly for pulpwood, predominantly for sawlogs, etc. Another class is the two-digit group 92, "noncommercial forest development," not in farms, which in turn is modestly subdivided. Still another class is the two-digit group 76, "parks," which is also modestly subdivided. This class might or might not have trees or "forest" by any desired definition; one would need further data on the natural qualities of the land to be sure. There is also a very large group, under the general two-digit designation 81, "agriculture," with nine types of farms defined at the three-digit level and further subdivision at the four-digit level. In a later section, we shall make a rather detailed comparison of farms so defined with farms as defined by the Bureau of the Census. The four-digit classes do not recognize farm forests; however, the *Manual* in its Appendix 2 sets up a system of farm use categories, somewhat similar to the auxiliary codes previously discussed. Farm use category 27, "forests," is subdivided according to whether the forest is grazed or not; but further subdivisions, comparable to those under 831, "commercial forestry production," noted above, could readily be added.

If data were available on a parcel basis for any area, using the coding system of the *Manual*, one could compile the acreage of "forests" by any definition he chose, using the foregoing specific categories as building blocks. If the data were recorded on some electronic data-processing equipment—as we assume would be the case—this grouping of detailed data into summary totals would be relatively simple.

Another activity, or group of activities, in which there is even more interest and even less agreement as to meaning, is recreation. Recreation, however defined, is the primary use of some land, and a secondary or other use of much additional area. Much will depend on the scale of inquiry or data recording. As we noted previously, on one scale a large area is used for forestry, meaning the production of commercial forest products; but on another scale the campground within it is shown separately. Likewise, school yards which are part of the educational plant may have additional recreational values. A much more difficult case arises when the land obviously appears to be in one use, such as farming or ranching or forestry, when in fact the owner owns and uses it because of the recreational value he gets.

Many "building blocks" might be considered for inclusion in a definition of recreation. A two-digit group 74, "recreational activities," is subdivided into several three-digit groups and these in turn into varying numbers of four-digit groups; generally speaking, this group or cluster of groups is concerned with sports. It does include 7491, "camping and picnicking areas" but with a footnote that this includes only such areas not identified with a larger activity, such as a park. There is also the two-digit group 75, "resorts and group camps," somewhat subdivided, and with fairly obvious specific activities. Then there is 76, "parks," only very slightly subdivided, and not following either the Outdoor Recreation Resources Review Commission's proposed uniform designation nor the one previously proposed by Clawson. There is also 73, "amusements," which includes fairgrounds, amusement parks, golf driving ranges (but not golf courses, which were in 74, noted above), and some other miscellaneous categories. Still another group is 72, "public assembly," with a considerable number of subgroups such as motion picture theaters, drive-in movies, race tracks, auditoriums, exhibition halls, and several others. Finally, there is 71, "cultural activities and nature exhibitions," with several subdivisions such as libraries, museums, zoos, botanical gardens, historic and monument sites, and others. All of these fall under the broad grouping 7, "cultural, entertainment, and recreational."

But there are other areas, within other primary designations, that might be included within recreation. Classes 68, "educational services," 69, "miscellaneous services," 6543, "hospital services," 6516, "sanitariums, convalescent, and rest home services," and 45, "highway and street right-of-way," might each include smaller specialized areas for some kind of recreation. The *Manual* does not have an auxiliary category as to recreation activities within a primarily different activity, as it does for parking on the premises of a factory, for instance; but such an auxiliary code for these incidental recreational areas and activities could readily be developed. If so, then one could readily designate such areas.

One could use any definition of "recreation" that he chose, and from these various building blocks assemble data on areas of land and their location used for the function as he defined it, if the basic data were coded on a parcel basis by the system proposed in the *Manual.*

Another grouping of land uses, for which there is much interest but which is even less clearly defined than the foregoing, is "urban" land use. Strictly speaking, "urban" is not an activity on land, or land use, in the sense that manufacturing, trade, or agriculture are. Rather, it is more a form of social organization, sometimes a legal form of government, or, in the land use sense, a grouping of certain uses in more or less definite density and other patterns. Nevertheless, frequently it is convenient to refer to a broad grouping of land uses as "urban." The postwar growth of urban populations, and more particularly their spread across the land, has focused a great deal of attention on land uses within urban complexes.

The land use coding system described in the *Manual* provides the building blocks to compile statistics on "urban" land uses, according to any definition of the latter. But the compiler must provide his own definition of urban. One could specify certain kinds of activities as urban, others as rural—forestry and agriculture would presumably fall in the latter, rather than in the former. A different approach would be to define as urban any grouping of dwellings of more than a certain number; or one could define as urban all or specified activities within specified distances of such defined concentrations of dwellings, in order to include the trade and industrial sites associated with urban areas, even though the factory was itself located outside of the defined urban area. If the land use activities are coded as outlined in the *Manual,* and if full information is obtained on parcel location and identification, then these or any other desired definitions of urban could be used.

Analyses Possible if Manual Is Used

A complete understanding of the potentials of the *Manual* may be facilitated by briefly considering some of the analyses that could be made, were accurate and comprehensive data about land available for any area, using the data system outlined in the *Manual.* First of all, the acreage of land used for any purpose would be known. One could start with the four-digit groups of the *Manual,* working upward to the three-, two-, and one-digit levels; or he could have information on some uses in the detail of the four-digit level, other uses at any one of the other levels. Or, as outlined above, he could regroup uses according to any definition he chose.

Secondly, these data on activity on the land could be summarized for any geographical area desired—by blocks, census enumeration districts, cities, counties, watersheds, or any other. Some data could be summarized in great detail for relatively small geographic areas, other data could be summarized by relatively large areas. Moreover, the same basic data could be summarized by one set of geographic areas at one time or for one purpose, and regrouped differently at another time for another purpose. Obviously, the flexibility in groupings according to use and according to location could be combined into any desired mixture of use and location groupings; for instance, certain kinds of trade activities could be analyzed in great geographical detail, while residential use of land would be summarized for larger areas, and agriculture and forestry grouped for the remaining parts of the county concerned. Or the latter could be treated in detail, with all uses within a defined urban area simply grouped, for some other kind of analysis. The same basic data could be used for any of these uses, at any time.

Moreover, always on the assumption that detailed activity and detailed location data are available, the data system outlined in the *Manual* can show the spatial interrelations of various uses. One could ascertain the number of land parcels used for residential purposes within one-half mile of a particular school, or within one-half mile of any school, or the number more than one-half but less than one mile, or one could substitute "park" for "school" in the foregoing. One could ascertain the interrelations of certain kinds of trade establishments—shoe stores to jewelry stores, shoe stores to large department stores, etc.—one could ascertain numbers of residential tracts within specified distances of certain types of factories or other employment places. The possibilities of such spatial-use interrelations are infinite, but it would be up to the analyst to specify what he wanted—merely because it is possible to get certain kinds of data interrelations does not prove that they have any economic or social meaning.

Data on land use could be related to data about other social and economic matters, if the latter were also available for the same or similar relatively small and well-defined land areas. For instance, data on numbers of people, in total or by age groups, could be related to areas of land used for residences, or to location of schools or parks, or the numbers and locations of specified trade establishments. Data on labor force could be related to certain types of employment opportunities; or one could show either shortest or quickest travel routes from certain areas of residence to certain areas of employment, if adequate data on transportation were available. Data on land area could be related to data on investment, output, employment, or anything else, always assuming that the latter data were accurate and sufficiently precise as to location. Obviously, all the possibilities for activity and geographic area groupings outlined above apply here also.

Moreover, were the *Manual* to be used generally, one could make comparisons between any land use, or any land use-geographic area combination, that he chose, for any pair or grouping of cities or counties or states that he might wish. One could analyze relationships of trade areas to residential areas in San Francisco as compared to Los Angeles, or Hartford as compared to Memphis, or any other combination that one chose. Here again, the possibility of making an analysis is not evidence that it would be meaningful if made; and one cannot assume that any analysis would be costless. Nevertheless, knowledge often comes from comparisons of experience in different places, and widespread or uniform use of the system outlined in the *Manual* opens up enormous possibilities for data analysis.

The same general situation exists if one considers analyses between different time periods, instead of analyses between different areas. If the data system outlined in the *Manual* were used in any city or other area over a period of years, with accurate and detailed data by activity and by geographic areas closely defined, then one could make any time comparisons he chose. He could show the changes in land area used for residential purposes as compared with the changes in total population; or the changes in trade areas as compared with changes in population. He could show changes in total land use within a defined part of the city, such as certain blocks. He could show the changes in spatial pattern—the extent of shifting of trade to suburbs in relation to population shifts to suburbs, or the degree to which certain types of trade tend to cluster, or the tendency of manufacturing of certain types to spread to more open area locations. This type of analysis could be as detailed or as general as desired. It could also be related to the physical or natural characteristics of the land; one could ascertain on precisely which classes of cropland, precisely in which locations, a certain crop had either expanded or declined in acreage or output.

A special variant of the foregoing is that it would be possible to trace what had happened over time to a specific tract or parcel of land. That is, one would not be limited by acreage totals for a county, city, or smaller geographic area; one could ascertain the activity on a particular parcel or spot at various dates in the past, for comparison with the present. This type of analysis today is generally impossible, and will remain so until detailed activity and location data are available over a period of years. Nevertheless, historical research could often ascertain past use, with at least moderate accuracy as to use and as to location; there are many historical materials which have been used little or not at all for this purpose. As time goes on, this type of historical analysis would often have great value. In addition to the previous assumptions as to detail and accuracy of data on activity and on location, this type of analysis must also assume that data from earlier time periods are preserved in a form suitable for use. This is much easier today, with modern data processing equipment, than it once was.

Lastly, data collection throughout the nation along the lines of the *Manual* would permit preparation of state and national, as well as of county, summaries of land use and changes in land use that could be much more accurate than any now available. As we noted in Chapters V and VI, the Census of Agriculture and the forestry statistics collected by the Forest Service provide national and smaller geographic area summaries of certain kinds of land use; and the Economic Research Service has compiled national summaries of all land uses. But these data are of unknown accuracy and coverage, since none accounts for the whole land area by a consistent and comprehensive system of land use classification. There has been no consistent, continuous collection of data on land use within urban complexes. To the extent that the *Manual* comes into general use, data will begin to accumulate which in time will permit more accurate and more meaningful summaries of land use, and its trends, than has been possible in the past.

Agriculture in the Manual and in the Census

"This land use coding system [of the *Manual*] has been developed primarily for use in urban area planning. However, this system is sufficiently broad and flexible enough for use in studies of the urban-rural fringe and of rural areas" (p. 15). These statements are accurate but the classification of agricultural activities in the *Manual* differs in several important respects from the long data series available in the Census of Agriculture, to which the USDA agricultural data generally conform. The system outlined in the *Manual* could rather easily be modified to bring the two into substantial agreement, and there would seem to be major advantages in so doing. A moderately detailed comparison of the two data systems therefore seems warranted at this point.

First, as to sources of data: The Census of Agriculture, as we noted in Chapter VI, gets its information predominantly by asking farmers about their operations. It is concerned with farms, not agriculture as we define the latter; that is, woods and other lands used for forestry, recreation, or other uses are included. However, the dominant factor usually is agriculture. The farmer is asked questions as to the total area of land under his control, the acreage of specific crops and their output, livestock numbers and their output, certain items of expense, and certain items of income, as well as a number of questions as to farm facilities. The amount of information that can be obtained in this way is limited by the farmer's willingness and ability to reply, but today these are each relatively high. The information obtained from the farmer is supplemented by state average prices, obtained by interview from sample farmers or otherwise, for calculation of certain farm income estimates.

Data for land coding, as outlined in the *Manual,* might come from any one of several sources: aerial photographs, observation, or secondary sources of data such as assessors' records. To classify some types of farms as outlined in the *Manual* (discussed below), it would be necessary to interview the farmer in order to obtain the needed information. The *Manual* also considers farms, not agriculture, but a supplementary farm use code separates forests and other non-agricultural uses. Some farms could be classified according to type on the basis of observable information. To be sure that each was properly classified, however, it would probably be necessary to interview all farmers, so that none escaped proper classification on the basis of data that could be obtained only by interview. For example, are the grains cash or feed grains; is dairying the major source of income, is it something else in this role? Since some, or most, or all farms, depending upon the kind of farming in a particular locality, would have to be interviewed in any case, a farm type classification based upon interview information is practical and not burdensome. The question then becomes one of the best definition of farm types. For many urban planning purposes, a classification by farm type would not be necessary. A general coding of the land as being "Agriculture" might be the only activity identification needed.

The *Manual* and the Census of Agriculture define a farm differently, as we noted above. Briefly, the Census includes places of ten acres or more if sales of agricultural produce exceeded $50, smaller places if sales exceeded

$250, or if the place normally would meet these standards but in that particular year fell short. The criterion is ten acres total land area; a considerable part of this might be in woods or other uses, if the value-of-sales criterion was met. The *Manual* includes as a farm a parcel or parcels of land if ten acres or more are under cultivation, in tree or bush crops, or are used for livestock or poultry purposes. Although it is not specifically stated, presumably permanent meadows cut for hay would be considered "under cultivation"; perhaps the same is true for permanent pastures, at least if the land is cultivatable. The *Manual* definition includes no value component; a specialized broiler enterprise on less than ten acres would not be included as a farm, no matter how large the value of its output. It is clear that these two definitions differ considerably; Census would presumably include some small farms omitted as farms under the *Manual.* In 1959 the Census of Agriculture reported almost a quarter of a million farms with less than ten acres total land area. Each would omit some very small tracts of land, as we noted earlier.

It is in their classification of farms by type, however, that the two methods or sources of data differ most. The Census of Agriculture makes an initial distinction between "commercial farms" and "other farms"; the latter include part-time, part-retirement, and abnormal farms.[2] "Part-time farms" are distinguished as "farms with a value of sales of farm products of $50 to $2,499 . . . . if (1) the operator was under sixty-five years of age and (2) he either worked off the farm 100 or more days during 1959 or the income he and members of his household received from off-the-farm operated sources was greater than the total value of farm products sold." Next, "part-retirement farms" were established: "farms with a value of sales of farm products of $50 to $2,499 were classified as 'part-retirement' when the farm operator was 65 years old or over." These two groups do not include all farms with less than $2,500 gross income; an operator less than sixty-five years of age who did less than 100 days work off his farm would be excluded from both of them. "Abnormal farms" included institutions, Indian reservations, and a few other unusual types.

The Census of Agriculture classifies commercial farms by type, based primarily on the source of farm income. Coffee, pineapple, and sugarcane farms are established for Hawaii but not elsewhere; we limit our discussion to the contiguous states. The farm types enumerated in the *Manual,* with their definitions as specified there, and the most nearly comparable types in the Census of Agriculture, with their definitions, are as follows:

[2] For a more detailed definition of commercial and other farms, see *Introduction, United States Census of Agriculture 1959*, General Report, Vol. II, Statistics by Subjects, Bureau of the Census (Washington, 1962).

Manual	*Census of Agriculture*
8111 Farms, predominant crop, cotton: subject to the general definition of a farm, and including all tracts under one management, the farm is classified according to the predominant use of land (the use taking up the greatest percentage of the farm area, excluding building areas, areas in feed crops, and grazed and nongrazed forested areas).	Cotton farms: sales of cotton (lint and seed) accounted for 50 per cent or more of total farm sales.
8119 Farms, other type fiber crops: same general criteria as above.	Not shown separately.
8120 Farms, predominant crop, cash grains: same general criteria as above.	Cash-grain farms: Combined sales of corn, sorghums (except for sirup), small grains, dry field and seed beans and peas, soybeans for beans, cowpeas for peas accounted for 50 per cent or more of total farm sales.
8130 Farms, field crops other than fiber or cash grain crops: same general criteria as above.	Other field crop farms: combined sales of peanuts, Irish potatoes, sweetpotatoes, sugarcane for sugar and for sirup, sweet sorghums for sirup, broomcorn, popcorn, sugar beets for sugar, mint, hops, and sugar beet seed accounted for 50 per cent or more of total farm sales. Tobacco farms: Sales of tobacco accounted for 50 per cent or more of total farm sales.
8141 Farms, predominant crops, fruits: same general criteria as above.	Fruit-and-nut farms: Combined sales of berries, and other small fruits, grapes, tree fruits, and nuts accounted for 50 per cent or more of total farm sales.
8142 Farms, predominant crops, tree nut: same general criteria as above.	
8143 Farms, predominant crops, vegetables: same general criteria as above.	Vegetable farms: Sales of vegetables accounted for 50 per cent or more of total farm sales.
8150 Farms, predominantly dairy products: 50 per cent or more of the	Dairy farms: Sales of milk and cream accounted for 50 per cent or more of

	Manual	*Census of Agriculture*
	value of farm products sold from sale of dairy products or sale of cows and calves.	total farm sales. Also farms with 30 per cent or more of total sales from milk and cream; provided one-half of the cows were milk cows and the addition of sales of cattle and calves to the sales of milk and cream accounted for 50 per cent or more of total farm sales.
8161	Farms and ranches, predominantly cattle: 50 per cent or more of value of farm products sold from sale of livestock, wool, or mohair.	Livestock farms other than poultry and dairy: Sales of cattle, calves, hogs, sheep, goats, wool, and mohair accounted for 50 per cent or more of total sales; ranches classified separately in West.
8162	Farms and ranches, predominantly hog: same general definition as immediately above.	Livestock ranches: Sales of cattle, calves, hogs, sheep, goats, wool, and mohair accounted for 50 per cent or more of total sales; provided the pastureland or grazing land amounted to 100 or more acres and was 10 or more times the acreage of cropland harvested; applies to 17 western states, Florida, Louisiana, Alaska, and Hawaii only.
8163	Farms and ranches, predominantly sheep: same general definition as immediately above.	
8164	Farms and ranches, predominantly goat: same general definition as immediately above.	
8169	Farms and ranches, other livestock, not elsewhere classified: same general definition as immediately above.	
8170	Farms, predominantly poultry: 50 per cent or more of value of farm products sold from sale of poultry and eggs.	Poultry farms: Sales of chickens, chicken eggs, and all other poultry and poultry products accounted for 50 per cent or more of total farm sales.
8180	Farms, general—no predominance: percentage of dairy, livestock, and poultry and products each less than 50 per cent of value of farm products sold, and three or more crops, none of which takes up 25 per cent	General farms: Sales of field seed crops, hay, and silage accounted for 50 per cent or more of total farm sales; or sales from 3 or more sources and none qualified for any other farm type.

Manual	*Census of Agriculture*
of total farm area (excluded areas eliminated by earlier definition).	
8191 Range and grassland pastures, not farm or ranch; used for grazing purposes, usually part of public domain.	(No comparable type.)
8192 Horticultural specialties: same general criteria as all farm types.	(Included with miscellaneous farms.)
8193 Apiary farms: same general criteria as all farm types.	(Not enumerated.)
8194 Farms or ranches, predominantly horse raising: same general definition as other ranches.	(Included in miscellaneous farms.)
8199 Other agriculture and related activities, not elsewhere classified.	Miscellaneous farms: Included farms with 50 per cent or more of total farm sales from (a) sales of forest products, or (b) sales of nursery and greenhouse products; or (c) sales of horses, mules, colts, and ponies.

A similarity of farm type classification is evident—a similarity which in many ways is misleading, since types with the same or nearly the same names may in fact include rather different content, since precise definitions vary. Farms with relatively small acreages of high-value crops and larger acreages of lower-valued crops would probably be classified differently, since many of the farm types of the *Manual* are based on acreage whereas all the farm types of the Census are based upon income. For instance, a farm with one acre of tobacco and ten acres of corn sold as grain would be classed as a cash-grain farm in the *Manual* but almost certainly as a tobacco farm by Census. Even with these differences, the definitions of farm types in the *Manual* could be brought into conformity with those of the Census (and thus with those of the USDA) without excessive difficulty. There would seem to be considerable advantage in so doing, and the permanent committee or other organization proposed in Chapter IX might well deal more intensively with this problem.

It may well be also that the *Manual* requires some supplementing in order to handle the various situations such as idle, fallow, crop failure, and other farm land uses other than crops harvested, in a manner which will be fully satisfactory to agricultural specialists. These land use situations are dealt with primarily in Appendix 2 of the *Manual,* where farm use codes are presented. That supplementary coding system could be expanded or modified easily, within the general framework proposed in the *Manual.*

The Census of Agriculture further defined commercial farms according to economic class, strictly on the basis of the value of products sold, as follows:

Class	I	$40,000 and over		
	II	20,000	to	$39,999
	III	10,000	to	19,999
	IV	5,000	to	9,999
	V	2,500	to	4,999
	VI	50	to	2,499*

* these excluded the non-commercial farms

The *Manual* does not provide for such a classification of farms by economic class. However, if data on value of farm sales were obtained, as would be necessary for classification of some farm types, then farms could be classified according to economic type. For many planning purposes, this would be useful information. On the cards, tapes, or other means of recording primary data required by the *Manual* procedures, additional columns or spaces could be used to record economic class, as measured by gross farm income, in a manner similar to that now used by Census; and thus additional analyses would be possible.

Some Unresolved Problems

Although the *Manual,* reproduced as Appendix I, is the most nearly comprehensive classification of activities using land which has yet been prepared, some problems remain in its use to meet all land use situations in the United States. These are explored briefly in this section.

The land use coding system was developed primarily for use in urban area planning, as we have noted. Many of the specific codes and categories are directed primarily at urban land use situations. For instance, within the broad group "highway and street right-of-way," code 45, there are seven specifically urban categories (different kinds of streets and alleys), one specifically between-cities category (freeways and expressways) but all other roads and all other streets are grouped under "other highway and street right-of-way, NEC" (not elsewhere coded). The latter would presumably include all classes of rural roads other than expressways—paved major federal and state highways, paved secondary roads, gravelled farm and other rural roads, and all dirt roads, as well as miscellaneous city streets. For many purposes, it would be desirable to subdivide this class. Or, since the streets are classified according to the functions they serve—arterial, collector-distributor, local access, etc.—this same classification might be extended to rural roads also.

Land uses of a generally urban character are indeed highly important in the United States. Most people live in an essentially urban environment, most manufacturing and trade are carried on there, most employment is there, and even the value of unimproved land is probably higher for all urban than for all rural land. Most new investment, public and private, is within generally urban areas. Nevertheless, all urban land uses—even by the most inclusive definition of "urban"—include less than 5 percent of the total land surface of the United States. The remaining 95 percent is highly important to many persons, including many who live within the urban areas. There are many federal and other governmental programs specifically concerned with privately as well as publicly owned farm, forest, grazing, and park land. Residents of urban areas are dependent on farms for food, forests for lumber and paper, and parks for recreation. Data on these extensive areas of mostly rural land are also highly important. Fortunately, it is *not* necessary to choose between a data system suitable for urban land uses and a system suitable for rural land uses; a single system can serve both needs and the system in the *Manual* is either presently adequate for both purposes or can be made so without major change in its basic structure.

The agencies and individuals responsible for the *Manual* tried to make its coding and classification system comprehensive and all-inclusive; they have succeeded very well, probably to as great an extent as could any single group. The *Manual* surely reflects discussions within the present Committee, where the views of persons of different background were expressed. Adjustments and adaptations can be made within its general system, without the necessity of basic changes in it. Some changes or elaboration may indeed be necessary, as suggested below; but this does not in the least deny the value of the system as a whole.

One part of the *Manual* which may require some revision or elaboration concerns agriculture, or farms, as we have noted in the preceding section.

The *Manual* may also require some supplementary categories and definitions for parks and other recreational areas. These are included in the broad group 7, "Cultural, entertainment, and recreational." Several specific categories are established: 7191, historic and monument sites; various kinds of public assembly areas, such as stadia and race tracks; various kinds of amusement areas, such as fairgrounds, miniature golf, golf driving ranges, etc.; various kinds of sports activities, such as golf courses, tennis courts, riding stables; playgrounds and athletic areas of different kinds, including swimming areas; resorts and group camps, such as dude ranches, ski resorts, and the like; and parks, which are divided between (1) general recreation, (2) leisure and ornamental, and (3) other. These various categories will fit a great many but perhaps not all of the situations that will be encountered and which are necessary in the study of recreation areas. The code as now included in the *Manual* could readily be expanded to include a great deal more detail, if desired in a specific inquiry. In particular, wilderness, natural area, and other relatively unimproved areas may need special recognition. By the use of additional auxiliary codes, it would also be possible to record recreation areas such as playgrounds attached to schools, hospitals, or other land uses which as a whole were not primarily for recreation. This would permit the re-aggregation of detailed land use data into new classifications which may be more suitable to particular recreation studies.

The *Manual* may also require some modest supplementation to deal with multiple levels of use on the same tract and with multiple uses of the surface. The former is dealt with, in the examples used in the *Manual,* in terms of floors above the surface; it could easily be extended to deal with various levels of use below the surface. This would be easiest for residential, storage, parking, and similar activities. But it could also be done for transportation and utilities, such as subways, buried power or telephone cables, buried water lines, buried sewer lines, and the like, if this were desired. In large part, the frequency and severity of the multi-use problem depends upon the scale of enumeration or observation in the field and in the subsequent analysis—or upon the size of the parcels or tracts separately identified. If the general principle of enumeration or observation of the smallest identifiable parcel or tract is followed, then a great deal of the problem of multiple uses of the surface of the same tract disappears.

Where genuinely multiple use of the same surface area does exist, this can be readily dealt with within the framework of the *Manual.* When primary data are assembled from any source, the major or primary use of the land can be recorded and coded by the system outlined in the *Manual* or by any agreed-upon modification of that system; elsewhere on the same form, the secondary, tertiary, and any other levels of use which it was desired to recognize could also be recorded and coded by exactly the same system of land use coding, and clearly identified as a separate level of activity. When the primary information was placed on cards, tapes, or other means of recording these data, the requisite number of columns or spaces may be used to record the codes for the primary land use, and additional columns or spaces may be used to record the secondary and other uses. Thus, five columns or spaces would be used to describe the primary use (four columns for the four-digit code, and one more for the auxiliary code); five more columns for the secondary land use; five more for the tertiary use, and so on. In practice, it is doubtful if more than three kinds of land use or activity should be recognized as existing at the same time on the same tract or parcel of land, but the system is theoretically capable of handling any number of concurrently existing uses, subject only to the physical capacity of the data processing equipment. Multiple uses of land are often particularly important for publicly owned land managed under a multiple use objective or philosophy, but this may also sometimes apply to private lands. The general framework of the *Manual* is adequate to handle this problem.

The *Manual* may also need some supplementing in the way water bodies are handled. Some recognition is given water bodies in codes 441, "marine terminals," 743, "swimming areas," and 744, "marinas"; but most water bodies are included under 93, "water areas," which in turn falls under the broad category 9, "undeveloped land and water areas." But many water bodies are intensively used, and competition for use of water surfaces as well as for the water itself is increasing. Use is mounting particularly for transportation and recreation. Many present water bodies have been created by man. In many instances, the water bodies might well be delineated separately but also classified as to their uses, primary and secondary. There will be many problems in doing so: How do you recognize a "parcel" of water? How small a body of water should be recorded separately from the land which surrounds it? On the latter point, the previous general remarks about scale or detail of inquiry apply here as well as to land areas. Some modification and refinement of the *Manual* may be necessary, at least to deal with some situations.

In various places, the *Manual* may need to be supplemented by the establishment of additional categories. This may be true within the broad framework established—a finer subdivision at the three-digit and four-digit levels, for instance. For some purposes, it may even be necessary or desirable to establish a five-digit breakdown. In other instances, the auxiliary code or codes may have to be subdivided further. For instance, the farm uses code in its Appendix 2 distinguishes only among the major crops—corn, barley, oats, wheat, cotton, alfalfa, sugar beets, etc.; for many purposes, a great deal more information than this would be necessary. However, the present codes could readily be extended, in all these instances, to incorporate any additional information which was needed in a particular survey.

All of the unresolved problems noted in this section can, we believe, be dealt with within the general framework of the system set out in the *Manual.* It does appear that testing in the field and in the statistical laboratory is required, especially as it applies to the various rural land uses. The *Manual* itself recognizes the need for this testing, even for the urban land uses to which it is particularly directed: "Over the next few years the proposed system of land use activity categories is expected to be used in a variety of urban development and transportation planning studies to test and refine the system. Categories may be added, changed, or reworded in order to make them more precise and operational. As field tests demonstrate the need for change, revisions of the system will be incorporated in subsequent editions of this publication" (pp. 6, 7). The same statement applies, possibly with greater force, to the categories of rural land uses and to the application of this system to rural land use situations. But the unresolved problems, as we have noted previously, can almost certainly be solved within the system, and do not require its abandonment or even major alteration.

The problems discussed in this section do, however, lend added weight to one of the major proposals in Chapter IX—the need for a continuing permanent organization to be concerned with land use statistics. The *Manual* still leaves unresolved problems; when, or if, they are resolved, there will almost certainly be others requiring attention. A perfect system of land use statistics probably cannot be devised but would in any case require revision as other circumstances changed. An organization to cope with this and related problems seems essential.

CHAPTER VIII.

Summary Classification of Other Data Relating to Land

In Chapter II we set forth briefly a number of concepts relating to land. Each of these is independent, but all are often interrelated. In the discussion thus far we have emphasized the value of "pure line" land classification systems—those which embody a single concept. In the chapter which follows, we shall emphasize this point again. Many economic and social problems demand a full and varied approach, hence data from different pure line classifications often must be interrelated in the analysis stage.

All data about land must be specific as to the location of the tracts which they describe. Tract location may be identified in any one of several ways, and one system of location and description may be translated into another by use of equivalency tables. Unless the location requirement is met, data have limited value, may often be meaningless, or could even be harmful by creating confusion. If location is specific, then data from two or more sources or data employing two or more concepts can be accurately and safely interrelated. It is in this connection that the *parcel* becomes so important; if parcels are the smallest separately treated units of land or geographical "building blocks," then data relating to parcels can be interrelated and summarized in any desired way. We have previously discussed the problems of identifying parcels; parcel identification or definition will depend on the scale and purpose of the inquiry, but should be the smallest unit of land identifiable under the circumstances of the basic data collection.

In this chapter, we shall assume that the locational problem is adequately dealt with in each instance, since it is basic to all land classification. But, as a general matter, location of land units or their relation to other land units does not enter into the classification system itself. That is, for instance, if a dwelling unit is properly located one can, by office analytical procedures, relate it to schools, shopping centers, or any other item of information, if these are also properly located; but houses will not be classified, in any of the classification systems, according to distance from schools or shopping centers. The latter would often be ephemeral, and in any case would unnecessarily confuse a single-line system of classification.

When it comes to collection of primary data, it is often practical to get several kinds of data at the same time. Primary data may be obtained from aerial photographs, by direct observation of field workers, by enumeration of responses from landowners and occupiers, from governmental records such as building permits, or in other ways. Data about activity on land, natural qualities of land, improvements, tenure, and various other concepts often can be obtained from a single source and recorded on a single data form. Such forms can be processed in a single way; thus, comparisons of different data for the same parcels are greatly facilitated. The different parcels can be combined into larger geographical units, and the different kinds of detailed data may be combined into different groupings, in each case as the analyst chooses, in accordance with the flexibility characteristics of ideal data systems previously discussed.

In Chapter VII, we briefly described and commented upon the rather detailed classification of land use activities presented in Appendix I. Hopefully, this classification system will be of value and interest to everyone in this country who collects or uses data about land. We described in Chapter VII some of the problems as yet unresolved in the actual use of this—or any other—classification system; and in Chapter IX, we shall point out further how this system needs refinement in order to be fully operational.

Information about land may be needed, using any one of the several other concepts about land which we discussed in Chapter II—natural qualities, improvements, tenure, etc. It may seem, at first glance, that one can simply record the "facts" on each of these concepts, as he finds them in the field, or from aerial photographs, or from other sources of information, in a manner comparable to the detailed recording and coding of activities on the land which is described in the *Manual,* and leave their classification and comparison with other data for a later stage. But what is a "fact"? An old definition of great value is: a fact is an opinion not now in dispute. That is, what is regarded as a "fact" to one person may well be only an opinion, and an unsupported one at that, to someone else. Perhaps more important for our purpose: what is a *relevant* fact? There exists an extremely large number of information items about any particular parcel of land—and this is true whether one considers all the various concepts or only one or a few of them.

For example, consider the kinds of information about the soil itself: it has texture, such as sand or clay; depth, to different horizons and to bedrock; slope, including micro-relief not well revealed by most topographical mapping; microbiology; fertility, including presence of harmful trace elements or lack of beneficial ones, sometimes in infinitesimal quantities per acre; *p*H, or acidity-alkalinity balance; bearing strength, for structures; drainage, both internal and surface; and many others—and each kind of information over a wide quantitative range whose differences may be critical for some purposes but unimportant for others. These different qualities of the soil have different meaning for the construction engineer and for the agronomist, to take but two examples among the professional interest groups. What constitutes a "fact," or at least a relevant fact, to one may not be accepted as such by the other; and the meaning of any "fact" about soil is likely to depend upon its relationship to a whole host of other facts about that parcel of land or other parcels.

Similar examples could be cited for other natural qualities of land than soil—climatic differences, for instance; and also for other concepts about land than natural qualities.

If one seeks to record "facts" about land, he must have some basis for deciding which items of information to record. As one member of the Committee remarked at a meeting, one man sees a red brick building while another sees a church.

It would be possible to develop detailed classification systems for each of the concepts other than land use, that were presented in Chapter II. Such classification systems could be the basis for choosing which facts to record, and for deciding how to record and classify them. But, aside from the space that would be required to present such classifications, the task of developing them is far from as simple as at first it may seem. Most of the other concepts have meaning primarily in terms of some specific activity on land. The meaningful natural qualities of land depend on whether it is to be used for agriculture, mining, recreation, residential, or other activity. Intensity measures also depend on the activity on the land. Likewise, the kinds of improvements and their most appropriate classification depends on the activities. A reasonably detailed classification according to any of the various concepts might well have to be made separately for each of the major activities. There are seven or eight activity groups, if one accepts the one-digit categories described in Appendix I, and many more if some of these highly aggregated groups are subdivided even by one step. If a classification system were devised for each of the eight to ten concepts discussed in Chapter II and for each of the major seven or eight activity groups, this would result in a very detailed amount of classification indeed.

In this chapter, we undertake a much more modest task. We outline briefly only the major points that would have to be considered in developing classification systems for each of the concepts other than activity; the actual development of such systems we leave for a further study. This might well be undertaken by the permanent organization we propose in Chapter IX.

Classification of Land According to Its Natural Qualities

The importance of the natural qualities of land is widely recognized, yet in practice it is difficult to establish broadly applicable classification systems of those natural qualities, for reasons outlined below. The natural qualities of land are sometimes confused with the activities carried out upon it. For instance, "forest" is a natural quality of land; it is the result of a combination of climate, soil, and other factors which tend to produce tree growth of specific kinds in the absence of forces too seriously disturbing. But "forestry" is an activity on the land, as we have noted above. Forests and forestry are highly associated, yet there are differences. Likewise, in as large and well-endowed a country as the United States, there is a high correlation between certain soil and other natural conditions, on the one hand, and agriculture as an activity, on the other hand.

The basic difficulty in classifying land according to natural qualities is that there are so many characteristics of land which might, or will under some circumstances, be considered a "quality," that one is simply overwhelmed in knowing what to include or to exclude and how to weight or combine the characteristics included. One soon comes to the conclusion that most characteristics of land are meaningful only in relation to particular activities on the land; the facts which are worth recording depend largely upon the kind of activity.

There are indeed some general characteristics of land, or at least some characteristics of wide applicability. There seems to be some correlation between the width of applicability and the unchangeability of a characteristic. For instance, position on the earth's surface (which we discussed in Chapter III), climate in the broadest sense of the term, basic geology, major topographic characteristics (including slope), and a few others are likely to be significant for almost any activity. They are also relatively unchangeable. But the precise importance of each of these characteristics, the critical ranges or zones of each which affect an activity, the nature of the interaction between two or more characteristics, and other relationships vary according to the activity carried on or proposed.

We come, therefore, to the conclusion that it is extremely difficult if not impossible to establish a *general* classification of land according to its natural qualities; such a classification must ordinarily be specific, for the activity to which it will be used. If the classification is to be specific, then the items of information which should be noted in the field, recorded, and coded must also be chosen with respect to the use that will be made later of the data. This does not in the least rule out general land resource surveys, such as those which facilitate mapping topography or soils; it does mean that the basic data so obtained, often plus specific data for the particular purpose, must be studied, combined, and evaluated in terms of a particular activity. To set up one or more classifications of natural qualities of land for each of the major activity groups and perhaps for each of the more numerous subgroups we established in Chapter VII and in Appendix I is a larger job than this Committee is capable of doing; moreover, such a classification would lead away from the central theme of this publication, which is upon activities using land. We may, however, briefly suggest some kinds of classifications of land according to natural qualities, especially for some uses.

Several systems of land classification according to natural qualities have been developed for land used for agriculture and grazing. The oldest is the soil survey, which identifies soils of defined similarities and outlines their extent upon the ground. In doing this, a considerable amount of information is obtained on soil texture, soil depth, drainage, slope, organic content, and various other specific characteristics of the soil which will help the soil surveyor decide how to classify it and how to interpret data about this particular soil. The United States Soil Conservation Service has developed a system of land capability classification, which is described in Appendix D. It evaluates soil types, slope, present conditions of erosion, and other factors, to determine a tract's suitability for continued or permanent agriculture, under defined degrees of soil conserving practices. Although soil surveys and land capability classifications use generally similar information about soil, somewhat different kinds of information are more significant to one than to another—and, above all, the different kinds of information are grouped differently. Yield or productivity ratings of soils have been developed in a number of countries and in various parts of the United States; they usually rest upon soil, climate, and other natural features. They use somewhat the same information as do soil surveys and land capability classifications, yet somewhat different or additional kinds of information are needed, as well as different groupings of available information. Range surveys define and identify forage types and range condition for the natural grazing land. Information is recorded on the ground as to forage plant species present, their relative density and growth, degree of their utilization by livestock, evidence as to trends in the thrift or health of various species, and the like—items of information significant in relation to later use of the information. Each of these systems of classifying land according to natural qualities is necessarily somewhat detailed and technical; we shall not attempt a description of each here.

Forest inventories and surveys have obtained information about forest lands which permit their classification for forestry as an activity. One important item of information is the forest type, or the species or combination of species which cover the land. By means of timber cruises or other surveys on the land, or from aerial photographs supplemented by field work, the species of trees, their relative density on the ground, their size, volume, vigor, and other qualities are noted in basic records, which may later be coded or otherwise tabulated and summarized. Some of these factors reflect the history of the area (harvest and fire, particularly) as much as they do any inherent characteristics of the land itself; hence, efforts are often made to obtain specific information about that history, and to record and analyze it in the same way as data about tree size or other characteristics. For a period of some years, until it can be changed by management practices, the present forest type and its condition is an important fact about any unit of forest land. The site class of forest land is a determination of tree vigor or rate of tree growth; it is affected by soil, slope, moisture, and other factors. In order to determine forest site class, information must be collected on each of these points—information which is relevant to this specific use. The potential rate of tree growth is rather closely determined by site characteristics; actual tree growth reflects management practices as well.

For mining and mineral extraction, various geological or other maps or studies measure depth to ores, richness of deposits, depth and other characteristics of overburden, and nature of waste materials in the ores or mineral deposits as these affect the refinement processes, etc. Some of these data would be observable at the surface, but many would require drilling or other subsurface exploration. Specific information items could be recorded and coded, and closely identified as to geographical location, including depth below surface. On the basis of these and other factors, mineral deposits can be classified in various ways with respect to their suitability for profitable mineral exploitation. The kinds of information to be recorded and the methods of analyzing the information would have to be chosen to serve the ultimate purpose for which the classification was intended.

For transportation and communication, a number of factors are important in classifying land according to natural qualities. Slope of land, its roughness, internal soil drainage, and many other characteristics affect the usefulness of land for these purposes or, to put it in another way, the cost of constructing transportation and communication routes to or across them. Specific items of information would have to be noted on the ground, recorded, coded, and later analyzed. Some of these same factors, as we have noted, are important for agricultural use of land—slope and soil drainage, for instance. But the precise items of information to be noted and the significant range of each variable might well be different for the two land uses. The need or demand for transportation and communication is dependent upon the volume and kinds of activities at each end of specified routes, and this in turn depends upon other land uses and other land qualities.

The natural land qualities important for recreation and leisure depend almost entirely upon the kinds of activities to be carried out, even within this broad activity or use group. For many intensive recreation activities, flat or nearly flat topography is best; for many more extensive activities, rugged terrain is an asset. The presence of water bodies and of trees (if not really forests) is nearly always an asset. Many specific features or qualities about land and water could be observed, recorded, coded, and later used to classify such areas. But the specific items of information to be recorded would depend in considerable part upon the probable activities. Information could be obtained on such matters as depth of water, freedom from pollution, temperature, and other characteristics. But the importance of these factors, and perhaps the specific facts to be noted, would vary depending upon whether the water body was to be used for swimming, for fishing, or for boating. Information about hazards to recreationists, ranging from bothersome insects to poisonous snakes, and from excessive temperatures to flood hazards, would be useful in any land inventory and classification for recreation.

Residential, commerce and industry, health and welfare, and governmental activities often require similar natural land qualities. Modest terrain differences, permeable and internally well-drained soils, bedrock sufficiently strong to bear needed buildings but not excessively difficult to excavate, absence of severe flood hazards, and other natural characteristics are important for each of these activities, although perhaps not to the same degree. Specific and quantitative information on these various points could be obtained by observation in the field or from other sources, accurately identified as to geographic location of each parcel, recorded, coded, and later analyzed. Some classification systems for these activities have been developed. Urban planning agencies commonly undertake land capability analyses and in this work develop classifications of basic physiographic features as well as classification of improvements to land. However, there are no standard classification systems used.

Classification of Land According to Its Improvements

We come now to the possibility of classifying land according to the nature of the man-made improvements on it. Although the idea of improvements is distinct from that of activity, yet in practice the two tend to merge or blend somewhat. Some activities are impossible without certain kinds of improvements, and the latter in turn are an inducement to the activities for which they are suited. In the discussion which follows in this section, it is assumed that the basic data on improvements are obtained at the same time as the basic data on land use or at least in generally similar ways—i.e., by recording observable facts for relatively small parcels of land. Our concern here is how to classify or group such facts in meaningful and useful ways.

The importance of improvements to land use is most dramatically illustrated in the case of residential or housing use of land. For this activity, the value of the improvements normally greatly exceeds the value of the unimproved land. By inspection on the ground, one can set aside certain areas as predominantly residential in character, now or prospectively in the future; but the kind of residential use depends upon the kind of improvements—single-family houses, row houses, apartments, and the like. Even more importantly, the quality of housing varies greatly. In some countries of the world, some people regularly sleep in the streets; even in our own country, some "have no fixed address"; at the other extreme, a few people in every country have magnificent quarters, sumptuously furnished. Even aside from these extremes, there is great variation in the quality of housing in the typical American city.

Quality of housing is hard to define and to measure. Some observable characteristics of housing, however, may provide an index to housing quality. One of the simplest is the number of rooms per person. While commodious quarters do not invariably mean good quality space, generally the two are associated, and cramped quarters generally mean poor quality housing. The age of the residential structure is another index factor; very old houses in most cities characterize slums or are perilously close to them. It is possible to establish qualitative descriptions of the conditions of dwelling space—"excellent," "good," "run down," "in need of major repairs," etc., which can perhaps be defined in terms such that different, experienced observers would place it in about the same classifications. Certain observable physical features, such as the kind of plumbing (if any), offer an index to the quality of housing. Perhaps the best over-all measure would be the value of the residential unit, per person housed, if comparable and reliable values could be obtained easily. The census obtains information on some of these points. Urban planning agencies frequently utilize classification systems in measuring the quality of structures and their environment; but there is no uniform and generally accepted classification system for structures.

It would be entirely possible to develop a uniform classification scheme for housing improvements, employing some or a combination of the factors mentioned or other factors, and with some of the same attributes of flexibility as we have included in our classification of activities on the land. The amount, character, and value of improvements are also relatively important for some other major activities on the land—transportation and communication, commercial and industrial, health and related activities, and government, particularly. It would be possible to develop classifications of improvements for each of these activities. Presumably such classification schemes would take into account the size, capacity (however measured), age, physical condition, usefulness for the purpose intended, and value of the improvements concerned. The relationship between improvements and activities, while perhaps less intimate than for residential uses, is nevertheless close for these activities. Any subdivision of these major activities into use groups inescapably implies something as to improvements; and the kind of improvements greatly influences the precise activities likely to be carried out.

Improvements on the land are generally less important for agricultural and recreational activities, than for the foregoing. The value of buildings on farms in most parts of the United States is much less than the value of the land itself. Improvements *to* the land are often more important than those *on* it; tile or other draining, clearing, levelling, removal of stones, tilth and structure of soil built up by rotations and fertility, and other factors affecting the productivity of the land are often highly important. Although there are some data on these matters, as we noted in Chapter VI, there is an even more impressive dearth of relevant data on improvements to the land itself, in particular as a result of public programs of the past few decades. In any case, there is no uniform and comprehensive system for obtaining, analyzing, and presenting such data, although one could be developed.

The more intensively used outdoor recreation areas have more improvements than the less intensively used ones; but, even here, the land is likely to be more valuable than the improvements. For some kinds of outdoor recreational activity, improvements have a negative value—in wilderness areas, for instance, improvements detract from the value of the area for this particular activity.

"Improvements" on land in forestry are rather unusual; they are the standing trees themselves, which are both productive "machine" and ultimate final product. The volume and character of the presently standing timber is both a reflecter of past activity and management, and a conditioner of future activity and management. In many instances, improvements are possible in the timber stand itself. There is necessarily a rather close relationship between the kind of forestry activity on the land, and the kind of "improvements," or timber stand, now on the land. Different classification systems have been developed to describe the character of the present timber stand in a forest.

The improvements in mineral extraction are also of a rather special kind.

Some are above ground, but even these are likely to be both highly specialized and highly localized in use possibilities. Some are likely to be below ground surface, in the form of drill holes, shafts, tunnels, excavations, casings, supports and other facilities. The value of these depends entirely upon the profitability of the mineral extraction enterprise; if that enterprise is profitable, these investments have great value, for they are necessary for the extraction of the minerals; if it is unprofitable and likely to remain so, then these "improvements" have no value, no matter what their cost. While this is true to some extent for all improvements on or to land, yet mineral extraction represents nearly the extreme in fixity and specialized character of improvements. As in the case of other activities, there is a close interrelationship between the nature of the improvements and the kind of activity carried on—oil wells for oil extraction, etc.

Classification of Land According to the Intensity of Its Use

The intensity of use of land for any purpose may be measured in different ways: first, primarily by differences in annual inputs of labor, capital, current outlays for productive materials, etc., per unit of land area; and secondly, by differences in annual output per acre, as measured by bushels harvested per acre, visitor-days of recreation per acre, etc. The former measure would generally be preferable, but sometimes data are lacking for its use. For some kinds of use the output per unit of area is more meaningful. In any event, input differences are presumably correlated with output differences, so that either to some extent serves as a substitute for the other.

In this section, we assume that data on intensity of land use, like data on improvements to land, have been collected at the same time or in similar ways as the collection of the basic data on activity on land. The emphasis should be upon observable facts, of a relatively detailed kind, recordable in the field with only a bare minimum of classification, which can be coded and analyzed later. Such facts should be obtained for small and closely identified parcels of land—the same parcels, ideally, as used to indicate activity on the land. But the kind of facts which should be observed and recorded to measure intensity of land use will depend in large measure upon the kind of activity on the land. Thus, intensity of land use in an office building might be measured in terms of numbers of square feet of floor space per employee, as well as in terms of numbers of floors in the building; intensity of residential use might be measured in terms of rooms per person; intensity of park use might be measured in terms of numbers of visits per acre, from data showing attendance and acreage of the park; and so on. Our purpose here is to suggest some of the problems and opportunities of coding and classifying such information.

Intensity of land use is more meaningful in comparison with a standard or normal, than it is as an absolute expression. In this country, we think that one room per person is about the minimum for decent housing; less space is crowding, and more is better. But, for many countries in the world, one room per person would be a most generous scale of housing. One tract of forest land may produce far more sawtimber per acre than another, or one tract of grazing land produce far more forage than another, each with identical treatment. If a scale of intensity of land use is drawn up for any particular activity, the approximate midpoint of the scale might roughly represent common current practice, so that less intensive and more intensive uses could be measured from this point.

The intensity of land use is often related to the improvements on the land. For instance, a more intensive residential use of land is easily obtained by larger capital investment in the form of higher buildings, apartments in most cases. These permit much greater housing "output" per acre without necessarily involving any loss in quality of output. In a great many other situations, more and better improvements permit more intensive use of a given land area.

Intensity of land use is also related to amount and quality of management of the activity carried on by means of the land. A modern supermarket, for example, handles a far larger volume of sales per unit of land area, including even the land used in its parking lot, than did the old-fashioned grocery store of a generation ago, whose customers either walked or parked on the street. By more careful stocking of items, by far greater emphasis on rapid turnover, and by quicker service to a much larger number of customers, the same area of land produces a far greater economic output. Competition among food processors is very keen for shelf space in the supermarket; its manager cannot afford to stock items which do not move. Other illustrations could be cited for other activities, to show how differences in management may lead to more intensive use of land.

The intensity of land use is also related to the scale of land use mapping or of data enumeration. For instance, a large wilderness area may show only a few hundred recreation visits annually per million acres of land—a very low intensity of use, over-all. But topography may force virtually all the visitors to follow closely along certain routes and to camp at certain spots; these may well become severely crowded, for this type of use, while the area as a whole is still lightly used. Similarly, a popular city park may average several thousand recreation visits per acre annually, yet there may be some spots within this park where no human foot has touched during the year. The same may be true within one's own house or yard; although the whole area is used at a relatively intensive rate, there may be some spots used but little or not at all. On one scale of mapping or enumeration, one level of intensity for the whole area would be shown; on a much more intensive scale of study, some parts would be shown to be used much more intensively than others, while other parts would be used much less or possibly not at all.

Scales or classifications of use intensity could be developed, but this would have to be done for each land activity or use; we consider it impossible to develop a general land use intensity scale, equally applicable to all uses. At the minimum, one scale would be required for each of the major activity classes—agriculture, forestry, mining, residential, recreation, etc.; and it might be necessary to establish separate scales for some of the major subclasses within these broad classes.

Classification of Land According to Its Tenure

It would be possible to devise a uniform classification system for data on land tenure; but the relevant tenure considerations would depend largely upon whether the land was used for residential purposes, for such business purposes as manufacturing and trade, for agriculture, for forestry, for recreation, or for others. A tenure classification would have to take account of private land ownership, private renting or leasing of privately owned land, public controls over private land uses, public ownership classifications, and private use arrangements on public land, as well as of other situations. Tenure involves legal, institutional, and economic aspects, as well as perhaps others, and these would all have to be considered in a classification system for land tenure. For reasons previously discussed, any data about land tenure should be accurately located and should apply to parcels, as previously described; thus, such data could be related to any other data about land quality, land use, improvements, or other items of information. Data on tenure would usually have to be obtained by interview or by questionnaire; differences in tenure are usually not observable.

Classification of Data on Land Prices, Land Market Activity, and Credit

The central focus of this study, as we have pointed out several times, is activity on land, but closely related to that is the matter of land prices, land market, and credit based upon land. In Chapter VI, we briefly noted some of the kinds of information available on these matters.

It would be possible, but we have considered it beyond the scope of our present interest, to develop a detailed classification system on each of these points. A comprehensive system for classifying land area units by means of data on land prices, on the structure and function of land markets, and on credit resources and facilities related to land, surely should be related to present use or activity on the land, and probably to the natural qualities of the land and to the improvements as well, because each of these factors would affect land prices, land market, and credit. The classification system probably should be a single, comprehensive one, rather than a separate one for each major land activity, because in many cases land is sold or improved when a change in use is contemplated. Any data on prices, market activity, and credit should be closely identified as to location of land, so that it could safely be related to other data about the same land.

Classification of Data Showing Interrelations of Land Use between Areas

In the modern world, few tracts of land stand alone, as far as their use is concerned. Their occupants or users buy products produced on other land and sell products or services to users of other land. Frequently a man lives on one tract of land, works on another, plays at others, shops on other land areas, etc. A downtown office worker makes the daily journey to and from his downtown business or professional location to his residence inside or more probably outside of the downtown district. He makes a weekend transition, possibly, to a rural retreat at a distance from both locations. A critical aspect of the daily movements, involving sometimes seven, but often five days a week, is the heavy demand at a brief morning period and a somewhat similar heavy demand at a brief afternoon period for use of highways, commuter trains, buses, etc. Those heavy demands involve much use of land for streets, highways, waiting spaces for passengers, rolling stock, etc.

Many tracts of land are thus woven into a complex pattern of use for a single family; and some of the people who use these areas also use many others, until a far-reaching network of interlocking land uses spreads over a substantial total area. Transportation and communication facilities provide the avenues between the various areas or tracts, permitting this complex interrelationship to function. Technological change over the past two centuries has greatly reduced the time, cost, and discomfort of moving people and goods from one location to another. This has had the effect of greatly increasing the supply of land; land previously unavailable is now readily usable. It has also had the effect of greatly increasing the demand for some tracts of land; since they were previously unavailable, there was no effective demand for them, but now demand may be very high.

By and large, the relationships between two or more tracts used for different purposes are complementary and supplementary. Each tract adds value to the other, and any single tract, if it had to stand completely alone, would have limited usefulness. This is a form of external economy of scale which is extremely important in the modern world. The relationship between tracts used for the same purpose is usually competitive; one tract is to a large degree a substitute for the others. But even here there may be complementary relationships, also growing out of economies of scale. For instance, the provision of two or more bodies of water may lead to the purchase of far more motor boats than would one body alone, for people like to have alternate places in which to enjoy their sport.

The land activity coding and classification system of the *Manual*, which is discussed in Chapter VII, deals with the activity on each parcel of land. It would not, by itself, show how different parcels of land were interrelated. That is, it would show which land parcels were used for residential purposes and which were used for manufacturing, but it would not show which residential parcels were related with which manufacturing parcels, via the worker who lived in one and was employed at the other. However, data to measure relationships between parcels could be obtained. In fact, some such data often are obtained in transportation studies. One could ascertain where the person who lives on one parcel works, shops, plays, or carries on other activities. Origin and destination traffic studies get such information. But there are other land parcel interrelations—between a residential area and its watershed, or between a power generating station and its load centers, for example—which would have to be measured in ways other than traffic origin and destination surveys. Data on relationships among land parcels could be obtained but ordinarily only by interview or from basic records, not by observation. Presumably, the activity on each parcel would be recorded, coded, and analyzed in terms of the system outlined in the *Manual*, with such modifications as may appropriately be developed.

Our concern, at this point, is to suggest some of the problems and opportunities that would arise in coding and classifying data on relationships among land parcels, each of which was used for a particular purpose.

As part of the classification of any tract of land, one could specify its distance from certain other tracts with differing land use. For instance, one could show all residential land within one mile of a school, within one to two miles, etc. Similarly, residential areas or potential residential areas could be classified as to their distance from water supply lines, sewer lines, roads, or from downtown facilities. Likewise, land could be classified in terms of its access to or distance from probable market outlets, labor supply, or other economic productive factors. It could be classified according to its relationship to areas with certain natural qualities—i.e., distance to the seashore or to the mountains. This type of classification would seem superficially to have considerable value.

However, there are at least two major objections to classifying land on this basis. In the first place, the classification of each tract would depend upon the use of each other tract. The maze of interrelations would likely create a very difficult classification problem, perhaps completely indeterminate—"neither could move until the other had passed." In the second place, when use of any tract, or at least of any important tract, changed, the classification of many or all other tracts for considerable distances would change also. A classification would get out of date as soon as made, and would be constantly subject to change, especially in growing urban areas.

We prefer a different approach to this matter of area relationships. Parcels of land should be classified according to their present use or activity—or according to their natural qualities, improvements, intensity of use, tenure, etc. If additional data were available, it would be possible to show the relationships between and among different parcels and uses, either statistically or on maps. Such relationships are obviously important, for many economic and social analyses. There are many ways in which important relationships could be shown; the physical distance between areas, the time distance, or the cost of moving are obvious measures for showing the relationship between different tracts or kinds of use areas.

In addition to showing which parcels are related, and for which uses, an ideal system of land data would also provide information on the closeness of the relationship. For instance, a homeowner with a permanent job has a very close interrelation with the land parcel on which he lives and the one on which he works; this will have major effects upon his demands for transportation between them. At a different extreme, an apartment dweller only temporarily in the city may occasionally go to a particular park; the tract on which he resides and the one on which he recreates are only loosely related.

It would be possible to develop a comprehensive scheme of land classification based upon one or more measures of distance between areas of different types or uses. Such a scheme would have to be very detailed and complex, in order to deal with the wide variety of situations existing in various parts of the United States. It would almost certainly have to include all present uses or activities—it could scarcely deal only with a single activity, for its essence is the relationship between areas of different types and uses.

Classification of Data on Land Use in Relation to Other Activities

As we have noted several times, the focus of our interest is activity on the land. What we are really talking about is *human* activities, taking place upon specified pieces of the earth's surface. We consider land in the foreground of our interest, with everything else relegated to the background and oriented to the land. We have considered primarily the *kind* of activity, and only secondarily how much of it, how profitable, with what capital values, etc.

But it would easily be possible to reverse this focus, to put human activities of many kinds first, and then to consider *where* they take place. Every human activity takes place somewhere, however, and this approach if carried to an extreme would classify everything as "land use."

For instance, all employment takes place somewhere. One might say that an important attribute of land was the amount and kind of employment that took place upon it. Likewise, all wealth-producing activities of any kind take place somewhere; one might take the national income account, and try to apportion each item of it to some tract or kind of land. And so on, so as to include the location of all present wealth, all leisure activities, all education, etc.

But if this were done under a label of "land use," it would be distorting the latter out of all proportion. Through long practice, other ways have arisen for looking at certain human activities. For example, employment and national income statistics are worked up and used with only a minimum consideration of *area*—they apply to the nation, a state, or a metropolitan area, but not to a tract or a particular kind of land. We think it desirable that such economic data series should continue on a broad basis, but such data would be much more usable if more specifically and accurately identified as to location. One must draw the line somewhere, even in economic and social data which form a continuum over a wide range, and say: up to this point or line, we shall call it "land use"; beyond it, primarily something else.

But data primarily concerning land—whether as to activity, natural qualities, improvements, intensity of use, tenure, or other factors—should be *relatable* to other kinds of data, to the maximum extent possible. Perhaps the best example is the use of the same definitions and divisions of land activity within the broad class *commercial and industrial* as are used in the Standard Industrial Classification, as has been done in Appendix I and as we have discussed it in Chapter VII, so that the hosts of data on employment, production, transportation, and other matters which employ this classification system can be directly related to the land areas concerned. For any economic or social activity, it would be desirable to relate the *land dimension* to any and all other data.

Conclusion

Land can be "classified" in any one of many ways. As Webster says, classification is the "systematic arrangement in classes" of data of any kind.

Any factor or character or any combination of them can be used as the basis of a classification system.

"Classification," as applied to land, unless delimited, is thus so broad as to be meaningless. Classification for what purpose? Classification by what criteria? Classification by use of which information? These are the necessary questions, if the term is to have any meaning.

The central concern of this book is classification according to *kind of activity,* which is what we mean by the term, *land use.* To achieve this, in Chapter VII we considered the detailed classification of land using activities presented in Appendix I. In this chapter, we have tried to show the relationship of other concepts, which we outlined in Chapter II, to this central theme of land use. But we have not developed detailed classifications for such other concepts; this would not only be a major task in itself, it would lead us and our readers too far afield from our central theme. These other concepts are related, more or less closely, to the matter of land use; some of them would use some of the same data, as well as others. But their focus would be quite different. As we have noted at several points, complex or hybrid land data classification schemes may have practical utility for dealing with some economic and social problems; but the concepts should be developed in as single-dimensioned a way as possible, with hybridization taking place only as a last step, in the analytical phase.

CHAPTER IX.

Elements of an Improved System of Land Use Statistics for the United States

Perhaps we should start a discussion of this subject by raising a question: Why bother? What evidence is there that existing data about land, evolved over a considerable period of time, are inadequate? Has any serious crisis or breakdown in such statistics occurred?

While admittedly no national crisis about land use statistics exists, in our judgment there are several major reasons why improved data about land are necessary for the future, if serious losses and unnecessary costs are to be avoided. Data systems which sufficed for the past, even though less than perfect, may not produce with tolerable results for the future.

In the first place, an increasing pressure of demand for land for many purposes is pressing upon a fixed total area of land. This situation has been summarized elsewhere: "Changes in major land use in the future will be made with more difficulty and will be accompanied with more stresses and strains, public and private, than past shifts in land use. As uses have become more firmly entrenched on a given tract, they can be displaced only with more difficulty. This is but the corollary to the idea of maturity in the general land use pattern."[1]

Anyone who has seen the political and economic stresses involved in pushing a major expressway through an urban area can well appreciate the difficulty of modifying established land use patterns. Anyone who has observed the very large rises in land value accruing to a relatively few persons, as suburban growth pushed into particular directions from the older city center, can understand the economic values involved in such land use changes. Very substantial capital investments have been made, where land use changes were also involved. Both public and private organizations have great stakes in such land use shifts, and thus in accurate and timely data about them.

[1] Marion Clawson, R. Burnell Held, and C. H. Stoddard, *Land for the Future* (Baltimore: The Johns Hopkins Press, 1960), pp. 476–77.

In the second place, the nation is developing increasingly complex and closely knit interrelations in the use of one land area and another. As we have noted earlier, it is the externalities of land use which give value and importance to a particular tract, more than its internalities—the job which gives value to the suburban home, the existence of nearby users which makes a park valuable, the more or less distant urban market which determines farm income, and the like. Interrelations in land use have always existed, of course; but they grow increasingly complex and significant as our total society and economy grow more complex. If either public agency or private organization is to plan the use of its land intelligently, then it must have a great deal of information about other land and about other landowners.

In the third place, numerous agencies are now collecting data about land—for the most part, independently and without coordination. Earlier parts of this report and the various appendices show how different federal agencies collect such information, starting from different bases or on different topics. Likewise, many cities or metropolitan areas collect land use data for their areas but usually employ different definitions and sometimes different methodologies. One could argue that some waste arises out of this multiplicity of effort, but one might also argue that each program has solid local or specific purpose which makes some waste a necessary cost. More significantly, however, many of these organizations expect to greatly extend their land data programs in the future, to meet needs now foreseen but not fully met. The more that present data programs are extended, the more important become efficient and better co-ordinated land data programs. If the extremely important interrelations of land uses are to be understood, data are often required which no organization could well collect for itself—data about land use in another political subdivision, for example.

In the fourth place there are great conceptual and analytical advantages to land use comparisons over time and through space. How does the land use situation in this city, or in this part of the city, compare today with what it was ten, twenty, or more years ago? How does the land use situation in our city compare with that in all other cities of the same general size class, or in some particular other city? These questions could be repeated for every major kind of land use, for every major kind of area. There is not only a close economic relationship between different land areas; there is a close conceptual or analytical one as well. The best guide to the future is often the past. At the least, there should be an attempt to solve problems with the greatest possible use of experience in other areas and in other times. And this requires accurate, relevant, and comparable data. This need will increase, not diminish, over the decades ahead.

Lastly, there is great need to relate data about land and its use to all manner of other data about economic and social factors. How does land use relate to health, law enforcement, or juvenile delinquency within different parts of a city? How does the development of new jobs in one part of an urban complex relate to the development of new housing in the whole urban area? What effect will a new superhighway have upon land use along it, or at its interchanges? These are but samples of the kinds of economic, social, and political problems constantly arising, on which accurately located data about land use and about other economic and social factors could be very helpful. As we have noted, land use records could be intimately related to other kinds of data, especially in cities. More or less comprehensive data banks can readily be developed, largely out of current operating programs of various kinds, which with little or no added cost will provide many valuable kinds of information to assist in the making of public and private decisions.

An Ideal Land Data System

Any system of data about land is likely to involve some compromises—compromises with administrative feasibility or with entrenched organizational interest, compromises to preserve continuity in an established data series, or compromises for other reasons. In any good compromise, more is gained than is lost. But it may be helpful to outline what an ideal land data system would consist of, and then make necessary compromises away from that, not compromises made too soon or too easily.

A prime requisite for a good system of land data is that it be built upon logical concepts, each on a "pure line" basis. In Chapter II, we outlined a number of different concepts about land. Data about land may be obtained from aerial photographs, by observation on the ground, from interviews with landowners or occupiers, from official records such as building permits or assessors' records, or in other ways. Every item of data must be identified with an accurately described and located piece of land, if it is to have any value at all; the advantages of the "parcel" approach have been discussed previously and apply here also. The same basic sources of land use data may also yield data on other aspects of land—its natural qualities, its improvements, its tenure, and others. The same system of electronic or other data processing can record, tabulate, and analyze data about these other aspects of land, as well as data upon land use.

However, the data collection, tabulation, and summarization should not mix indiscriminately different ideas about land in one system or plane. Each concept should be kept pure, as far as possible, and data on each idea or concept kept separate, up to the stage of analysis. For many purposes, one may wish to know how activity on the land, physical quality of the land, ownership, and improvements interrelate. If data have been obtained on each of these points, as well as perhaps on others, each accurately recorded as to physical location but kept separate throughout the data collection and recording processes, they can be interrelated at the analysis stage.

This apparently simple rule cannot always be followed as strictly as one would like. We have stated, for example, that residential use of land in single family dwellings is different from residential use of land in row houses or apartments, but the obvious measure of the difference in activity is the difference in kind of improvements on the land. Likewise, we have distinguished between certain kinds of outdoor recreation which are highly demanding as to natural features of the land and other kinds which are not so demanding; again, we distinguish between different kinds of activity, but the obvious measure is the difference in physical character of the land. Some compromises may be unavoidable, even at the conceptual and enumeration level, but they should be kept to the minimum.

Secondly, all data about land should relate to a specific area, exactly defined. Data may apply directly and only to the specific defined tract, or the data may apply to it as representative of a larger but defined area. Data from complete enumeration of all land should apply to individual parcels, and summaries for larger areas should be compiled from such data by parcels; data from sample areas apply to the specific parcels but also serve to represent the larger area of which they are a part. As we noted in Chapter III, the one, absolutely basic characteristic of land is its location. Data which apply to an unknown or poorly defined area may be worthless, or even worse—they may lead to inaccurate conclusions. If data on different characteristics of land or from different sources are to be compared, then it becomes even more important to know that the different data relate to exactly the same tract or area. Obviously, accuracy of defining land location, like all other kinds of accuracy, is relative. For extremely valuable downtown city property, boundaries may have to be defined on the ground to a small fraction of an inch; for extensively used grazing land, the fence should be more or less on the legal boundary line. The accuracy and detail of land location should be adequate to support the further analysis of the data about each piece of land.

Thirdly, an ideal system of land data should be based upon securing maximum detail in the basic enumeration stage, with groupings and summaries only at a later stage. All data about land rests ultimately upon some enumeration on the land, even if it is only from an aerial photograph, but more typically by observation of the land itself or by interview with landowner or occupier. The way data are collected at this point often completely determines the later use of those same data. If forms are properly devised, the field enumerator can often record what he sees or hears, with a very minimum of classification and interpretation. It may take him no longer to record that a field was in spring wheat, than it would to indicate that the land was within a cash-grain farm, for instance; or that a particular establishment was a shoe store, than that it was used for trade. The data so obtained, including data on any of the concepts we have discussed, can then be summarized and interrelated with other data, in any way desired, in the office and statistical laboratory. Office editing and coding of field data and recording it on suitable, electronic equipment takes time and involves cost; but this makes it all the more important that the right data be collected, adequately identified, and properly recorded. This is a matter to which we return below. In an earlier day, when the time and cost of office tabulation was relatively much greater and when there were sharp physical limitations on the comparisons that could be made between different kinds of data, a considerable degree of classification and summarization at the field level may have been not only desirable but essential. The value of detailed data at the enumeration stage, and the fact that it may cost little if any more, makes detailed enumeration today an essential characteristic of a good land data system.

Fourthly, an ideal system of data about land is flexible, in at least two ways: it can be used in great detail, or the data can be summarized into broad groups, as desired; the same basic data can be grouped differently to meet different uses. Flexibility may involve either different groupings of uses, or different groupings of areas for summarization. A rigid system of land data can, at best, meet only one, carefully defined set of needs. In practice, however, many different groups require the same or similar basic data, to answer their questions—the highway planner, the urban planner, the housing specialist, the recreation planner, the education administrator, and others may each require the same or nearly similar data about a city, yet each will need these data in different forms. By far the greatest part of the cost of getting the data each needs is the basic enumeration in the field and the primary stage of data analysis. If the needed detail is obtained in the field and the data are properly placed on modern data handling equipment, then later summaries are relatively easy, quick, and inexpensive.

Fifthly, an ideal data system about land provides the data readily to anyone who needs it. Some users want only summaries, for general comparisons, and they want them quickly and without need for manipulation of the basic data. For them, the printed summary of land data is adequate. Others will want access to the basic data themselves, to compile summaries upon local areas significant for their purposes. For them, use of the electronic equipment to analyze the data as they choose is likely to be necessary. The would-be user of land data not only wants to get the answers he needs; he wants them at a cost in time and effort proportionate to his interest.

A special feature of this matter of data accessibility is the retention of data for earlier time periods, in form for ready comparison with data for the most recent time period. In many instances, data about land today would be greatly more valuable if it were possible to make comparisons with the past. We may need to know how farmland is used today, or what the occupancy of a residential area is, or what the condition of a forest is; but, almost always, the present absolute condition or number is no more important, and may be less so, than the trend in use or condition. Data for different time periods should be comparable, if at all possible. But this often imposes serious problems. How far shall one adhere to a less than optimum system of land data, in order to preserve comparability with an earlier data series? Shall one make changes ("improvements," hopefully) in some data series, thus destroying or impairing a comparison with the past, and with at least the real possibility that similar changes in the form of the data in a few years will render less meaningful any comparison with the data now being collected? There is probably no place where compromises between the ideal and the facts of life are more common and more difficult than in this matter of data comparability over time. But one can continue to assert that a characteristic of ideal land data is the future availability of comparable data for earlier periods.

Lastly, an ideal system of data about land should be efficient, in the sense of least cost for the results obtained. Data always cost money—often less money in the end than their lack, but still money. The costs are borne not only by the public or private organization which collects, summarizes, and publishes the data; they are borne in some part by the landowners and others who provide the basic data. No one can argue with the goal of minimum cost; the difficulty comes in attaining it. In general, this means a minimum of duplication between sources of data, especially duplication in the expensive data-collection and initial statistical processing. Different private and public organizations need data about land, and different organizations may each need to analyze the same basic data for their own purposes. But the analysis of data available on tapes or other electronic equipment is relatively inexpensive. The big savings are in collection and early processing, and it is here that our earlier comments about getting full detail at this level are most important.

A matter of great practical importance, and one about which there is often a lot of confusion, is the matter of *scale*—scale at which different parcels or tracts are distinguished, scale at which data are recorded and tabulated, and scale in later summaries. At one extreme—a typical road map obtained from a filling station, for example—all forms of land use within an urban area are shown lumped together, and perhaps not very accurately bounded. By progressively larger scales, one can distinguish on the land and in the data the other kinds of land using activities described in Appendix I, to any degree of detail desired. We have stressed the importance of noting the smallest recognizable tract or parcel. Ideally, a parcel should be defined as the smallest unit with a single use, single tenure, or otherwise uniform condition throughout. Where activity changes, as from residential to trade, or from one kind of trade to another, then separate parcels should ordinarily be recognized. Likewise, where ownership or control changes but activity stays constant, as between one home or lot and another in a single residential area, different parcels should also be recognized. This is ordinarily as far as the land planner would go, in the direction of larger scale. But the architect or landscape architect might go much further; he might analyze land use within a single suburban lot, and prescribe quite different programs of land management for different parts of the lot. The same might be true for different parts of a single retail store. One can only say the scale of enumeration, tabulation, and analysis should be appropriate to the ends sought, and the mechanisms employed should be adequate to support the scale used.

U.S. Society Is Multi-centered

The United States society is a multi-centered one, and this directly affects the form of any land data program. There is no single center for decision making at the political, economic, or social level in the United States. One attribute of our relatively open (not class-structured) society and of our relatively dispersed system of government is the multiplicity of centers of decision making. There are great virtues to such a society, and this attribute of it is deeply imbedded in the American culture. Some forms of private and public action are possible and others are not, under such a structure. This applies to programs for data about land, as well as to many other larger economic and political issues.

In the United States, government (at all levels) makes some decisions; private business makes others. Each influences the other, in numerous and often subtle ways. But neither can control the other, in any absolute sense. Neither the federal nor any other level of government can require private organizations nor local governments to collect, analyze, and publish data about land in any particular way, or to refrain from doing as they choose in this matter, as long as no general laws are broken in the process.

Within the broad governmental structure, there is a wide diffusion of power between federal, state, city, and other local units of government. Although some kinds of authority and some kinds of revenue have been reserved to each, in practice there is a very wide overlap between these so-called "levels" of government. Moreover, within a given level of government—most noticeable at the federal level—there are several agencies, each with a clientele or body of supporters, each with rather specific duties to perform in accordance with enabling legislation and continued appropriations. But the activities of these various agencies do not in all cases completely dovetail into a comprehensive and logical program, whether for land data or in any one of many larger issues. The explanation lies not primarily in the selfishness of the various agencies, but rather in the complexities of modern life; it is easier in any field to undertake a series of rather specific programs than it is to try to devise a single, all-inclusive, completely integrated program.

This general situation has significance far beyond the matter of data about land, of course, and this is not the place for a discussion of its meaning in national life. But it does have direct and immediate importance for a land data program. Its meaning can be simply stated: co-operation to the end of improvement in land data is possible, but coercion to the same end is not generally possible. The several federal, state, and city agencies, and the private organizations, may be persuaded that a given system of data about land is mutually advantageous, and in time may each come to adhere reasonably well to it. This has happened in other cases—there are such obvious advantages to a standard industrial classification as a means of ordering data about many economic activities, or such obvious advantages to a uniform definition of standard metropolitan statistical areas as a basis for summarizing numerous data, that most public and private organizations have adopted these uniform definitions. But this was a choice on their part, not a compulsion imposed by higher authority. We think it completely unlikely that any agency of government or any single private organization could compel national adoption and use of any system of data about land—it might persuade, but it cannot order.

One of the virtues of this multi-centered structure of American government and life is that it permits, perhaps encourages, experimentation and innovation. New programs can be begun in one place without the necessity of application nationally. The possibility of innovation has some merit in the land data field, as elsewhere; but the innovation should be within a general common framework, as far as possible. Some metropolitan areas have experimented with data banks, where data about land and data about many other aspects of urban life are assembled and can be interrelated. This is excellent; but such data would have greater utility if broadly comparable to similar data for other cities and areas.

This general situation in the American culture has led to special arrangements between the so-called higher levels of government and the lower levels, or between them and private groups. A typical American approach has been the use of grant-in-aid or subsidy to achieve a desired end. This device has a long history—land grants for railroads and canal companies and for schools, financial grants for highways, and in more recent years for agricultural production, slum clearance, and many other purposes. In the land data field, a great deal of the effort expended at city and other local governmental levels today is financed, at least in part, by funds provided as part of federal housing or transportation programs. It is likely that the relative importance of these grants will increase, not diminish, in the future. It is widely recognized that a granting agency or organization has some responsibility for establishing the conditions under which grants are available under the applicable law and for checking to ascertain whether the conditions of the grants are adhered to. In matters where direct control or compulsion would be resented, specification of conditions of grants—which might well be called indirect control—is accepted, if not loved. The right of the man who pays the piper to call the tune is generally accepted; if one does not want the grant on these terms, he is not compelled to take it. Some students of American government feel that the federal government has in general exercised too little, not too much, control over the use of grant funds.

As far as land data programs are concerned, a greater degree of control could be established and exercised by the Bureau of the Budget in approving requests for appropriations for the various federal agencies for their own programs, and in specifying conditions under which grants would be made to other units of government for similar programs. However, such control will be the more effective, the more it rests upon conviction and agreement among the agencies and units of government concerned. That is, a program of land data which had been widely considered and which represented a consensus of most groups could be pushed toward more general use by administrative actions of the Bureau of the Budget and other federal agencies. But such actions could never be completely determinative.

Potentialities of Modern Data Processing

The potentialities of modern data processing strongly affect the practicality of any program of land data. This book is not the place for an extended discussion of modern data processing; that is available in other specialized publications on the subject. Although several members of the Committee possess expertise in this field, the Committee chairman does not. However, modern methods of data processing have such great importance for the form of a land data program that some general statements can safely be made without attempting to translate them into details.

Modern processing of land data must start with information on land location. Any tract of land which can be identified on the ground or on a map can be described in modern electronic data processing. Parcels of land can be identified on the ground or described in the data records by any one of several systems of land identification; data described by one system can be translated into other groupings by means of equivalency tables. Since latitude and longitude is the one universal system of land description which includes all areas by unique description, there would be great advantage in preparing equivalency tables which would identify any other system of land description with latitude and longitude description. For many uses of data, the land description system actually used in urban areas should be converted, by equivalency tables, into lot numbers, block numbers, census tracts, and other larger area descriptions based upon these units. For a large part of the United States, where cadastral descriptions are based upon the rectangular survey system, equivalency tables could convert whatever system was used for data collection into the cadastral survey system. For still other purposes, the Standard Location Areas established by the Bureau of the Census have great utility, and data described by any other system could be converted into their terms. Sometimes, especially for presentations to local groups, it would be desirable to use various locally used systems of description. For most uses, it would be helpful to have the equivalency tables show the unit of government within which various tracts of land lie—state, county, city, township, and others.

When land parcels have been properly and unequivocally identified on electronic data records by any competent system of land description, it is then possible for summaries of any available data to be prepared for any specified area—a unit of government, a quadrangle defined by latitude and longitude, a census tract, a group of city blocks, a group of townships in a grazing district, a watershed within a national forest, or any other, as long as the basic data are on the record or as long as the data on the record are translatable in terms of such areas. Moreover, data can be assembled as to lands adjacent to or within specified distances of described tracts—the use of the land across the road, the number of families within a specified distance of a playground, activities on land bordering a road as contrasted to those lying further back, etc. All the externalities affecting land that we have discussed previously can be explored, subject always to the limitation that the necessary data be upon the electronic records.

Any information about land which can be ascertained in the field can be placed upon punch cards or electronic records. This includes information as to activity on the land, its tenure, its physical characteristics, the intensity of its use, its improvements, or on any of the many other points discussed previously. Such information can be recorded in any degree of detail desired. As we have noted, there are great advantages in detailed recording at the field enumeration level; and anything that can be recorded on paper can be put onto electronic data equipment records. Obviously, data do not become more accurate simply by being recorded on more sophisticated machinery than an adding machine tape; and recordation does not make them economically or socially significant. However, the data processing possibilities are so great as to make possible the use of any data that can be found in the field and that it is believed may be meaningful.

Electronic data processing machines can sort out and summarize any data they have on their records, by any arrangement of those data, if the machines are given the proper instructions. One can ascertain the simple acreages of different land use activities within a defined district, for example; or one can find out the area that meets a certain activity description and simultaneously meets a certain physical description category; or that does both of these and also has certain tenure characteristics; etc. The machine can do its part, if its instructor can do his; but each is limited by the accuracy, relevance, and detail of the basic data; and the user of the data must consider further how much detail he can possibly use. More detail can reveal more, but it may also so overwhelm the analyst as practically to be useless.

Reference is made to Appendix B, the report of the Bureau of Public Roads, wherein a number of recent land use studies for urban areas are summarized, and some discussion is presented as to the methodology used in each. The possibilities of the new machines are almost unlimited. Their operations, once data have been properly recorded into their data system, is *comparatively* inexpensive—that is, it is much cheaper than "hand" tabulation of the same data would be. But it is far from costless; not only do the machines cost significant sums of money per hour of use, but the cost of "programming" or instructing them may be large, as well as the relatively large prior costs of securing the data and placing it within their record system. Moreover, as we have noted, the very capacity of the machines to spew out data summaries may lead the unwary to ask for more detailed data than he can possibly digest after it is available. The potentialities of the machines are great indeed, but they are also very demanding in terms of the thoughtful planning that must be put into their best use.

One special attribute of this modern data processing equipment deserves further discussion. If this kind of machinery is to be used competently and efficiently, a significant staff of well-trained (and hence well-paid) technicians is required; and this, together with the costs of the equipment itself, requires a substantial volume of work, if costs per unit are not to be excessive. If the volume of data is large and the processes of its necessary analysis complex, then electronic data processing equipment may be highly economical; but if either volume of data is small and/or processes for its handling are simple, then such equipment may be uneconomic. The possibility of renting equipment, or of having analyses made on a job basis, may solve the problem of full use of the machine; but the problem of having competent staff available to the data agency itself is not so easily solved. It is not possible to give hard and fast limitations on volume, but a small rural county would almost never find an electronic data processing machine economic for land data—nor perhaps for any data it had to process. A large city, on the other hand, might well have its own data center, fully equipped, where land data and other kinds of data could be analyzed to meet needs. To the extent that the same specialists and same machines can handle other kinds of data also, the land use data are correspondingly made less onerous.

Special thought might well be given on the role that state organizations could play in this process, especially for rural areas. The federal agencies concerned with land data can usually solve their own problems efficiently; so can, or should, the larger cities or metropolitan areas. But smaller cities and towns and especially smaller rural counties cannot develop efficient land data processing by themselves; their volume is simply too small. While groups of such towns and counties might pool their interests co-operatively, often it would be simpler for some state agency to undertake the land data functions for them, either on a voluntary agreement or on a compulsory basis. Sample legislation and sample administrative arrangements to this end might well be prepared by the central continuing organization described in the following section.

A Continuing Organization Essential

If any proposal for improvement in data relating to land is actually to be achieved, then some form of continuing organization is essential.

The present study, in spite of the wealth of talent on its Committee and in spite of the valuable comments from its reviewers, is not perfect. But, even if it were, it only blocks out the broad lines of a many-featured program of improved data on land; we have called attention at various places in this report to the need for further work. In particular, the classification of activities on land should be carried into greater detail, and the smallest classes defined carefully; classification systems for concepts other than activity on land need to be developed. There is a long way from a basic system like this, no matter how soundly conceived, to actual operations on the ground and in the statistical laboratory. At the best, we have devised a soundly serviceable process, which must go through pilot plant testing and refinement before being put into large-scale operation.

Further, if the present proposals, refined and tested fully, were readied for application, there would still be need for a continuing organization, because new ideas and new problems would surely arise. The demands for land change, and with such changes come new demands for data about land.

No small part of the present confusion and deficiencies in land data arise out of changes which have been incompletely digested. Before the days of the auto, there was no need for data to compute traffic demands on largely non-existent roads by non-existent modes of transportation, for instance. No system can be devised that will not require some modification as time goes on; the problem arises in knowing when to change and how—how to retain the best of the old, including data comparability with former sources, and how to include the new in an integration. Some form of continuing organization is essential if such updating is to be orderly.

Still further, if a perfect land data system could somehow be devised and kept current, some form of central data organization is necessary to provide advice and help to local or specialized units of government or of business which propose to use it. We have stressed that no system of land data can be centrally operated or controlled; many units of government and business will collect, tabulate, and perhaps publish data about land, for their own purposes. Granted that many such organizations will see substantial advantages in conforming to a uniform system of data definition, they are very likely to need or want help in translating such a system into their own operational terms. A particular metropolitan area may wish to undertake a transportation study, for which data on present and possible future land use are basic, for instance; it may wish to use the uniform system of land data, but it may also wish to preserve some comparability with its own earlier data sources. How can this best be done? This is but one illustration of the need of local agencies for technical help from a central and continuing organization.

The three major activities of a continuing organization would thus be refinement, updating, and technical help. Without such an organization to carry out these functions, relatively few improvements in land data are probable or likely to be effective over the long pull. Standardization of data and sometimes of techniques has been stimulated by the federal government and by trade organizations and otherwise in the past; in almost every case, some continuing organization to give continued attention to the problem is essential. These problems can rarely be solved, once and for all, and forgotten.

What kind of an organization is needed at the national level? Numerous possibilities exist, and we can set forth here only the broad outlines. Two attributes or parts seem highly desirable, if not essential: (1) a committee or group of reasonable size, representing most if not all the numerous groups concerned with data about land, which could bring to bear specialized knowledge and viewpoints about land, which no small group could possibly possess; and (2) a small staff of highly competent professional workers, who could give full time and attention (or virtually so) to the problems of this field. It is impossible, and perhaps unnecessary, now to specify exactly how large the latter need be. Once a system got functioning, perhaps no more than two or three able professional workers would be needed; only time and experience can tell. But a committee without a staff is virtually helpless, and a staff without a committee, no matter how able its members, is almost sure to lack knowledge about many important aspects of land use.

Where and how might such a continuing organization be formed, financed, and affiliated on a long-term basis? Numerous possibilities exist here also, and it is not possible in this report to do more than outline in the broadest terms a few of the possibilities. Some might argue that there is no one way of doing it which is so superior to all others that it clearly must be adopted; it might well be argued that the enthusiasm and interest which the lead agency might be prepared to give is perhaps more important than all other considerations combined.

First of all, any efforts at improvement in data about land, and any program developed for this purpose, must include several of the federal agencies most directly concerned—the Bureau of the Census, the Housing and Home Finance Agency, the Bureau of Public Roads, and the various bureaus of the Department of Agriculture, such as the Statistical Reporting Service, the Economic Research Service, the Forest Service, and the Soil Conservation Service. It has been no accident that individuals from these agencies, in an individual rather than an official capacity, have been represented on the present Committee; these agencies have too long a history, too important a role, and too great a need for data about land, for any one of them to be excluded from any program for improvement of data about land. Other federal agencies are interested also—the Bureau of Land Management, the National Park Service, the Fish and Wildlife Service, the Bureau of Outdoor Recreation, the Corps of Engineers, the Bureau of Reclamation, the Tennessee Valley Authority, the General Services Administration, and perhaps others; but, by and large, these agencies do not produce general data about land to the same extent as do the first-listed group of agencies.

The federal government has a clearly recognized responsibility for collection and publication of economic data. Section 103 of the Budget and Accounting Procedures Act of 1950 (31 U.S.C. 18b) states in part: "The President, through the Director of the Bureau of the Budget, is authorized and directed to develop programs and to issue regulations and orders for the improved gathering, compiling, analyzing, publishing, and disseminating of statistical information for any purpose by the various agencies in the executive branch of the Government." Pursuant to this law, Executive Order 10253 was issued on June 11, 1951. It directs the Director of the Bureau of the Budget to develop programs for improving statistical information, and to make continuing studies of the needs and programs for various statistical data. The Director is authorized to issue regulations to effectuate his programs, and to consult both affected federal agencies and interested private groups. This authority is all in general terms, but it is applicable to data about land and its use.

If the federal agencies are to participate in, and more particularly if they are to lead, an effort to improve data about land, then the encouragement or at least the consent of the Bureau of the Budget is essential. Interagency committees and undertakings normally must have its approval, by formal order or otherwise; and transfer of funds between agencies, or from agencies to an inter-agency committee, or even appropriations for data improvement within agencies, require Bureau of the Budget approval. Its role is thus a key one. It can forbid on the one hand or encourage on the other; but it cannot really compel agencies to carry out effectively what they do not want to do, unless the Bureau itself is prepared to direct a data improvement program of its own. In other words, cooperation rather than compulsion may be as necessary within the federal government as outside of it.

In whatever manner such a continuing organization were put to work within the federal government, there are important interest groups outside that should be drawn in, in some way. A few states have significant land data programs; their number may increase in the future. Virtually all larger cities and some urbanized counties have some form of land data programs—many of them financed in whole or in part by federal funds, either as urban planning (701) grants under the housing programs or as highway planning and research funds under the federal highway programs. The agricultural colleges and many other institutions of higher education have a great interest in data about land. County and other assessors produce a great deal of data about land, and some of them use data from other sources. So do hundreds of private organizations. A few of the latter are directly operative in the production or analysis of data about land—the Sanborn Company and other organizations compile maps on landownership and other matters relating to land, the R. L. Polk Company compiles city directories, and so on. Many more are interested in data about land, as affecting their decisions about business operations. Still other business organizations, such as International Business Machines Corporation, are primarily concerned with data processing and with equipment for this purpose.

The range of interests in data about land is very great indeed. It would be impossible for all these interests to be represented directly on a continuing committee or organization, if the latter were to be kept to any reasonable operating size. If the continuing organization were a federal interagency committee, normally none of these interests outside of the federal government would be directly represented upon the Committee; however, this would not preclude consultation with them, either informally or by means of more or less formal public hearings from time to time. If some other form of continuing organization were established, some representation from these non-federal groups would be possible; but even in this case, not all could be, from sheer numbers alone, and consultation with others not members of the group would be necessary.

A federal interagency committee, to serve as a continuing organization for the improvement of data about land, might get started in one of several ways. The simplest, perhaps, would be for the Bureau of the Budget to organize and direct such a committee. It performs a similar role with respect to the Standard Industrial Classification and the Standard Metropolitan Statistical Areas. However, its staff and funds for this type of activity are limited. Alternatively, the Bureau might designate some other federal agency to act for it, in organizing and directing an interagency committee for this purpose. If the designated agency were able to enlist full co-operation and agreement from the other affected federal agencies, then Budget's role could be no more than that of approval of the results; if disputes or differences arose, then Budget might have to step in as arbitrator. A different approach would be for some agency or group of agencies with a direct interest in this subject to request the Bureau of the Budget to authorize it or them to form an interagency committee, broadening it within federal government if need be. In practice, there might not be too much difference in these approaches; if the Bureau of the Budget took leadership, it would surely want to enlist the active participation of the other agencies, while if they initiated the effort, the Bureau would shortly have to be drawn in. In any event, an interagency committee would be recognized by an executive order, which would spell out its functions and responsibilities. Presumably funds would be transferred from the constituent agencies to provide a central staff, or the chairmanship agency would supply the necessary staff. These administrative details, while extremely important in affecting the actual operations of the organization, are not especially difficult to solve, and there is ample precedent for handling them.

The procedures for forming a continuing organization where nonfederal organizations are directly represented is not so clear, nor is there as much in the way of precedent for guidance. The critical element is some organization of sufficient professional capacity and reputation that could find itself ready to devote some funds and time to the matter. It could invite various private and local governments to be represented, as well as the federal agencies. There would still be difficult problems of choosing organizations and individuals most directly interested, and yet of keeping the whole organization down to a manageable number. If the sponsoring organization could provide the necessary staff, this would greatly simplify the process. However, there is much to be said for requiring participating groups to contribute modest financial support—doing so certainly serves as one concrete measure of their interest. Something of the foregoing process has been followed in the establishment of the present Committee, with Resources for the Future as the sponsoring organization. As a research organization, RFF naturally does not wish to be the leader of a continuing operation which bridges the gap between research and operation. Moreover, the financial cost of an adequate continuing organization, while very modest in terms of governmental activities, would be beyond the capacity of such a research organization to bear.

It is quite difficult to identify a private organization which might be willing to assume the leadership role in a continuing organization for improvement in data relating to land, even if the necessary costs could be met by sharing among the interested groups.

The conclusions of an interagency committee could be made binding, in the sense that an executive order would require all federal agencies to adhere to the data systems elaborated by the committee. This could also be made binding upon all other organizations which accepted federal grants for collection or processing of data about land. Obviously, no program should be made binding until it had been hammered out thoroughly in consultations and discussions, and probably not until it had been tested on a sample basis in the field.

There might well be data co-ordinating organizations at state and larger municipal levels also. A great many agencies of local government now collect many kinds of data relating to land in some way; typically, these separate efforts produce data which are not related, one to another. By careful planning, the same data could be made to serve several purposes. Not only might some direct economies be achieved in data compilation, but the availability of much more data, more directly relevant to the problems of the various units of government, would permit analyses and plans which in the end could save a great deal. The Urban Planning Assistance Program of the New York State Department of Commerce has established certain standards for land data enumeration and compilation by cities which obtain 701 grants, for instance; and the Department of City Planning of the City of Pittsburgh has developed a method for bringing into a single system all data relating to land, or based upon land areas, which are collected by the various units of the city government. It is felt that substantial economies in data handling can be achieved in this way; but, as suggested above, the real benefit will come in terms of the more accurate, more meaningful, and more current analyses of significant economic and social changes which can be made, once the relevant data have been brought together efficiently.

If a continuing organization were established on a national level, one of its functions should be to help states and municipalities develop co-ordinated data programs, especially for land data. The national organization could not compel the formation of such co-ordinated data programs at the local level, but it could advise about how they could be established and in various ways could encourage their establishment.

An Attainable System of Land Data

Suppose that all the suggestions made in this report were carried out, to the maximum probable extent. What kind of a land data system would the nation then have?

First of all, let us assume that as a result of their own conviction, or from persuasion exerted by the continuing organization, or from modest compulsion exerted as a condition of grants, most public and most private organizations interested in data about land—as recorders, collectors, analyzers, or users—would have adopted the major characteristics of the land data system we have proposed. These would include the positive identification of individual land parcels, the use of pure line concepts for data acquisition and analysis, the use of uniform classification systems under each of the concepts, and the enumeration in the field in maximum detail, as well as other less essential points. Data could be collected on either a complete enumeration or on a sampling basis, as seemed most appropriate. The system would be flexible, to permit local variation within the general framework, and also to permit recombinations of the same basic data. With reasonably uniform methods used everywhere, or nearly so, comparisons between areas and between time periods would be greatly facilitated. More meaningful national or major regional summaries and analyses could be made; and data about land could be related more readily and accurately to other data about other aspects of economic and social life. Ambiguities, omissions, and overlaps would be reduced to a minimum.

In practice, of course, we could not expect complete conformity to a national system of land data, no matter how well formulated it might be; given the multi-centered character of the American society and economy, there would almost surely be some divergences in application—and some which outsiders would be hard put to accept as rational. But the present condition of extreme diversity could be sharply changed, toward more uniformity.

Secondly, the continuing organization discussed above would strive not only to persuade various organizations to use the common system, but would help them apply it in particular cases. In addition, it would work constantly to update and refine the system itself, as conditions changed and as experience accumulated. Uniformity at the core, but flexibility and modernization, would be the objectives.

Thirdly, the data so obtained and analyzed would be deposited in a modest number of data centers, where it could be integrated with other data, retrieved to meet needs, and generally scheduled for the greatest possible usefulness. Some such data centers might be maintained by federal agencies, others by metropolitan planning organizations, and others by still other organizations. Flexibility should be striven for here also. One of the functions of the continuing organization would be to work out arrangements for such data centers. Duplication of data and effort should be avoided, while maximum use and interrelation of available data should be sought. In many instances, one organization could maintain the data center, and other organizations could both use it and help pay some of its costs. Small localized pools of limited amounts of data about land are extremely expensive, in relation to the services they provide. Much larger pools of data, uniformly organized to take full advantage of all available data, can produce much more useful information, and sometimes at no greater cost.

With such a system of land data for users throughout the nation, many kinds of economic and social problems could be answered more accurately and with less cost. There would be major gains from such better information, but it is not a panacea. Information from the data system would not be better than the data that went into it, nor the results more meaningful than the intellectual analysis which governed their compilation. Land data, while important, are obviously but one aspect of the total national economy. But, within this particular sphere, much progress is possible and could contribute materially to the improvement in both the quality and quantity of usable information on land.

Appendices

APPENDIX A.

Some Historical Materials on Land Use Data[1]

Developments Affecting Land Use Information Needs and Availability: Some Important Dates in United States Land History

Prior to 1785	Tax assessments in various provincial and state areas varied according to observed quality grades of land, as improved and located (see below).
1785	Land Ordinance established rectangular system of cadastral surveys of public land in Northwest Territory (north of the Ohio River). Field notes in first public domain survey shows surveyor's observations of land quality differences.
1790	First census of population.
1792	Virginia builds turnpike, Alexandria to Shenandoah Valley, this year and next. Philadelphia and Lancaster turnpike chartered, turnpike era extending to 1820.
1796	Act of Congress provided for administration, survey, and sale of public lands in central part of Northwest Territory, surveyors being required to describe the nature of soil, water, vegetation, etc. Salt springs and salt waters were designated to be reserved by the federal government.
1802	Cumberland Road authorized for construction between Potomac and Ohio Rivers; completed in 1818. Various arterial transportation routes and local land use roads developed by federal and local action.
1807	Lead mines on public lands first leased by the federal government to private enterprises. This policy was continued for about forty years.
1810	First census of manufacturers.
1812	General Land Office established in the Treasury Department.
1828	Senate resolution required land offices to estimate relative acreages of various classes of public lands not yet sold.
1829	First steam locomotive used in America, on railroad from Carbondale to Honesdale, Pennsylvania.
1832	Hot Springs area in Arkansas was set aside by the Congress. In 1921, the Hot Springs National Park was created.
1840	First census of agriculture and mineral industries.
1841	The Preemption Act.

1 This appendix was prepared for this study by Charles L. Stewart.

1849 First grant of swamplands in the public domain for reclamation. Other acts followed in 1850 and 1860.

1850 United States Census collected information on "improved" and "unimproved" land in farms.

1852 Federal grant of land to three states to hold in trust toward the completion of Illinois Central Railroad. During next twenty years over 115 million acres were certified to railroads from public lands. Similar state grants added 52 million acres.

1862 Act establishing the United States Department of Agriculture and directing the Commissioner of Agriculture to collect statistics.
Homestead Act passed, effective the first of the following year.

1864 Morrill Land Grant Act set aside land areas as supports for state universities. Second Morrill Act was passed in 1890.

1865 The first state or territorial law for irrigation passed by Utah.

1866 Mining Act declared all mineral lands of the public domain open to exploration and occupation. The Placer Mining Act of 1870 and the General Mining Law of 1872 followed. In 1897 public lands chiefly valuable for petroleum were placed under placer mining laws. In 1910 came the act creating the Bureau of Mines and in 1920 came the Mineral Leasing Act.

1873 Timber Culture Act, followed in 1877 by Desert Land Act, in 1878 by Timber and Stone Act (repealed 1955), in 1913 by Burnt Timber Act, in 1916 by Stock-Raising Homestead Act (repealed in 1934) and by many other acts supplemental to the Homestead Act.

1879 Act of March 3 established the Geological Survey. Major John Wesley Powell advocated classification of various types of land in western half of the United States mostly marked by aridity. Public Land Commission authorized that year recommended in 1880 classification of public lands as arable, irrigable, pasturage, timber and mineral.

1891 Forest Reserve Act passed, which began national forest system.

1894 Carey Act provided for patenting large areas of desert lands to several states on condition that the land be reclaimed by irrigation and sold to actual settlers.

1902 Division of Reclamation established in the Geological Survey, U.S. Department of the Interior. In 1907 the Reclamation Service became a separate agency in the Department of the Interior.

1903 Public Lands Commission appointed by President. Its report in 1905 recommended reservation of land for livestock grazing, classification of public lands, etc.

1906 Bureau of Forestry established in U.S. Department of Agriculture. This became the Forest Service shortly thereafter, and national forests (transferred from Department of the Interior to the Department of Agriculture in 1905) placed under it.

1907 American Antiquities Act authorized national monuments on public lands. Inland Waterways Commission appointed by President. It gave attention to protection of lands from soil erosion.

1909 Act of Congress reserved mineral rights to the federal government. USDA initiated annual series of data on cropland uses.

1912 Land utilization studies began in USDA under O. E. Baker.
1913 *Classification of the Public Lands* authored by G. O. Smith and others, directed primarily to mineral lands and water power.
1916 National Park Service established in U.S. Department of the Interior.
1919 Land utilization research established in newly formed Division of Land Economics, Office of Farm Management, USDA, subsequently in Bureau of Agricultural Economics and Agricultural Research Service, Economic Research Service, USDA.
1920 Mineral Leasing Act.
1922 R. T. Ely and others published *Outlines of Land Economics;* Michigan Land Economic Survey initiated first of several state surveys of land uses.
1923 USDA Yearbook was largely devoted to agricultural land problems.
1924 Upper Mississippi Wildlife and Fish Refuge Act. Fact Finders Act for classifying lands preliminary to approval of Bureau of Reclamation projects.
1926 General Reclamation Act.
1928 Forest Research Act provided for making and keeping current a nationwide forest survey.
1929 First census of business.
1931 Conference on land utilization called by Secretary of Agriculture.
1933 National Planning Board, later called National Resources Planning Board, established in the Public Works Administration, July 20. Soil Erosion Service established in USDI, transferred to USDA two years later.
Tennessee Valley Authority created.
Report of the National Land Use Planning Committee.
Land Utilization article appeared in Encyclopedia of the Social Sciences, 9, 132–37.
1934 Science Advisory Board's Land-Use Committee published *Soil Erosion and Critical Land Margins,* by I. Bowman and others (Appendix 8), and *Land Resource and Land use in Relation to Public Policy,* by C. Sauer and others (Appendix 9). Taylor Grazing Act passed; Division of Grazing, USDI.
Land Utilization Projects established under the Land Policy Section of Agricultural Adjustment Administration, USDA; transferred and carried out under the Resettlement Administration, 1934–37; assigned to the Soil Conservation Service, 1938–53; and to the Forest Service, 1954.
1935 Soil Conservation Act.
1937 Land Utilization Projects provided for in Bankhead-Jones Farm Tenant Act (Title III). O&C Act provided for sustained yield management of valuable federally-owned forest lands in Oregon.
1938 *Soils and Men,* USDA Yearbook.
1940 Office of Land Utilization established in USDI; renamed Division of Land Utilization in 1950. First National Conference on Land Classification held at Columbia, Missouri.
First full-fledged census of housing.
1941 National Resources Planning Board's Land Planning Committee issued report on Land Classification in the United States.

1943 Effective August 31, National Resources Planning Board was abolished.

1948 First major application of land use data in determining trip generating characteristics of land in United States in the San Juan, Puerto Rico, Area Transportation Study.

1949 Housing Act established Urban Renewal Administration.

1953 First major application of methods of forecasting future travel based on existing land use and travel relationships begun in Detroit, Michigan, Area Transportation Study. This study was brought to first-phase completion in 1955.

Submerged Lands Act approved.

Public Law 167 reclaimed to federal government the right to manage surface and subsurface resources in subsequent mining claims.

1958 *Land,* USDA Yearbook.

Office of Minerals Exploration established in USDI.

Outdoor Recreation Resources Review Commission established; report published in January 1962.

1960 *Soil Classification: A Comprehensive System* (7th approximation) published by USDA.

National Forest Multiple Use Act approved.

1962 Resource Development Economics Division established in Economic Research Service, USDA.

Rural Areas Development sections of Food and Agriculture Act of 1962 given additional rural renewal authority.

Approved on October 23 was Public Law 87–866 setting July 1, 1965 as a date applicable to cities of 50,000 and more population. Their urban highway projects, to be approved under section 105, must be based on a continuing comprehensive transportation planning process carried on co-operatively with states and local communities, presaging emphasis on land use studies.

1963 *A Place to Live,* USDA Yearbook.

1964 Public Land Law Review Commission created.

1965 *Standard Land Use Coding Manual,* by Bureau of Public Roads and Urban Renewal Administration, published.

Public Revenues from Land as Occasioning Land Use Data

Governments in older settled and in newer areas had to be supported by contributions or levies of some sort. These efforts were not carried through without at least sporadic attempts to take into account differences in quality of resources used by taxpayers.

A summary of early tax assessment policies and an indication of the need for insights into quality differences in land units is afforded in a report made in 1796. Some thought was being directed in the Congress toward a proposed federal tax plan. Secretary of the Treasury Oliver Wolcott sent to the House of Representatives a statement on Direct Taxes. Much of this report dealt with real estate assessments. The report contained information for the original states and for the two states admitted in 1795, Vermont and Kentucky.[1] In the assess-

[1] While Tennessee had been admitted to the Union in 1796, there was no evidence in the Wolcott report of a statute having been enacted in that state prior to the preparation of that report. The report was made to the 4th Congress, 2d session, and was dated December 14, 1796. (American State Papers, Finance, Vol. 1, Document No. 100, pages 414–465.)

ment of real estate, distinctions that reflected differences in quality and location were made in a number of states. Many of the practices reported in 1796 had been in effect prior to statehood. Some of the distinctions being made in the early days of the Republic, to say nothing of the colonial period, show that even some seventeen decades ago, those concerned with administration needed information not altogether unlike that which continues to be needed.

In *Kentucky* lands, except town lots, were divided into three classes on which were laid an annual tax per hundred acres of a half dollar, quarter dollar and an eighth dollar, respectively. For a year cited, 4 per cent of the acres of Kentucky lands had been listed as in first class, 30 per cent second class, and 66 per cent third class.

In *Georgia,* under an act of 1796, tide swamps of the first quality were rated at ten dollars and thirty-nine cents per acre, and pine-barren lands at twenty-one cents per acre. Lands of intermediate qualities were rated according to their advantages either of soil or situation.

In *South Carolina,* lands were classed by general description indicative of their value as resulting from natural fertility or situation, and to each class a specific value was assigned. All lands falling within a given class were to be uniformly taxed. For instance, all tide swamps "not generally affected by the salts, or freshes," when of the first fertility were given an assessed value of six pounds per acre; those of second quality, four pounds per acre; and those of the third quality, two pounds per acre. All pine-barren land contiguous to such swamps, when considered with respect to the benefit of water carriage, were rated at ten shillings per acre. All prime inland swamp, cultivated and uncultivated, was rated at an average of three pounds per acre; second quality, at two pounds per acre; third quality, at one pound per acre. Pine-barren land contiguous to such prime inland swamps was rated at five shillings per acre.

Lands lying within the parishes of St. Philip and St. Michael near Charleston were excepted from the foregoing general rules for South Carolina. In these parishes lands, lots and buildings lying within any city, village or borough were assessed in detail, with reference to the local advantages and value of each separate lot or building, all in a relative proportion to lands in "the country." As many as twelve grades were shown in each part of South Carolina. Ratings ranged from 1 to 120 shillings.

North Carolina showed at that time a reluctance to classify land, as indicated by the provision that "all patented lands, except lots in town, were assessed without regard to quality or situation. On all entries of land, whether disputed or not, the rate was eight pence per hundred acres. The rate on every hundred pounds of town lots, with their improvements, was two shillings."

During the period 1784–1814, trials of land classification systems were proposed and to some extent used in parts of North Carolina.[2]

In *Virginia,* an act of 1781 gave justices the duty to ascertain the average price per acre for which each tract or parcel of land might be sold, for immediate payment in specie, excluding from valuation all reference to buildings or other improvements. Lands under a lease for years were directed to be valued, in

[2] Hugh Hill Wooten, "Land Valuations of Iredell County in 1800," *North Carolina Historical Review*, 29, 4 (October 1952), pp. 623–639. See also Francis J. Marschner, "Land Use and Its Patterns in the United States," p. 13, wherein is shown a map of a North Carolina area where land was classified for taxation, 1784–1814.

the first instance, without regard to the rent, but where such valuation exceeded twenty years' purchase, computed upon the rent reserved. The landlord was assessed for the amount of the twenty years' purchase, and the remainder was apportioned to the tenant. (Twenty years' purchase is the same as capitalization at 5 per cent.) In October 1782, the counties of Virginia were arranged into four districts; in this classification of counties, reference was made to their soil and situation, with the view of obtaining a "general and equitable standard of value" for the lands of the several counties.

In *Maryland,* under a law of November, 1776, lands in each county were given by the Legislature an average valuation, chiefly between twenty-two shillings three pence and thirty-three shillings nine pence per acre, but in one instance as low as four shillings per acre. A right of possession of fifteen years, without payment of rent, was held to be equivalent to one-half of the value of the fee simple.

In *Pennsylvania,* under an act of 1785, assessments for general property taxes were based on estimated values.

In *Delaware* the year 1796 witnessed a shift from an income tax system in which each person's annual income had been estimated, to a general property tax. The stated purpose was to "remedy the inconveniences and inequality experienced from arbitrary assessments." Assessors were required to take an accurate account of the lands in their respective hundreds, specifying . . . "what part is improved or unimproved, with the buildings and improvements thereon, and the value of each part in ready money."

In *Delaware, Maryland* and *Pennsylvania* special attention was given to ground rents. These were valued in the case of rural lands at one hundred pounds for every eight pounds of annual rent, and lands subject to ground rents were valued according to the actual value after deducting one hundred pounds for every eight pounds rent. In the case of lots and houses, Delaware and Pennsylvania used the figure twelve pounds, and Maryland the figure sixteen pounds. One might ask whether the competition of good farm land available on easy terms in areas to the west may have been at the base of this differentiation between rural and town land in these states.

In *New Jersey* there were ten grades of "improved" land, five grades of "unimproved" land, and five grades of houses and lots. The values were graduated according to an equitable scale, with reference to the relative fertility and local advantages or disadvantages of the several counties.

In *New York* according to the Wolcott report, no general or direct tax had been levied by the state following the year 1788. No objects of taxation were defined in the laws, nor any principles of valuation prescribed.[3]

In *Connecticut* taxes were imposed according to a system obtained from an early period, without any radical changes or alteration. Plowland was rated

[3] See, however, John Christopher Schwab, *History of the New York Property,* for indications that from as early as 1658 vacant lots in New Amsterdam were assessed at 6½ percent of their value until built upon, that traders in New Amsterdam and Beverwyck and along the Hudson River were not reachable too well by property taxes, and that even in the agricultural districts of Long Island and the Delaware Valley, the property tax when introduced was collected only with difficulty. In the twenty years preceding 1713, moves to assess arable and pasture land according to its annual yield culminated in a law that remained in force until Revolutionary times. The Schwab volume was a publication of the *American Economic Association,* V, 5 (September 1890).

at ten shillings; meadowland in Hartford and Middlesex counties at fifteen shillings, in all other counties, seven shillings six pence; upland mowing and clear pasture, eight shillings; boggy mead, mowed, five shillings, not mowed, two shillings; bush pasture, two shillings; unenclosed land, first rate, two shillings, second rate, one shilling, third rate, six pence. Of Connecticut's total assessed acreage, 23 per cent was in miscellaneous uses, 21 per cent in upland mowing and clear pasture, 28 per cent in bush pasture, 15 per cent in unenclosed third-rate land, and 13 per cent in plowland.

In *Massachusetts, New Hampshire, Rhode Island* and *Vermont* rating by value was early established. In Massachusetts, assessors, when rendering lists of lands, were directed to distinguish them by the following criteria: the number of acres of pastureland, with the number of cows which the grass of each entire farm would support, together with the number of barrels of cider produced, on an average of several years, upon each farm; the number of acres of tillage land, with the number of bushels of grain or corn, of all sorts, usually produced; the number of acres of salt marsh, with the tons of hay usually produced; the number of enclosed acres of woodland; the number of acres unimproved, owned by individuals and by towns; and acres of land unimprovable, or used for roads, or covered with water; distinguishing each by estimate.

In *New Hampshire* orchard and arable land of less than an acre, and pasture land of less than four acres apparently was exempted from assessment. A one shilling six pence an acre tax was laid on orchard land of sufficient quantity to produce, on an average of several years, ten barrels of cider or perry. At a shilling an acre, arable land was taxed where there was a sufficient quantity to produce, on an average of several years, one ton of English hay, or other hay equivalent. At five pence an acre, pastureland was taxed where there was a sufficient quantity to support one cow. Unimproved lands and all buildings, whether owned by inhabitants or non-residents, were taxed at a half of one per cent of the real value.

In *Vermont* lands were taxed at ten shillings per acre, after being improved two years, either for pasture, plowing or mowing, or stocked with grass and within enclosure. There is little evidence of quality differentiation at that time in Vermont.

Secretary Wolcott stated that "if . . . it shall be determined to establish a uniform mode of taxation for the United States, it is conceived that an eligible plan of assessment can be easily extracted from the acts of New Hampshire, Massachusetts, Pennsylvania, Delaware, Maryland and Virginia." No such uniformity has been achieved even to the present writing.

Of the fifteen states included in the 1796 Wolcott report on the use of state-wide direct taxes on real and other property, it may be noted that only Kentucky, Georgia and Maryland continued in the 1960's to provide funds from the general property tax for the support of the state governments.[4] The application

[4] Prior to 1930 five of these states, Delaware, New York, North Carolina, Pennsylvania and Virginia, had given up the general property tax for state purposes. Prior to 1930 the only other state in the Union that had withdrawn from this form of tax for state support was California.

Data for 1961 are largely from the Advisory Commission on Intergovernmental Relations, *The Role of the States in Strengthening the Property Tax*, Vols. 1 and 2 (June 1963). The Census of Governments reports, especially for 1956 and 1961, published in 1957 and 1962, were also used.

of these taxes for purposes below the state level within the states has continued to be emphasized. In 1961, in the United States as a whole 46.3 per cent of all state-local taxes were from general property levies. The ratios in the Wolcott states ranged from 22.7 per cent in Delaware to 67.2 per cent in New Jersey.[5]

Across the nation, the property tax, although it has declined in relative importance in most states over the years, has continued to be the largest single source in the state-local tax systems.[6] Of the nearly $356 billion of property assessments for taxes in the fifty states in 1961, $328 billion, or all but 7.8 per cent, was on properties locally assessed. Of this amount $271 billion, or nearly 83 per cent, was on real estate. For another expression of pervasive local activity in assessing real estate, it may be noted that 67,449,000 properties were reported in 1961 to the Census of Governments as having been so assessed.[7]

Adequate data on which properly to base property tax assessments has never been available to assessors from early colonial time to the present. Increase in tax burdens, federal, state and local, have made for some improvements in these assessments, but the call for better methods, better data, and better use of data has not subsided.

As stated by one group of students of the general property tax, reviewing in 1963 a considerable span of history, rudimentary methods of administering the property tax which worked only fairly well in colonial days are still cherished in some areas with what has been described as "a touching though misplaced fidelity. . . . Fortunately enough, there also have developed, here and there, well organized, well staffed, well equipped establishments for scientific property assessment that point up the requirements for its extension."[8]

In cities, low-income families have pressed to occupy inadequately equipped and poorly serviced apartment houses and other places of residence. Here, too, temptations have influenced some to create nuisances and fire and other hazards in and near places of residence and employment, and others to connive at their continuance. A result has been to confront police and others with problems of protecting people and property and have made various improvement

[5] Among the fifty states, least relative dependence on the general property was shown in 1961 in Hawaii, 12.7 per cent, and highest in Nebraska, 70.5 per cent. See preceding footnote.

[6] Even as late as 1927, 77.7 per cent of all state-local tax revenues came from the property tax.

[7] Of these, the numbers listed in five classes of property were as follows: industrial, 468,000; commercial, 2,098,000; vacant lots, 12,876,000; acreage and farm, 13,348,000; and non-farm residential, 37,336,000 properties. Compared with numbers reported to the Census of Governments five years previously, there had been a decrease of 800,000 acreage and farm properties, an increase of about the same number in three classes, taken together, industrial, commercial, and vacant lots, and there had been an increase of 6,300,000 non-farm residential properties assessed.

Unassessed, because tax-exempt, were properties used for public beneficial purposes (such as governmental holdings, church properties, non-profit hospitals and educational institutions); in most states, some particular classes of property were unassessed, rarely real estate. New industrial plants were accorded temporary exemption in certain states in an effort to attract new industry.

Partial exemptions from tax payments were applied to assessed properties in some of the states. The percentage of gross assessed value relieved of liability to local property taxes because of various classes of partial exemptions in 1961 was 3.2 per cent.

[8] Advisory Commission on Intergovernmental Relations, *The Role of the States in Strengthening the Property Tax*, Vol. 1 (June, 1963), pp. 3 and 4.

programs difficult. Definite descriptions of land sites and of structural conditions have been needed to detect the repetitions of offenses. Retrieval of past records has often been hampered. Such data have their bearing upon the delineation of urban renewal project areas.

The capacity of many a county, levee district, irrigable or drainable area, or of many a city "commuter" shed, to know itself in its subareas or in its entirety and to reveal itself as against a competitive jurisdiction has been lamentably inadequate, decade by decade, through the history of every part of the country. Exceptions in these respects have been, like those in property tax assessments, not too strong and all too lonely.

Nor have assessments of land units for general property tax purposes been the sole occasions for citizens and officers in states, counties, cities, towns and minor civil divisions to have their land units come under adequate identification and to have information about them subject to facile retrieval. Special assessment districts, largely devoted to real estate development and protection, have been incorporated in state after state. Drainage districts and supplemental districts within them have had a long and significant history and have proceeded with a breadth of local support often surprising to those who ventured to develop them from their initial stages. Other real estate improvement and protective districts operating on a special assessment basis without federal charter have included levee districts, irrigation districts, fire protection districts and many others. For these and for federally authorized reclamation and other districts a large amount of local initiative has evolved, often with too little light on the economic performances and potentials of the units involved. Civil engineering and other techniques have long been called into service in specifying the structures to be installed or erected, the channels to be created, widened or deepened, the boundaries to be set for the area to be served, and gradations imputed to individual units for the allocation of estimated benefits and corresponding cost shares. Economic considerations at least crudely envisaged have entered into the judgments made in non-tax as well as tax matters from the earliest application in this country of the ideas with which settlers came from England, France, Holland, Spain, Sweden, and other countries. It is safe to say, however, that the prestige of some elements in the major and minor civil divisions and dependence upon unsystematic impressions as to the actual or potential productiveness of land units in use or withheld from use kept at no higher than half-mast the flag of accuracy and impartiality that careful economic analyses might have pushed toward the top.

Within urbanized districts as well as in rural territory the lack of land unit identification and of adequate economic information prevented anything more than the roughest approach to equalization between costs and benefits. There are illustrations of property units that escaped being reckoned to exist for tax and other specific purposes, to say nothing of their potentiality being soundly recognized, until air photography made prints available for complete checks.

APPENDIX B.

The Interest of the Bureau of Public Roads in Land Use Data[1]

Background

Although the Bureau of Public Roads itself does not collect land use data, the Bureau does provide financial assistance to many state highway programs for planning activities which may include the collection and analysis of land use information for highway planning. The federal-aid highway planning and research funds contribute to such studies and programs as: the impact of highways on community development, variation in land values, highway mapping, and urban transportation planning. In the discussion that follows only one of these programs will be described, i.e., the urban transportation planning program. Urban transportation studies are initiated and usually directed by state highway departments in cooperation with local communities.

Since the spatial distribution of land use activities is the basis for the movement of persons and goods, the collection and analysis of land use information is an important part of transportation planning. For many years it has been recognized that travel is related to land use activity. However, until 15 years ago, very little work in highway transportation was done to study and measure the nature of this functional relationship. One of the earliest landmarks in developing an understanding of land use-travel relationships was the work done in the 1948 San Juan (Puerto Rico) Transportation Study. The next major contribution came from the work of the 1953 Detroit transportation study. Subsequent to the Detroit study an increasing number of transportation studies collected land use data and made travel forecasts based in part on the analysis of existing land use-travel relationships and on some type of land use forecast.

Section 9 of the 1962 Federal-Aid Highway Act amended Chapter 1 of Title 23, United States Code by the addition of a new section 134 which reads as follows:

> It is declared to be in the national interest to encourage and promote the development of transportation systems embracing various modes of transport in a manner

[1] A statement prepared expressly for this study, by Jacob Silver, Urban Development Branch, Bureau of Public Roads.

that will serve the States and local communities efficiently and effectively. To accomplish this objective the Secretary shall cooperate with the States, as authorized in this title, in the development of long-range highway plans and programs which are properly coordinated with plans for improvements in other affected forms of transportation and which are formulated with due consideration to their probable effect on the future development of urban areas of more than fifty thousand population. After July 1, 1965, the Secretary shall not approve under section 105 of this title any program for projects in any urban area of more than fifty thousand population unless he finds that such projects are based on a continuing comprehensive transportation planning process carried on cooperatively by States and local communities in conformance with the objectives stated in this section.

This section of the federal-aid legislation places a new and greater emphasis on the need to integrate urban development planning with transportation planning. Among the common denominators to both processes that allow such an integration are a land use inventory and a land use forecast. A survey of land use activity and the continued updating of this information, together with a forecast of the future growth and distribution of land uses, are essential in the preparation and continued evaluation of any comprehensive transportation plan.

The policy of the Bureau of Public Roads toward the collection of land use information by urban transportation studies is stated in its Instructional Memorandum 50–2–63(1) of September 13, 1963. The intent of this memorandum is one of establishing general standards or goals for the several elements included in the comprehensive transportation planning process. In the case of land use data, the intent is to insure that this element of transportation planning is tied in closely with the land use data requirements of local communities. Land use data are needed not only for transportation planning, but as is often the case, they are also needed by local communities for a variety of other planning programs. For this reason, the Bureau believes that the most desirable and the most economical approach in many urban areas is to collect the data for all users through a jointly planned and jointly financed land use inventory.

Urban transportation studies differ widely as to the type of land use analyses contemplated, the land use forecasting techniques to be used, and the needs of the particular local communities for land use data. Because of this, the decision as to the type and the detail of land use data to be collected in each transportation study is made by the study staff. Several questions the staff will usually consider before making these decisions are as follows:

A. What funds are available from the transportation study budget for the land use inventory, and also, how much time is available for this phase of the study?

B. What type of land use data and what level of detail is required by the transportation study to satisfy the needs of its own forecasting procedures and for possible study-related research, both in the current and continuing phase of the study?

C. What is the value to other existing or anticipated planning programs of recording land use data in a detailed and flexible form?

D. What contributions are the local communities and other planning programs willing to make to cover the costs of the land use inventory?

Function of Land Use Data in Urban Transportation Planning

Existing techniques of transportation planning make use of land use information in the following ways:

A. Land use activity data constitute one of three interrelated categories of information used to develop estimates of the number of future trips that will be produced and attracted, by traffic zones. The other two categories are population and economic data, e.g., employment, retail sales, etc.

B. The land use inventory provides the transportation planner with a "quantitative" picture of the current distribution of activities within the urban community. This statistical framework in turn forms the "base year" community and is used as one of the data inputs to forecasting the distribution of land uses at some future date.

Land Use Inventories

Types of Inventories

The type of information collected in a land use inventory is the location, identification, and the area measurement of an activity. This information is collected either by the transportation study agency, the local planning office, or by planning consultants under contract.

The availability for transportation planning of reliable, consistent, and up-to-date detailed land use information has varied considerably from one community to another. Consequently, the actual procedures used to collect data have had to vary. The numerous inventory practices that have been used by transportation studies, however, can be grouped into one of the following two categories:

1. A combination of existing records and field inventory.—This group includes all studies in which existing records (e.g., Sanborn maps, local land use planning maps, directories, assessors' records, etc.) are used as the major source for identifying land use activities. In most instances, however, the source material is neither complete nor consistent for the whole area in terms of time, units of measurement, or classification system used. Consequently, segments of the study area must be field inventoried to complete, correct, verify, or update information. The Chicago, St. Paul-Minneapolis, and Puget Sound (Seattle-Tacoma) transportation studies are examples of studies which have used this method.

2. A complete field inventory.—Several studies have made a complete field inventory of activities and have relied on secondary sources only to a limited extent. A complete field inventory provides one or more of the following types of information to the transportation study:

a. Detailed information concerning the location and identification of every residential and nonresidential activity in the study area.

b. A complete listing of all households within the study area. From this list a sample of homes is selected and residents are interviewed as to their previous day's travel.

c. A complete inventory of streets and street intersections.

d. A listing of address numbers that could be used as a guide for coding the information collected by a home interview survey to traffic analysis zones.

Among the studies that have made a complete field inventory (or a field inventory over a major portion of the study area) are Pittsburgh and Philadelphia (Penn-Jersey), Pennsylvania, and Akron, Ohio.

Procedures Generally Used in an Inventory

The procedures generally used by transportation studies in collecting land use information, using either of the two previously described methods, can be generalized into the following six separate phases:

1. Preparing for the inventory.
2. The identification of land use activities through the use of secondary sources and/or through field listing.
3. The classification and coding of the identified activities.
4. The measurement of land and/or floor area of the classified activity.
5. The key punching of the data on data processing cards.
6. The contingency checking of all data in phases one through five.

The first two phases of the land use inventory each include a number of steps. The first phase, that of preparing for the actual data gathering, can be divided into several operations, each of which is discussed briefly in the following paragraphs.

First, all available source materials are assembled and are grouped into three categories of use: those to be used only for identifying activities, those to be used only for measuring the area of an activity, and those that can be used for either of these purposes. The following is a list of source materials and selected studies where such sources were used:

1. Sanborn insurance maps—Chicago, Illinois; Buffalo-Niagara Falls, New York (Niagara Frontier); Pittsburgh, Pennsylvania; Denver, Colorado; Salt Lake City, Utah.
2. Land use maps or special inventory data supplied by local planning offices—St. Paul-Minneapolis, Minnesota; Chicago, Illinois; Seattle-Tacoma, Washington (Puget Sound); Denver, Colorado; Los Angeles, California.
3. Aerial photographs—Seattle-Tacoma, Washington; Buffalo-Niagara Falls, New York; St. Paul-Minneapolis, Minnesota; Akron, Ohio; Pittsburgh, Pennsylvania; Boston, Massachusetts; Denver, Colorado; New York City, New York.
4. City directories, telephone directories, and reverse telephone directories—St. Paul-Minneapolis, Minnesota; Chicago, Illinois; Seattle-Tacoma, Washington; Denver, Colorado; Salt Lake City, Utah.
5. U.S. Geological Survey Maps (Scale 1:24,000)—Seattle-Tacoma, Washington; Buffalo-Niagara Falls, New York; St. Paul-Minneapolis, Minnesota; Chicago, Illinois; Pittsburgh and Philadelphia, Pennsylvania.
6. Utility Records—Chicago, Illinois.
7. Building information supplied by building owners and managers association—Seattle-Tacoma, Washington; Denver, Colorado; Salt Lake City, Utah.
8. Tax assessors records—Rochester, New York; Phoenix, Arizona; Waco, Texas.
9. Miscellaneous other sources which include city and county engineering maps, property ownership plats, 1960 census of block statistics, and redevelopment studies—Seattle-Tacoma, Washington; St. Paul-Minneapolis, Minnesota; Chicago, Illinois.

Second, base maps are developed for the study area if suitable ones are not already available. In some of the studies, there has been no complete or consistent series of base maps available to work with. As a result, the studies develop their own series of base maps. This was the case in Philadelphia and in Pittsburgh.

The method usually used is to have planimetric maps made from aerial photographs and annotated from supplementary sources. The aerial photography and the drafting of the base maps are operations that are contracted to qualified consultants, since transportation study agencies will not normally have the proper equipment and the technical specialty for this work.

Several transportation studies have carried out their programs without developing a complete series of base maps. The Chicago study is one such example. Here, the data were put on acetate overlays of aerial mosaics.

Next, to identify one location from another in the study area, a master control of geographical location is developed. One system that is often used is a series of cartesian coordinates. An X-Y grid coordinate system is established over the entire study area, and each block is identified by the X-Y coordinates that intersect in the middle of that block. This procedure was used by the Seattle-Tacoma, Akron, and Buffalo-Niagara Falls studies. Several studies (e.g., the Phoenix, Arizona, and Oahu, Hawaii, studies) have also used county or city assessors' records in developing geographical controls of parcel location.

A land use classification system is then developed or adopted from another study to code the land use activity descriptions collected in the survey.

Finally, forms are developed upon which the land use information is listed, controlled, and coded. There has been no particular set of forms that has been used consistently from study to study. In the more recent studies the forms used in the field listing phase have shown a marked similarity. In general, space for the following types of information are included on the form:

1. Geographical identification of the block or pseudo block being listed.
2. Street address of each building within the block.
3. Location of the activity within the building.
4. Description of the activity.
5. Code for activity.
6. Floor area and/or land area measurement of activity.

The second phase of the land use inventory is the actual identification of land use activities through the use of secondary sources and/or field listings. As previously discussed, the type and amount of source material available for identifying land use activities varies considerably from one community to another. Hence, one major difference between many studies is the amount of field work necessary to supplement the secondary sources available for identification. The following are examples from particular transportation studies.

In the St. Paul-Minneapolis study each of the two cities had a city planning office that supplied the study with an establishment survey and floor area measurements for their respective central business districts. In addition, the Minneapolis city planning office made available base maps that contained platted parcels, streets, existing structures, and some indication of the use of the parcels. Similar information was supplied by the St. Paul planning office, though not in as much detail.

Within the city limits of these two cities, then, there was some field work, but a good deal of it was done merely to check the accuracy, to update, and to complete the identifications supplied by the two planning staffs. Outside of these two cities, a field inventory combined with other sources, e.g., aerial photographs, U.S. Geological Survey maps, local planning maps, etc., was made to identify land use activities.

On the other hand, the Buffalo-Niagara Falls study identified activities within the urbanized portion of the study area through a complete field inventory; outside of this area, aerial photographs were used. Sanborn maps and aerial photographs were both used to measure the land area and floor area occupied by each activity.

Differences in Information

The specific information obtained in a land use inventory is often significantly different from one study to another. These differences are primarily in the level of detail collected, classified, or stored on data processing records. The staff members of a study will usually decide on the level of detail required after considering the cost and the difficulty in obtaining data in detail and weighing this against the benefits that will be realized in the various uses of the data.

One of the prime differences in the type of detail collected is the extent to which each study identifies land use activities. Most studies in the past (e.g., the St. Paul-Minneapolis study) identified only the major activity at the ground floor level, i.e., the activity occupying the largest area on the first floor of a structure. However, a survey of major activities on the first floor in an area of multi-storied buildings (e.g., found in the central business district) will not give any indication of the concentration of activities that are located in these relatively small areas. Hence, in these special locations, all the activities taking place on each parcel of land were identified and recorded.

In most instances a detailed survey of activities was conducted only in densely built-up areas, e.g., a central business district. There have been variations of this however. In the Seattle-Tacoma study, every activity was identified and recorded in those blocks where at least one-fourth of the block contained buildings two stories or higher and where at least 30 per cent of the activities on the second floor were in nonresidential use. In the St. Paul-Minneapolis study a detailed survey of activities was made in 45 suburban shopping centers in addition to the central business districts of the two cities.

A second, but much smaller group of studies (e.g., the Philadelphia study) recorded all activities on every parcel of land within the entire survey area. This procedure is akin to the detailed survey of central business district activities mentioned above, except that it covers the entire study area.

A second major difference in land use studies is the classification systems used to group the data collected. Even though there were similarities between many of the classifications systems used, there was no real consistency in the number, grouping, and definition of categories. In the Chicago study there were approximately 88 two-digit classifications used; the Pittsburgh study had 45. In the Denver study there were 94 two-digit land use categories, in the St. Paul-Minneapolis Study 68, and in the Buffalo-Niagara Falls study 64.

In 1959 a classification system was devised by members of Public Roads staff, and until 1964 it was recommended to the state highway departments for use in urban transportation studies. Even though the 1959 classification system was accepted by many studies, there were those that developed their own systems. Buffalo-Niagara Falls, Madison, Wisconsin, and Boston, Massachusetts, for example, have all developed their own system for classifying land use activities. At the present time Public Roads is recommending the use of the coding system presented in the *Standard Land Use Coding Manual,*[2] which was developed jointly by the Urban Renewal Administration and the Bureau of Public Roads.

Land use studies also differ in the amount of land use information that is stored on data processing cards or on computer tapes for use in subsequent analyses. Many of the older studies (e.g., the 1955 Washington, D.C., study) summarized land use by one-digit classification and stored land use information only by transportation analysis zones or grid squares. However, the trend now is to maintain greater detail in both geographic location and land use identification. The Akron and Seattle-Tacoma studies are good examples of this trend; as a minimum, land use is summarized by block and two-digit classification.

Publication of Land Use Information

Although a large amount of detail is collected during a land use inventory, only very generalized summaries of the data or analyses of the data are published. This is usually included as part of a transportation study report. Much of the land use information collected remains unpublished, usually stored on data processing cards or electronic computer tapes.

Several studies, e.g., the Chicago and Pittsburgh transportation studies, have published research reports which have a limited distribution. However, this is the exception rather than the rule.

[2] *Standard Land Use Coding Manual,* Urban Renewal Administration, Housing and Home Finance Agency, and Bureau of Public Roads, Department of Commerce (Washington: U.S. Government Printing Office, 1964).

APPENDIX C.

Land Use Data Collection by the Forest Service, USDA[1]

PREFACE

The Forest Service has been collecting data on land use since it was established in 1905. Most of the data gathered has been associated with management of the National Forests but the Nation-Wide Forest Survey is an example of more widespread activity. This report highlights current land use data collection activities of the Forest Service. A wide range of related information such as forest fire statistics, detailed recreation use statistics, reforestation and timber stand improvement data, and road and trail mileage is not included. A list of materials is included to illustrate the scope of some Forest Service land use data collection activities.

The Forest Service cooperates closely with other USDA agencies in compiling comprehensive land use reports and interpreting land use data to formulate basic policy relating to land use adjustments, development of resources, land classification, or similar matters. States, industries, and other private land owners co-operate in gathering data on forest resources, forest uses, and forest protection.

The necessity of having reliable land use statistics have been amply demonstrated in Forest Service experience. Periodic national appraisals of the current and prospective timber situation have been used to guide program planning and to set basic forest policy. Recreation use data on the National Forests have been essential to set the framework of an appropriate resource development program. Timber inventories provide the basis for establishment of critically important cutting cycles for harvesting National Forest timber products. Range surveys have been essential in planning and executing rehabilitation work on National Forest grazing land. Analyses of Forest Survey data have guided the location and development of wood-using industries in many cases. Snow surveys have provided vital data in critical western watersheds and soil surveys have strengthened land stewardship in areas with critical erosion potential.

The Nationwide Forest Survey provides up-to-date information on the use of one-third of the Nation's land area or that portion classified as forest land. Basic forest resource facts include ownership of land and timber; character

[1] Prepared by the Forest Service for this report.

and condition of forest land; kind, volume, quality, and location of standing timber; amount of timber grown and amount lost due to fire and other natural causes; amount and kind of timber cut for timber products. These facts are provided by states and counties. In some instances they are accompanied by maps on which forest and other types of land are shown in place.

There is both commercial and noncommercial forest land. Commercial refers primarily to timber producing land while noncommercial generally refers to lands unsuitable for commercial timber production. Some forest land is set aside exclusively for recreation as in the National Parks or primarily so as in National Forest wilderness areas. Most is devoted to more than one use.

Repeat surveys are made for most states about every eight or fifteen years. Reports feature the present situation and changes between surveys. About every ten years the data for all states are brought up to date in a national reappraisal report which takes stock of our timber situation. The purpose is to provide guides for forest policy—both public and private—on a national, state, and local basis.

Another phase of land use data collection by the Forest Service relates specifically to the 186 million acres of National Forests and National Grasslands which it administers. Virtually all of these lands are open to public use in one form or another. Administrative restrictions are few and where they do occur, reflect considerations of fire prevention, public health and safety, or similar aspects of resource or visitor protection.

A wide range of climatic, biologic, topographic, and other conditions exists on the National Forest System, offering great diversity in public use and posing a wide array of problems for management. Data are collected on a host of activities for general purposes of resource planning and the development of detailed management plans. These data vary greatly in kind, intensity, and frequency of collection. Usually involved is a type of information directly related to the functional pattern of resource management. Much of the information secured comes from periodic reporting and special surveys having as their purpose the description of current conditions on the land, the determination of relative usefulness of given areas of land, the definition of land development needs, or the establishment of significant trends in land conditions.

The production of public values in outdoor recreation, timber, grazing, wildlife, and mining creates use data and other pertinent information generally published annually in the Chief's Report to the Secretary of Agriculture and other reports and publications.

Timberland data for example commonly includes the area of land administered, the amount of commercial forest area and the useful timber volume, volume and value of timber cut, and the area planted and seeded to trees. Grazing statistics are maintained on the number of permits in effect on the system lands and the types, kinds, and quantities of livestock grazed. Outdoor recreation use by type of facility and kind of activity is regularly reported. Wildlife use of National Forest lands, estimated harvest numbers of game animals, areas of habitat improvement completed, and similar information is available. Mining claims and oil and gas lease permits are recorded also because of the large areas subject to mineral location and entry. All of these data relate to some phase of land use on the National Forest system.

The Forest Service has long advocated the principle of multiple use of lands and resources. Public Law 86–517 specifically directs that the National Forest System be managed for multiple use and sustained yield of all surface resources. The establishment and maintenance of areas of wilderness are consistent with the purposes and provisions of this Act.

Much of the Nation's public and private land has long been used for more than one purpose, and multiple-purpose development of water resources is generally accepted. Improvement of cropland, pasture, and forest management will benefit watershed runoff and water quality. Much can be done on private lands to improve wildlife habitat and develop recreation as an income producing enterprise to supplement other sources of farm income. Possibilities for further encouraging the multiple use of private lands are particularly significant. Any collection of land use data should clearly reflect the multiple nature of such uses wherever appropriate.

The Nationwide Forest Survey

I. *Introduction*

A. Purpose and Scope

The purpose of the Forest Survey is to assemble and maintain information for guiding forest policy and program decisions on national, state, and local levels. This information includes facts about the present timber inventory, supply available, and timber harvests. The future timber supply-demand relationships are also projected. The information is released in periodic reports on national, state, and geographic subdivisions covered by the survey.

The Forest Survey is one of the major fields of research provided for by the McSweeney-McNary Forest Research Act of May 22, 1928. Section 9 of this basic charter for the forestry research program of the U.S. Department of Agriculture (as amended) provides:

> The Secretary of Agriculture is authorized and directed, under such plans as he may determine to be fair and equitable, to cooperate with appropriate officials of each State, Territory or possession of the United States, and either through them or directly with private and other agencies, in making and keeping current a comprehensive survey of the present and prospective requirements for timber and other forest products in the United States and its Territories and possessions, and of timber supplies, including a determination of the present and potential productivity of forest land therein, and of such other facts as may be necessary in determination of ways and means to balance the timber budget of the United States. There is authorized to be appropriated, out of any money in the Treasury not otherwise appropriated, not to exceed $1,000,000 annually to complete the initial survey authorized by this section: Provided, That the total appropriation of Federal funds under this section to complete the initial survey shall not exceed $11,000,000. There is additionally authorized to be appropriated not to exceed $2,500,000 annually to keep the survey current.

This continuing long-range program of applied research is administered primarily through the field experiment stations of the Forest Service. Essentially all of the 775 million acres of forest land in the United States has been inventoried at least once. Resurveys to provide up-to-date information and to determine trends in timber supplies, forestry problems and forest industrial development opportunities are being made at intervals of from 8 to 15 years. These resurvey cycles depend on the rapidity of changes in forest conditions and the nature of wood supply problems in different areas.

B. History

Through the years a number of estimates of the forest resources in the United States—or in its major forest regions—have been made. Until authorization of the Nationwide Forest Survey in 1928, these estimates were primarily "guestimates" by informed people. In some instances they were based on fragmentary field data such as inventories of small tracts of timber.

At fairly frequent intervals since late in the nineteenth century various public and private agencies were called upon to produce estimates of forest resources. One of the first was in 1880 when C. S. Sargent of Harvard College compiled for the Bureau of the Census the statements of timberland owners and state land agents into volume estimates for certain timber species only. Redwood was the only western species included in these estimates. Another similar survey for certain species was made by Henry Gannett of the Geological Survey in 1900. In 1908 R. S. Kellogg of the Forest Service made the first attempt at a comprehensive estimate of all timber in the country—drawing upon every available source. He recognized, however, that these ". . . estimates . . . are at best only approximate"; and continued with the statement that ". . . great as the need for it, there has never been a timber census of the United States, nor, with one or two exceptions, any close estimate of forest resources of any individual State."

So it went, with estimates called for and made every few years, until 1928 when Section 9 of the McSweeney-McNary Forest Research Act called for a comprehensive survey of the requirements for timber and timber supplies. Under an authorization of a total appropriation of $3 million, and annual appropriations of $250,000, field work was started in three major forest regions—the Pacific Northwest, the South, and the Lake states in the early 1930's. Within two decades work was expanded into the northern Rocky Mountains, Central, and Northeastern states; and by 1950 initial inventories were completed in about two-thirds of the forest land in the continental United States. Reinventories had also begun in the South, Northwest, and Lake states to keep resource facts current in pace with activities of forest industries in those regions.

Because of the demand for greater details on the forest and in view of rising costs for production, in 1944 an amendment to the original Act increased authorization for completion of the initial survey to a total of $6½ million (of which up to $750,000 could be appropriated annually) and also authorized not more than $250,000 annually for resurveys. In 1949 the authorization was again increased to provide total appropriations up to $11 million (with annual authorization of $1 million) for completing the initial survey and to provide up to $1½ million annually for resurveys. Subsequently (in 1962) the authorized ceiling for resurveys was boosted to $2½ million.

By 1963, virtually all the field work had been done in all 50 States on the initial survey although completion of office compilations of the data were scheduled to take another year to two years.

For some years total Survey appropriations have been more than $1 million annually. During recent years they have been approximately $1½ million annually. Most of these funds have been expended outside National Forests, since information essentially suitable for Forest Survey purposes is obtained on National Forests as a regular procedure on inventories needed for management planning. Such inventories are coordinated with Forest Survey and both kinds of inventories use similar procedures and standard specifications and definitions.

Forest Survey progress had been significantly supported through the years by cooperation of non-Federal agencies. During the last decade, for example, more than 10 per cent of the Survey effort was contributed by such agencies—mainly by State Conservation Departments. These agencies contributed manpower, funds and loans of equipment with the dual objectives of speeding completion of surveys and gathering more intensive data on the forest resource than could be financed by federal money alone.

II. *Planning and Co-ordination*

The survey is under the general technical direction and co-ordination of the Forest Survey Branch of the Division of Forest Economics and Marketing Research of the Forest Service, to insure maintenance of national uniformity and comparability in collecting and analyzing resource data. The Survey is conducted as part of the activities of 10 regional Forest Experiment Stations and specifically by regional staffs of the Division of Forest Economics who are responsible for all detailed phases of the work in their respective regions. Each Forest Experiment Station has its own handbooks of procedures and a system of personnel training and inspections to maintain effective work. However, these regional handbooks are expanded within the framework of a National Forest Survey Manual which outlines subject matter standards, definitions and specifications and covers general operational procedures. As part of the national controls, inspections of all phases of the Survey are made periodically by members of the Washington Office of the Forest Service. These inspections not only provide means to insure that field operations are within policy guidelines; they also provide opportunities for field offices to suggest and receive information on latest survey methodology. In all these contacts, attention is given to incorporation of latest proven methods of photogrammetry and statistics and other techniques which can improve efficiency of surveys.

III. *How the Survey of Timber Supplies Is Done*

Although details of inventory procedures vary somewhat between regions, depending partly on variety of forest conditions, the main phases of the supply inventory are generally the same in all parts of the country. These main phases are: (a) Photo interpretation to collect part of the information on timber supplies, (b) field sampling to get details on the forest conditions and timber, and (c) automatic data processing and analysis of results.

A. Photo Interpretation

On initial inventories the best recent aerial photography is used. If suitable photography is not available from flights flown for other purposes, photography may be financed from Survey funds or other cooperative funds. Generally photography not more than a few years old and at scales of 1:20,000 or greater has been available.

A systematic pattern of photo plots is located on the photography by using plot templets to sample the gross land area within a project to be surveyed at an intensity of approximately 1 photo plot per square mile or even greater intensity. Each photo plot (representing approximately one acre) is classified according to major land use (commercial and other forest land, agricultural land, wasteland, etc.). Any plots falling in doubtful areas are noted so that these locations (or some of them) may be checked later on the ground. In a common variation of this procedure all photo plots falling on commercial forest are classified further into subclasses based on such items as cover type, stand-size, crown closure and gross volume. The photo sample provides a preliminary basis for obtaining estimates of classes of forest; information from a subsequent more limited field sample is used to adjust these estimates for errors in photo classification. The photo sample also is the basis for stratifying field plots in some significant respect and thus permits more accurate estimates of items determined in the field than if field plots were not stratified. Photo stratification has generally been employed to increase accuracy of timber volume estimates for particular geographic areas such as a county.

In the photo interpretation process a number of aids are used, including magnifying stereoscopes, special templets and measuring scales.

B. Field Sampling

Locations of field plots are determined by random or systematic selection from the universe of photo plots falling on forest land. The number of field plots is a small fraction, only, of the total number of photo plots.

Each field plot location is pinpointed on an aerial photo which is used in turn as a reference by the field crew in locating the plot in the field. After the desired location for a field plot has been determined on the ground, the field crew (generally two men) carefully reference it on the ground with an appropriate center stake and marks on reference trees, as means of identifying and relocating the plot on a resurvey. Virtually all field plots are now referenced for use in resurveys to provide accurate and detailed records of changes in the forest with the passage of time.

Each field plot is divided into subplots which comprise a heavy sample of the acre classified as the photo plot. Careful measurements and estimates are made on each tree on each subplot to determine a large number of details about the timber such as: tree species, diameter, height (total, utilizable for sawlogs, and for other products), amount and kind of defect, and damaging agents, tree vigor, quality and crown class and, for dead trees, estimates of causes of death. Other details are determined and recorded about the plot location, such as the timber-growing capacity of the site, stand age, ecological cover type and condition class. The condition class is based on averages of objective records made at each subplot to indicate whether trees are desirable, acceptable, or culls, and whether the subplot is adequately or inadequately stocked. If stocking is inadequate a determination is made of whether the stocking is likely to be improved by natural means or whether some cultural treatment is probably needed such as scarification of the ground, removal of inhibiting cull trees or other vegetation and/or planting or seeding.

Most items are recorded in standard numerical codes to facilitate automatic machine processing of field data.

Field procedures on a reinventory of previously established plots are similar to those on an initial inventory, except that measurements indicate changes in the dimensions or conditions of trees during the interval between inventories. Those trees cut or dying in the interval provide accurate indications of timber cut on the plot and of mortality due to fire, disease, insects, or other natural causes.

C. Automatic Data Processing and Analysis of Results

After the records of field plot data are edited for completeness they are forwarded to the office where machine punch cards are prepared for each plot and for each tree. These form a master file which is drawn upon for the computations of items needed in standard statistical tables and for special tabulations on the timber resource, all on modern data processing equipment.

One of the many operations performed during the data processing is to determine areas of various forest and other land use classes by applying adjusted proportions of plots in all of the various classes to the total gross acreage within the inventory project. Also volume (in both cubic and board feet) is computed for every tree recorded on the field plots using formulas based on diameters and lengths recorded in the field and appropriate factors reflecting variations in form class of trees by species and size. Data on sample plots are also expanded to an acre basis to derive per acre averages which may be applied to appropriate acreages to obtain estimates of total volume of timber in the territory included in the survey project.

Not only are a number of tables produced which show current areas, volumes, growth, mortality and cut of timber by various categories; projections are also made of future supplies of timber. Starting with current information on inventories, growth, mortality and cutting rates in the timber, projections are made in increments of short periods of 1 to 5 years under assumed rates of growth and cutting which are actually or anticipated to be changed over time.

IV. *Ownership of Land and Timber*

Areas of the commercial forest lands, and some subclasses of those lands, and main volume growth and cut classes (for the softwood and hardwood groups) are estimated and reported by ownership. The following separate kinds of ownership are recognized: national forest, other public, forest industry, and farmer and miscellaneous private. On some inventory projects commercial forest acreages have been broken down by size-class of ownership also (i.e., amounts in tracts less than 25 acres, 25 to 100 acres, 100 to 500 acres, etc.).

Some information on forest ownerships is obtained from interviews with landowners during the course of field work to collect physical data on the forest resource. Much of the information is obtained from county offices holding land records and some from questionnaires mailed to a sample of the owners in a geographic area.

V. *Timber Losses*

Losses of timber due to killing of trees by insects, disease, fire, weather, animals and other destructive agents are large. Estimates of mortality from these agents indicate that insects generally have been killing the largest volume of timber, with disease next in importance. Another serious kind of loss, not as spectacular as outright killing of trees, is the loss in growth caused by disease, fire and insects. An important portion of losses of this kind is the slowdown in growth on live trees resulting from lowered tree vigor, temporary defoliation and reduction in soil productivity after a damaging attack. Other losses have been resulting from delays in restocking of the forest after an attack. The annual loss of volume attributed to growth losses is estimated to be significantly higher than the loss of volume due to mortality. Disease is estimated to be the most serious agent causing growth losses.

Tallies of recently dead trees on field inventory plots provide the basis for estimates of mortality by cause. Estimates of growth loss are more difficult to appraise and are based to a large degree on judgment of experts who specialize in research in forest protection.

VI. *Product Output*

The magnitude of the impact of timber cutting on the forest resource is, of course, indicated by the volume of timber products output, which is indicated in turn by census of the forest industries. The Forest Service makes extensive use of the data published by the Bureau of the Census such as the periodic estimates of lumber production made by that office. In some instances the Service co-operates with the Bureau of the Census in surveys of lumber production in order to get detailed estimates of production within a state. The Service also finds it necessary to conduct some separate canvasses of certain parts of the timber industries, to get estimates of output of specific timber products such as mine timbers, fuelwood and fence posts from producers who are not usually canvassed by the Bureau of the Census. The normal procedure on such canvasses is to canvass all producers (or a large number) by mail questionnaires with a field follow-up of nonrespondents.

Particular attention is given to timing of co-operative surveys and separate surveys of timber products output so that they coincide with inventories of the timberlands. This coordination permits the growth of the forest and the drain on that resource to be compared quantitatively.

Before direct comparisons of growth and cut may be made, however, estimates must also be made of the amount of residue of potentially useful wood which remains in the woods from waste in logging. Special studies are made periodically to determine amounts of residues and thus provide utilization factors which are applied to volume output of timber products to convert it to the volume of the timber before felling. Generally there is under-utilization, and thus, for example, the measured amount of sawlogs delivered to a mill must be inflated by some percentage to get an estimate of actual timber cut (the fellings).

Cross checks of the estimate of timber cut can be made by estimating what timber volumes were taken from the woods from the evidence of stumps on field inventory plots. Since stump tallies do not indicate what parts of the timber inventory were converted to particular timber products such as saw logs, veneer, pulpwood bolts, etc., periodic canvasses of forest industries continue to be important procedures for estimating all components of timber cut.

Industry canvasses also provide a means of estimating the amount of residues produced at industrial plants during the manufacturing process. One part of the questionnaire used in canvasses of sawmills and other industrial plants is aimed at determining not only the total quantity of residues produced in primary manufacturing (e.g., slabs, and sawdust at sawmills) but also determining what portion, if any, of these residues is used subsequently. Many slabs and edgings from sawmills, for example, are chipped for use at pulpmills and thus are by-products of sawmills.

VII. *Productivity Ratings*

Recently a method was developed and incorporated into Survey procedures for determining key conditions which indicate the current and potential productivity of timberlands. This forest area condition classification is derived from data collected on standard Survey field plots. The following major classes of condition are recognized. Some classes indicate essentially satisfactory conditions of the timberland, whereas others indicate areas where stand improvement or reforestation measures should be applied to improve productivity of the timberland. Statistics on acreages by these classes are very useful in planning forestry programs:

1. Areas 70 percent or more stocked with desirable trees (i.e., productivity condition good).
2. Areas 40 to 70 percent stocked with desirable trees, and with 30 percent or less of the area controlled by other trees and/or inhibiting vegetation, slash, or other trees and/or conditions that ordinarily prevent occupancy by desirable trees (i.e., current productivity is fair to good with prospect that productivity will increase significantly without cultural treatment).
3. Areas 40 to 70 percent stocked with desirable trees and with 30 percent or more of the area controlled by other trees and/or conditions that ordinarily prevent occupancy by desirable trees (where prospects for future productivity are generally not as good as prospects in previous classes—cultural treatment needed).
4. Areas less than 40 percent stocked with desirable trees, but with 70 percent or more stocking with growing-stock trees (where cultural treatment is desirable for young stands in this class; but where, for reasons of economy, treatment in older stands might best be deferred until harvest cutting).
5. Areas less than 40 percent stocked with desirable trees, but with 40 to 70 percent stocking with growing-stock trees (a somewhat lower productivity class than the preceding one; decision on whether treatment is needed varies by age class, also).
6. Areas less than 40 percent stocked with desirable trees and with less than 40 percent stocking with growing stock trees (planting and/or other regeneration treatment being needed to bring forest to satisfactory productivity).
7. Old growth areas 40 percent or more stocked with desirable trees (where cutting might be deferred with little risk of loss in timber values from mortality or growth loss).
8. Old growth areas less than 40 percent stocked with desirable trees (where harvest cutting is needed to minimize loss of values by mortality and to increase productivity).

VIII. *Requirements for Timber Products*

Estimates of potential demand for timber products, together with timber supplies, are necessary to indicate prospective resource problems, to establish timber growth goals, and to guide formulation of forest policies and programs aimed at keeping the Nation's timber budget in balance.

Demand projections have been made from time to time under specified assumptions of population growth, construction trends and other items. Trends in consumption of forest products such as lumber, veneer and plywood, are determined using data from other special Forest Survey studies, from wood-using industries and from other agencies. Factors influencing wood use such as housing starts and price differentials between wood and substitute construction materials are also studied as bases for projections. Studies of wood consumption are generally made by end uses, i.e., for wood used in manufactured products, for residential construction, on the farm, and for various non-residential construction uses.

IX. *Use of Forest Survey Findings*

Survey information has been used by federal agencies and Congress and by State Conservation Commissions and Legislatures as bases for policy decisions pertaining to forest protection, tree planting, timber management and other measures necessary to balance the timber budget of important forested states and of the nation as a whole. Forest resource data also constitute guides for short-term emergency programs relating to maintaining timber products output or expansion of forest industry capacity.

Survey findings are also basic to programs of wood-using industries and private forest landowners. Information on timber supplies, timber growth and timber cut provides guides to wood-using industries in answering questions of plant location and wood procurement areas and in shaping plans for long-term management.

Among other users of Survey releases are livestock ranchers, real estate operators, timber consultants, bankers, insurance companies, county assessors, railroads and chambers of commerce. All these many different users are interested in accurate, up-to-date information on the timber resources which can only be obtained through a Forest Survey project, as witnessed by the continuing demand for the various kinds of Survey releases, for analytical and statistical reports on the timber resources and industries of particular states, for county statistical reports, and for special reports such as the annual report on production of pulpwood for the South which indicates, by counties, the production of pulpwood species groups and the location of all pulpmills. All Survey reports deal with facts on the timber resource and/or the timber industries. Some of them have graphic presentations to highlight data in the tables. Some include maps showing distribution of the timberlands and some go into considerable detail in the text to interpret the significance of the findings.

An example of a report which highlighted and interpreted trends in supplies of timber is "Timber Trends in the Southeast," issued in November 1961. Another example of a special interpretive report is "Potential Timber Supplies and Forest Industrial Development in the Southeast River Basins," issued in February 1961. As implied by the title, this publication contains projections of both timber supplies and demand for several decades.

Periodically, the Forest Service makes comprehensive reports on the national timber situation based largely on Forest Survey information. The latest such report, issued in 1965 as Forest Resource Report No. 17, is "Timber Trends in the United States." (265 pp. illus.)

X. *Forest Survey Definitions*

Acceptable trees. Trees meeting the specifications for growing stock but not qualifying as desirable trees.

Area condition classes. A classification of commercial forest land based upon stocking by desirable trees and other conditions affecting current and prospective timber growth.

Commercial forest land. Forest land which is producing or is capable of producing crops of industrial wood where such land is not withdrawn from timber utilization by statute or administrative regulation and not currently developed for nonforest use.

Commercial species. Tree species presently or prospectively suitable for industrial wood products; excludes so-called weed species, such as sassafras and hawthorn.

Cull trees. Live trees that are unmerchantable for saw logs now or prospectively because of defect, rot, or species. (Also see sound cull trees and rotten cull trees.)

Desirable trees. Growing-stock trees having no serious defects in quality limiting present or prospective use of relatively high vigor and containing no pathogens that may result in death or serious deterioration before rotation age. They include the type of trees forest managers aim to grow, that is, the trees left in silvicultural cutting or favored in cultural operations.

Farmer-owned lands. Lands owned by operators of farms.

Forest industry lands. Lands owned by companies or individuals operating wood-using plants.

Forest land. Land at least 10 percent stocked by forest trees of any size, or formerly having such tree cover, and not currently developed for nonforest use (also see commercial forest land, noncommercial forest land, productive-reserved forest land, and unproductive forest land).

Forest trees. Woody plants having a well-developed stem and usually more than twelve feet in height, including both growing stock and cull trees.

Forest types. A classification of forest land based upon the species forming a plurality of the stocking in the present tree cover.

Growing-stock trees. Sawtimber trees, poletimber trees, saplings, and seedlings, that is, all live trees except cull trees.

Gross growth. Net annual growth plus annual mortality.

Hardwoods. Dicotyledonous trees, usually broad-leaved and deciduous.

Industrial wood. Commercial roundwood products such as saw logs and pulpwood, but excluding fuelwood and fence posts.

Log grades. A classification of logs based on external characteristics as indicators of quality or value.

Logging residues. The unused portions of cut trees plus unused trees killed by logging and unused trees killed by land-clearing or cultural operations.

Mortality of growing stock. The volume of sound wood in live sawtimber and poletimber trees dying annually from natural causes during a specified period.

Mortality of sawtimber. The net board-foot volume of sawtimber trees dying annually from natural causes during a specified period.

National-Forest lands. Federal lands which have been designated by Executive Order or statute as National Forests or purchase units, and other lands under the administration of the Forest Service, including experimental areas and Bankhead-Jones title III lands.

Net annual growth of growing stock. The annual change in volume of sound wood in live sawtimber and poletimber trees during a specified period resulting from natural causes.

Net annual growth of sawtimber. The annual change in net board-foot volume of live sawtimber trees during a specified period resulting from natural causes.

Net volume. The gross board-foot volume of a tree less deductions for rot, sweep, or other defect affecting use for lumber.

Noncommercial forest land. Unproductive forest land incapable of yielding crops of industrial wood because of adverse site conditions and productive forest land withdrawn from commercial timber use through statute or administrative regulation.

Nonforest land. Land that does not qualify as forest land. Includes land that has never supported forests and lands formerly forested where forest use is precluded by development for nonforest uses, such as crops, improved pasture, residential areas, and city parks. Also includes improved roads and certain areas of water classified by the Bureau of the Census as land. Unimproved roads, streams, canals, and nonforest strips in forest areas must be more than 120 feet wide, and clearings in forest areas must be more than 1 acre in size, to qualify as nonforest land.

Nonstocked areas. Commercial forest lands less than 10 percent stocked with growing-stock trees.

Ownership. The property owned by one owner, regardless of the number of parcels that it may consist of, in a specified area such as a state or the United States as a whole.

Ownership classes. A classification of forest land based on the following types of ownership:

1. National-forest lands.
2. Other federal lands.
3. State, county, and municipal lands.
4. Forest industry lands.
5. Farmer-owned lands.
6. Miscellaneous private lands.

Plant byproducts. Wood material from primary manufacturing plants (such as slabs, edgings, trimmings, miscuts, sawdust, shavings, veneer cores and clippings, and screenings at pulp mills) that is used for some product.

Plant residues. Wood material from primary manufacturing plants that is not utilized for some product.

Poletimber trees. Live trees of commercial species at least 5.0 inches in diameter at breast height but smaller than sawtimber size, and of good form and vigor.

Quality classes. A classification of sawtimber volumes in terms of specified log or tree grades.

Rotten cull trees. Live trees that do not contain a saw log now or prospectively primarily because of rot.

Roundwood products. Logs, bolts, or other round sections cut from trees.

Saplings. Live trees of commercial species 1.0 inch to 5.0 inches in diameter at breast height and of good form and vigor.

Saw log. A log meeting minimum approved log grade specifications, or, for species for which approved log grades are lacking, meeting regional utilization standards.

Sawtimber trees. Live trees of commercial species containing at least a 12-foot saw log meeting approved or regional log grade specifications. Softwoods must be at least 9.0 inches in diameter at breast height, except in California, Oregon, Washington, and coastal Alaska where the minimum diameter is 11.0 inches. Hardwoods must be at least 11.0 inches in diameter in all states.

Site classes. A classification of forest land in terms of inherent capacity to grow crops of industrial wood.

Softwoods. Coniferous trees, usually evergreen, having needle or scale-like leaves.

Sound cull trees. Live trees 5.0 inches and larger in diameter at breast height that do not contain a saw log now or prospectively primarily because of roughness, poor form, or noncommercial species.

Stand treatment classes. A classification of forest land in terms of cultural measures required to increase harvest yields of desirable trees.

Stocking. A measure of area occupancy by trees of specified classes. Three categories of stocking are considered in the Survey: (1) all live trees, (2) growing-stock trees, and (3) desirable trees. Stocking in terms of all trees is used in the delineation of forest land and forest types. Stocking in terms of growing-stock trees is used in stand-size and age classifications. Stocking in terms of desirable trees is used in delineating area condition and stand treatment classes.

Stocking percentage. Current area occupancy or stocking in relation to specified stocking standards.

Stocking standards. The number, size, and spacing of trees considered necessary to make effective use of specified forest types and sites.

Timber cut from growing stock. The volume of sound wood in live sawtimber and poletimber trees cut for forest products during a specified period, including both roundwood products and logging residues.

Timber cut from sawtimber. The net board-foot volume of live sawtimber trees cut for forest products during a specified period, including both roundwood products and logging residues.

Timber products. Roundwood products and byproducts of wood manufacturing plants.

Tree size classes: A classification of trees chiefly according to diameter at breast height outside bark, including sawtimber trees, poletimber trees, saplings, and seedlings.

Unproductive forest land. Forest land incapable of yielding crops of industrial wood because of adverse site conditions.

Volume of growing stock. Volume of sound wood in the bole of sawtimber and poletimber trees from stump to a minimum 4.0-inch top outside bark or to the point where the central stem breaks into limbs.

Volume of sawtimber. Net volume of the saw-log portion of live sawtimber trees, in board feet International ¼-inch rule.

Volume of timber. The volume of sound wood in the bole of growing stock, cull, and salvable dead trees 5.0 inches and larger in diameter at breast height, from stump to a minimum 4.0-inch top outside bark or to the point where the central stem breaks into limbs.

Productive-reserved forest land. Productive public forest land withdrawn from timber utilization through statute or administrative regulation.

Some sample Forest Inventory reports:

1. Minnesota's Forest Resources; Forest Service, USDA; Forest Resource Report No. 13, 1958; 52 pp. illus.
2. Potential Timber Supplies and Forest Industrial Development in the Southeast River Basins, Forest Service, USDA; 1961, 38 pp. illus.
3. Similarities Among Owners of Small Private Forest Properties in Nine Eastern Localities; T. A. McClay, *Journal of Forestry*, Vol. 59, No. 2, February 1961, pp. 88–92.
4. A Summary of the Timber Resource Review; Forest Service, USDA, Forest Resource Report No. 14, 1958; 109 pp. illus.
5. Timber Trends in the United States, Forest Service, USDA, Resource Report No. 17, 1965; 265 pp. illus.
6. Report of the Chief of the Forest Service, 1961; USDA, 1962; 47 pp. illus.
7. Development Program for the National Forests; Forest Service, USDA; Misc. Publ. No. 896; 1961, 26 pp. illus.
8. Trial Program of Public Land Range Appraisal; Bureau of Land Management, USDI and Forest Service, USDA; Senate Document 119; 1962; 35 pp. illus.
9. Forest and Wind Barrier Planting and Seeding in the US, 1961; Forest Service, USDA; 1961, 13 pp. illus.
10. Biennial Report on Special-Use Permits, 1961; Forest Service, USDA; 1961; 6 pp. illus. (unpublished).
11. Soil Survey, Fraser Alpine Area, Colorado; Forest Service-Soil Conservation Service, USDA; Soil Survey Series 1956, No. 20; 1962, 55 pp. illus.

APPENDIX D.

Land Use Statistics of the Soil Conservation Service, USDA[1]

Land use information is collected, interpreted, and used in varying degrees by the Soil Conservation Service. It is used in formulating and carrying out sound soil and water conservation programs, including watershed activities and associated work for which the SCS is responsible. SCS collects its own data only after all available and applicable land use statistics from other agencies are fully used. And it collects the data in such a way that they will best serve other agencies for their programs and the general public, to the extent practicable.

For example, data on land uses, land use potentials, and land use adjustments were needed in connection with the "National Inventory of Soil and Water Conservation Needs" taken by USDA. As a basis for this inventory, the following procedure was used.

Recent Mapping of Land Use on Sample Areas

In 1956 the Soil Conservation Service adopted a plan to obtain soil and land use information on sample areas for every non-urban county in the United States. The samples in each county consisted of fifty or more separate "blocks" selected by a method developed jointly by statistical laboratories at Iowa State University and Cornell University. Each county was laid out in areas or strata of twelve square miles (slightly smaller in the Northeast). In the sectionized part of the country these were one-third of a township of the land office survey. Within each stratum two separate sets of sample units were selected by a system of randomization. These samples were 100 acres in size in the Northeastern States and 160 acres (quarter sections) in the rest of the country. Farm boundaries were not considered. Each set of samples represented approximately two percent of an average-sized county. In small counties the rate of sampling was increased by adjusting the number or size of the sample units. Similarly, the rate of sampling was decreased in large counties to give an equivalent statistical reliability to the information from all counties in the country.

[1] Statement prepared for this report by the Soil Conservation Service.

Each non-urban sample unit in one set was mapped by standard soil survey methods with the land use maps superimposed on the same sheet. This mapping covers a total of 25 to 30 million acres of land in the United States. Samples on federally-owned land were not mapped. The maps were measured by grids or planimeters (in some states by cutting and weighing) and the data were (or are in the process of being) recorded on punch cards and tapes at the statistical laboratories at Cornell (13 states), Texas A & M (5 states), and Iowa State (32 states) Universities. Each card contains the following information about the physical conditions of each delineated area on a map: acreage, land use, soil type, slope (gradient) class, degree of past erosion, and land capability unit (an interpretation of the last three items so that a large number of different entries are combined into a few groups).

In addition, each card carries code symbols to show the location of the individual delineation so that the data may be compiled by state, county, sample unit, soil conservation district, major land resource area and watershed. In a few cases there is a breakdown into private and state or county ownership.

The acreage figures for all separations were then expanded to equal the total for the county, and county tables were prepared. State tables are also prepared.

Use and Modification of the Information in Making the Conservation Needs Inventory

The first use of the data was in the Conservation Needs Inventory. In each county a group of local technicians from several government agencies, plus other local residents well acquainted with county conditions, was furnished with the data from the sample area survey, the U.S. Agricultural Census, the Forest Survey (Timber Resources Review) of the U.S. Forest Service, reports of county assessors, and results of other surveys conducted by state or county agencies. Because of differences in definition of land uses and in method of obtaining the information, the acreage figures varied. The county committees were instructed to arrive at a satisfactory set of figures which they believed most accurately represented the present land use acreages in the county. (Most of this work was done in 1958–59, so the term "present land use" applies to that period.)

In many cases, the figures agreed upon were those from the sample area surveys. In other counties they were not. In the latter case, new county tables of land use by land capability units were prepared by factoring the existing data. The differences between the original and revised sample area figures are relatively large in some counties, but when compiled on a state basis, they compensate and the figures are in rather close agreement. The revised acreages of present land use and estimates of land use by land capability units in 1975 have been recorded on punch cards in the Statistical Reporting Service computing center of the U.S. Department of Agriculture. So we now have two sets of data on cards—the original, as taken from the sample maps, and the revised as used in the Conservation Needs Inventory.

Availability of the Information

The recently published "Basic Statistics of the National Inventory of Soil and Water Conservation Needs," USDA Statistical Bulletin 317, and a more popular pamphlet "Agricultural Land Resources," USDA Agriculture Information Bulletin 263, contain some nationwide interpretations and groupings of the revised data. Several states have published similar material based on their own data and other state reports are in progress.

The original basic data from every state are being put on cards at the statistical laboratories with all of the identifying factors and location factors adequately coded. Considerable use, however, has already been made of the material in papers discussing nationwide conditions and in the preparation of some river basin studies.

The data on both sets of cards are or will be available for use by other agencies, organizations, and individuals on a reimbursable basis. In addition, copies of the maps and of the measured data from each sample unit are on file in the local offices.

This account gives the picture of the methods used in nearly all states and counties in the country. Where exceptions occurred, steps are being taken to bring them into line as rapidly as possible.

Future Uses of Data from Sample Areas

Since the location of each sample is recorded accurately, these sample areas afford a means of comparing land use at different periods. Changes in other items, such as erosion, conservation practices, irrigation, and drainage can be noted and compared over a period of time.

Land Capability and Land Use

With data on land use and a grouping of soils according to their agricultural capability, estimates can be made on such items as:

(1) acreage now in cropland but not suited for this use; and

(2) acreage not now in cropland but suited for cropland.

The land capability classification system is explained in Agriculture Handbook No. 210, SCS, USDA.

The National Cooperative Soil Survey

The Soil Conservation Service of the U.S. Department of Agriculture, in cooperation with state and other federal agencies, makes and publishes soil surveys of individual counties, combinations of counties, and of other areas approximating county size. Each published soil survey consists of a soil map of the soil survey area and a narrative containing descriptions and interpretations of the soils. Tables of predictions of soil behavior in the several adapted land uses are included. Soil maps have been made and published for more than sixty years. Published soil surveys are available for more than 2,000 counties or other survey areas. Their usefulness depends on their age which reflects the state of knowledge and soil classification system being used at the time. The more recent published soil surveys contain detailed soil maps and specific soil predictions for many soil map users.

About one-half of the land in farms in the United States (about 822 million acres) has been covered by soil surveys that show enough detail for conservation planning.

In 1964 fiscal year about 65 million acres were mapped in more than 2,900 soil conservation districts in cooperation with land grant universities and other agencies. Soil surveys were published for thirty-four areas (mostly counties) in fiscal year 1964. Thirty-five sets of maps and edited manuscripts were sent to the Government Printing Office for printing. There were fifty-two sets of maps and edited manuscripts in the Government Printing Office awaiting printing on June 30, 1964. The SCS working with the cooperating agencies has prepared a long-term schedule to complete soil surveys of all land in the United States. The speed of this work depends upon the availability of funds and trained soil scientists.

Plans for a Survey

Plans for work in each area to be surveyed are developed cooperatively by the agencies involved. These plans show by name who is to be the local survey party leader, who is to do the mapping, and who is to write the report, and also give a time schedule. The scale of maps and the intensity of detail of mapping are agreed upon as are the plans for publication.

Mapping Legend

At the beginning of the survey a soil scientist, usually from the state SCS office, takes the leadership. He and the local survey party leader and representative of each cooperating agency travel over the area to be covered, studying the soils. They prepare a mapping legend. The legend lists and describes the soils they then know will be shown in the survey. It also gives the symbol to be used to identify each.

Examining Soils in the Field

The soil scientists in the survey party then map the soils in the field. Their knowledge of the relation of landscape features, climate, parent material, relief, and vegetation to soil properties aids them in predicting the kinds of soil they expect to find. But to study the soil adequately, they dig or bore numerous holes deep enough to examine the underlying layers.

They record the total thickness of the soil, the thickness of each horizon, and its position in the profile. Commonly, properties of each horizon are contrasting; so for each one they note its texture (size of soil particles), structure (arrangement of soil particles), color, and acidity or alkalinity. They also record other characteristics, especially those having to do with the behavior and potential productivity of the soil as a whole.

Slope of the soil surface, significant losses of soil by erosion, stoniness, salt accumulation, and evidence of imperfect drainage or flooding and the like are also recorded.

From these observations, supplemented in some instances by laboratory data on samples of the horizons, they estimate permeability of the soil, erosion hazard, and other qualities important to soil use.

Of course, no two soils examined are exactly the same. But those soils that do not have differences that are significant in soil genesis and soil use are placed together and given a symbol, and the boundaries are plotted on the map.

Many soil mapping units merge into one another through a transitional belt several yards or more wide. Hence, the boundary on the map may indicate an abrupt or a gradual change in soil.

The soil scientist includes additional information about the landscape needed by users of the survey such as the drainage pattern (how and where water flows from the land) and the position of rock outcrops, lakes, ponds, levees, roads, railroads, power lines, geographical boundaries, buildings, and the like.

Equipment Used

To see the many soil characteristics—to mentally integrate them into mapping units to be recorded on the map—the soil scientist must not only be properly trained, he must also be properly equipped. The methods and the tools he uses depend on where he is working. After having a few deep trenches dug mechanically, in some places he needs only a spade or hand auger to examine the soil characteristics. But in another part of the country, he may use a power auger and other equipment to get the information he wants.

Much information can be uncovered with a spade—the depth of the surface horizon, the soil texture (coarseness or fineness), and the structure of the surface soil and the top part of the subsoil. And the spade does not distort the soil structure as do some soil augers. If deeper examinations are needed, he uses a soil auger.

Laboratory Work

While making the survey, the soil scientist also collects soil samples by soil horizons to be studied in the laboratory. This means he must dig a pit deep enough to reach through all the horizons and into the material beneath the true soil and large enough so that he can get into the pit and work effectively.

The samples are placed in bags or cans, labeled, and sent to a laboratory. The samples taken depend on the type of examinations to be made. And these in turn depend on the problem of soil classification, of genesis, or of behavior to be solved. For most analyses loose samples of about a gallon from each horizon are satisfactory.

The soil scientist takes undisturbed core soil samples where laboratory analyses are needed to study how porous the soil is, how fast water moves through it, how dense it is, and similar physical measurements.

In the laboratory a scientist measures particle-size distribution to help estimate the water-holding capacity. He measures the rate that water moves through the soil. He studies thin sections of the soil under the petrographic microscope to learn the distribution of certain important minerals.

These laboratory studies make it possible to use the information available on one soil for predictions about other soils with similar characteristics and qualities.

At the same time they reveal information that helps in putting all soils information into use. For example, tests on water-holding capacity may open up new possibilities for the irrigator. Or the drainage engineer who knows the rate of water movement through the soil can space tile for effective water disposal or know where tile will not work so well as open ditches.

Data from laboratory tests for calcium, magnesium, potassium, and other elements in soils help the scientists predict how these soils will respond to certain fertilizers. Also, the results of laboratory studies help the soil scientist in the field by giving him standards to go by; for example, he estimates soil texture in the field by rubbing soil between his thumb and finger. The laboratory measurement of the percentage of sand, silt, and clay gives him a good check on his ability to estimate texture in the field.

Where information is needed for highway construction or other engineering uses, 30-pound samples are taken. This provides enough soil for the mechanical analysis and other tests to determine how the soil may be compacted, and its other engineering properties. Most of these determinations are made by the Bureau of Public Roads and State Highway Department laboratories.

Soil Descriptions

As the soil scientist does his mapping, he adds new or improved information to the mapping legend and writes descriptions of the new soils he maps. During the course of the survey he writes several descriptions of each mapping unit. These include the location and description of a representative profile in each. From his several descriptions he prepares a composite description of each mapping unit and a statement explaining how much range was allowed in the various characteristics. He describes "inclusions" outside the range of the soil that bears the name assigned to the mapping unit.

He describes soils in standard terms so they can be used by other soil scientists who map in the area or who make use of his work. This provides enough information so that the soils can be classified properly and related properly to other soils outside the area.

The notes taken by the soil scientist are organized systematically for reference during the survey. As soon as the work is well begun the notes are assembled into handbooks and technical guides for use in conservation planning and other applications, and for preparing the published soil survey.

Collecting Additional Information

To give technical soil assistance for some special purposes, such as in designing drainage systems, deep borings must be made to add to the information normally collected. Checking foundation material on which to build heavy structures or highways and checking the porosity of deep layers that may cause a pond to leak are other examples of this kind of on-site assistance.

Information on flooding usually is recorded in making a soil survey. This kind of information is used in interpreting soil maps in planning and carrying out watershed protection and flood prevention work.

Strongly alkaline soils and those containing harmful amounts of salts are mapped separately from other soils. Soils having enough soluble salts or alkalinity to interfere with growing crops are largely confined to the arid and semiarid regions in the United States. They also occur, however, in humid regions in coastal strips affected by tides and in local areas affected by seepage of salty waters. One of the principal purposes of detailed soil surveys in such areas is to identify soils that cannot be irrigated practicably.

Soil Investigations

Research develops new ideas that increase our understanding of soils, make soil surveys more useful, and increase efficiency of mapping. For example, the results of a study on landscape evolution and soil genesis in an arid area near Las Cruces, New Mexico, are increasing our understanding of the nature of soils and erosion processes in desert areas.

Other projects such as (1) relations between soil-moisture movement and horizons of clay accumulation, (2) gullying in western Iowa, (3) soil-plant relations on rangeland, and (4) relations of deficiencies of cobalt and toxicities of molybdenum to soil classification are revealing data that make possible soil surveys of higher quality.

Results of studies on the relations between climate and crop yields by soils in the Great Plains and other areas are improving the placement of soils in the land capability classification and making other soil predictions.

Soil Correlation

To extend information obtained on one soil to like soils in other areas requires that these soils be given the same name. One of the immediate purposes of soil correlation is to assign names to the soils in the mapping units that are shown on soil maps. These, of course, must be consistent with and fit into the nationwide system of soil classification. Moreover, the name of a soil in a given area must carry the same name as soils in other areas that do not differ significantly in soil genesis.

Accurate mapping and interpretation depend on accurate classification, and, in turn, the mapping and interpretation serve as tests of the classification.

Cartographic Work

After the field mapping is completed for an area, usually a county, the soil information is transferred from the field sheets to a photomosaic base for printing the soil map.

By using a photomosaic base much drafting is eliminated and at the same time more background detail is included. The photomosaic shows such details as field boundaries, broad land use, and minor roads or trails that usually are not shown on line base maps.

The publication scale is commonly 1:20,000, which is usually large enough for users to see clearly the relation of soil boundaries to local land features in specific fields.

Using Soil Survey Information

Information about how soils respond to different management and treatment is gathered from many sources. Landowners' own experiences and field trials provide much information. More precise information is gained by experiment stations and other laboratory and field experiments where tests are made under controlled conditions. As information is collected on one soil or on a group of related soils, it can be projected to other soils.

Because there are so many kinds of soils, there are many individual soil interpretations. Most users of soil surveys want more general information than that of the individual mapping unit. They would like to have grouped together, for example, soils that behave alike in response to management and treatment for specific uses. Such grouping results in wider and more efficient use of what is known about soils.

The land capability classification is one interpretative grouping. It helps to introduce agricultural users to the detailed soil map. Soils are grouped according to their adaptability for common farm crops under permanent agriculture, to what they can be expected to do, to their limitations for sustained production, and to the risk of soil damage if they are mismanaged.

In this classification the individual mapping units are first grouped into capability units. The soils in any one *capability unit* have similar risks and limitations for agricultural use, respond to the same broadly defined practices, are adapted to about the same farm crops, and return about the same yields of these crops under comparable systems of management. Thus they are a basic management unit for common farm crops.

Capability units are then grouped into *capability subclasses,* a grouping that suggests both the degree and the kind of problem that a farmer or rancher will encounter in longtime use of the soil.

Capability subclasses, in turn, are grouped into *capability classes,* a grouping that expresses only the degree of limitation and risk for agricultural use.

This interpretation is widely used in giving technical assistance to landowners and operators through soil conservation districts. Soils also are grouped for special crops, for range sites, and for woodland suitability.

Land appraisers have found that soil surveys provide useful information on which to base land values, not only for individual tracts but especially to provide common standards for all holdings.

The use of soil surveys has expanded tremendously in the past few years. Originally farmers and ranchers and technical people working with them were the greatest users of soil maps and soil predictions. It is common now for soil map users to include highway engineers, planning commissions, consulting firms, tax appraisers, sanitary engineers, credit agencies, city and town governments, contractors, oil and gas companies, and many others.

In urban-fringe areas[2] the purpose of the soil survey is to gather soil data, plot them on suitable base maps and present predictions useful to planning groups and others who must make decisions on land use and treatment. The soil characteristics considered are those significant to the intended use—those that reflect the potential of the soil and the limitations and hazards involved in its use. These are the same soil characteristics that are used in making soil maps and predictions for work in areas used for cultivated crops, grasslands, and woodlands. The weight given a soil characteristic or soil property depends on other associated characteristics and is different for different kinds of pre-

[2] Areas with reasonable expectation of being urbanized in ten years.

dictions. Even where agriculture is not an important alternative land use within the urban fringe, essentially the same soil classification is needed for predictions about housing, industrial development, sanitation, drainage, parks, pipelines, and road and street construction. The detail of mapping, however, may be greater and often greater care is used in delineating areas of different soils in urban-fringe areas. Special emphasis is given to the engineering properties of soils that influence their suitability as subgrades and foundations for houses, roads, streets, and the location of pipelines and buried cables.

The kinds of soil make a real difference in these uses. Since man with the use of heavy equipment is capable of modifying the landscape, he needs to know a great deal about the soils. Soil texture of the different layers is important. The topsoil may or may not be good for covering cuts and fills, and other areas to be vegetated. The texture of the lower layers of the soil is important since it may not permit the percolation of water readily and hence would not be suitable for septic tank disposal fields. This is demonstrated over and over where subsoils are dense clays or hardpans (cemented layers) that will not handle the effluent from septic tank systems and thus the effluent appears on the soil surface or in roadside ditches. Depth of soil to rock and other restrictive soil materials is important in construction, especially in laying out pipelines for water, gas, and other utilities needed in the area. Putting utility lines through bedrock is very expensive.

Soil drainage is important. Soils with high water tables, those seasonally wet and dry, those wet most of the time, and those periodically flooded are problem soils in urban development. Predictions about these soils must take into account also what the soil is like after drainage. Soils periodically flooded are not suitable for housing or industrial development. These should be left in agricultural use (cultivated crops, grasses or trees) or used for parks and other recreation developments.

The kind of clay is important since some clays are unstable with a high shrink-swell potential. Buildings on these clays shift, crack and deteriorate. Expensive reinforced foundations are necessary for houses on these soils. Usually a reinforced concrete slab is the foundation requirement. Fortunately, all clays do not have a high shrink-swell potential and the design of the foundation can be based on the shrink-swell potential of the individual soil and not designed for all soils based on those with high shrink-swell potential.

Slope is an important feature in the soil survey. Slope gradient is an important factor in predicting soil erodibility. Special care is needed in laying out a development to avoid leaving the soil bare and exposed to the rains and subsequent erosion damages, and silting of water developments and clogging of sewer systems with soil sediment. In urban areas the runoff to be handled is much greater during and after construction than it was in the natural state, since roof tops, concrete streets and roadways produce virtually 100 percent runoff.

Some soils have a low bearing capacity. That is, they slip and slide when wet and do not support heavy loads of buildings and foundations. Organic soils especially have very low bearing capacity and are to be avoided in selecting construction sites. They may, however, be ideal for development into a park or wildlife sanctuary.

The completed soil map, descriptions of the soils, and predictions of soil behavior provide the soil map user basic information for making planning decisions on the use and treatment of the soil.

Conservation engineers also have many uses for soils information. For example, they need to know how fast water enters the soil (intake rate) and how rapidly water passes through the soil. They need such information to lay out terraces and irrigation and drainage systems and to determine the size of dams needed to retard floods.

Foresters are learning a great deal about the relationships between kind of soil and woodcrop production, as well as related values such as for watersheds, recreation, and wildlife.

Wildlife conservationists find soil surveys helpful in planning and developing measures for protection and improvement of wildlife habitat. They may be used for evaluating habitat; for locating and building ponds for waterfowl; and in locating recreation, hunting, and fishing sites.

Oil and gas companies use soil surveys to plan the routes of pipelines where corrosion and cost will be least and to plan for erosion control after pipelines are installed.

Food processors and canneries want to locate their plants where they can be assured of a reliable source of raw materials. Soil facts help them.

Investors, bankers, insurance companies, and building and loan companies find soil surveys helpful in determining the soundness of proposed investments in land. Farmers, or anyone who plans to buy a farm, will want to look first at the kind of soil and its potential productivity.

Manufacturers of earth-moving equipment need soils information in the design of certain types of machinery. The points of plows, blades of scrapers, and other similar cutters are affected greatly by the amount of sand and gravel in soils and must be designed to fit the soil to avoid excessive wear.

Various organizations such as soil conservation districts, watershed associations, and drainage districts have need for soils information in developing district programs. A detailed soil survey actually forms the foundation for a soil conservation district's work by showing where in the district the most urgent work is needed, as well as what kind of program will be most beneficial.

The increasing importance of a watershed as a natural land unit for the application of soil conservation and water resource development programs recognizes the need for soil survey information in watershed activities.

Research workers in experiment stations use soils information to set up crop and fertilizer studies. Soils data are used to predict soil responses to different levels of management. Extension workers and teachers use soil maps to help inform farmers and students on how to do a better job of farming.

Published Soil Surveys

The findings of a soil survey are published as a soil map and a printed text that describes each of the soils, summarizes what is known about them, and explains their potential uses.

Most of the present manuscripts are written primarily for agricultural users of the map. Most of them include additional information of value to engineers, foresters, geologists, land appraisers, and others. Since they report basic soils information, other interpretations for specific purposes can be made from them.

If the units on the map are properly described, the survey can be interpreted and reinterpreted as economic or other conditions change. Since yield predictions and management recommendations about a soil depend upon both the soil and the state of the agricultural arts, the development of new technology commonly requires new interpretations.

Most soil surveys are published by the Soil Conservation Service in co-operation with the state agricultural experiment stations and with other co-operating agencies. The map scale is usually 1:20,000 which is slightly more than three inches to the mile. These maps are suitable for use in farm planning in most areas although in some a larger scale is needed.

While a survey is being made, work copies of unpublished soil maps are maintained usually in the local field office of the Soil Conservation Service, or in the soil conservation district office. Local soil handbooks and technical guides, available for reference only in the field office, are needed to interpret and use these unpublished maps.

Each soil conservation district cooperator is furnished a copy of the soil map of his farm and needed interpretations as a part of his farm conservation plan.

Published soil surveys of the U.S. Department of Agriculture that are still in print may be purchased from the Superintendent of Documents, Government Printing Office, Washington, D.C.

A copy of a published soil survey for a particular area is available free from the Soil Conservation Service to landowners or operators in the area and to professional workers who have use for them, if the supply is not exhausted.

Extension services, experiment stations, and members of Congress may have copies of published soil surveys for areas in their states.

County agencies and SCS field offices usually have copies of the local published soil survey. A few state agencies also publish soil surveys.

Many libraries have soil surveys in their collections.

APPENDIX E.

Land Use Statistics of the Resource Development Economics Division, Economic Research Service, USDA[1]

PREFACE

The Resource Development Economics Division and antecedent Divisions have been collecting and analyzing statistics on major uses of land periodically for over fifty years, or since about 1912. This research provides a systematic and continuing national inventory of major land uses, farm and nonfarm, national and regional; analyzes trends in the nature and intensity of land use by states and regions, including shifts in major agricultural uses, reversion of cropland to grass and trees, acreages absorbed by nonagricultural uses; and appraises the situation with respect to present and prospective changes in the use of rural land.

Data on separate uses of land from various state and federal sources are assembled, analyzed, and the segments fitted together to account for the entire land area. The gaps in the data assembled from available reports and records are filled, as far as possible, by co-operative studies with state Agricultural Experiment Stations, federal, and private agencies. The work of the Resource Development Economics Division is carried on in close co-operation with other federal agencies engaged in preparing reports on land and water resources for formulation of policies and programs of use, adjustment, conservation, and development. A series of publications shows major uses of land at five-year intervals since 1910. The land use inventory project is continuing; plans include an over-all inventory in 1965–66 and annual estimates of cropland used for crops each year.

LAND USE INVESTIGATIONS

1. A national and regional research program is conducted on land utilization, including: (1) Inventories of land use; (2) analyses of development potentials; (3) analyses of competing and complementary uses; and (4) income and value relationships of different uses.

The national land use inventory is an organized project, a principal objective of which is to provide a balance sheet of basic land use statistics for the entire land area, not otherwise available except in scattered sources, or un-

[1] A statement prepared by the Resource Development Economics Division, Economic Research Service, for this report.

published, in files of public agencies. It now provides uniform information at five-year intervals on the land in agricultural production, including total cropland, pasture, and grazing land, and related land uses. Fairly complete estimates have been assembled since 1920. Annual series on cropland used for crops and crops harvested, beginning in 1909, are prepared. Only partial estimates on cropland and pasture, however, are available from 1880 to 1920.

Segments of land use data are compiled, analyzed, and fitted together systematically into a composite whole for the entire land area from a number of federal and state sources (none of which cover the entire land and water areas in detail as to acreages and economic classes of land used in agriculture). The inventory includes private and public land. Special attention is given to assembly and analysis of data on total acreages of cropland, pasture, and range by states and regions of the country.

Recent publications resulting from the national land use inventory are "Major Uses of Land and Water," Agricultural Economics Report No. 13, Economic Research Service, U.S. Department of Agriculture, 1962; and "A Graphic Summary of Land Utilization," A Co-operative Report with the Bureau of the Census, 1962.

The national land use inventory is designed especially to supply data for departmental and other studies of agricultural production; land and water requirements; land development, conversion, and management. Participation has been active in several national surveys, including the following Department of Agriculture Committee Reports:

(1) Land and Water Resources, A Policy Guide, 1962;
(2) Basic Statistics of Soil and Water Conservation Needs, 1962;
(3) Agricultural Land Resources, Capabilities, Uses, and Conservation Needs, 1962;
(4) Land and Water Potentials and Future Requirements for Water, 1960; prepared for the Senate Select Committee on National Water Resources.

2. Primary land use data are collected first-hand and analyzed in several specific county, state, and regional land use surveys of land development and use potentials in each five-year period. The objectives are to supply data and other information needed in the solution of agricultural problems. Analyses cover competing and complementary uses of land, income and value relationships, and studies of farmland being shifted to urban, industrial, transportation, recreation purposes, and for related public facilities. These surveys are important supplements to the national land use inventory.

These surveys are cooperative, either by written co-operative agreements, or informally with state agricultural experiment stations, universities, and federal agencies. Participation in three to five such surveys has occurred in each five-year period since 1945. In a number of instances, contracts or agreements have been made for collection of specific data by other state and federal agencies and by university departments.

3. Land use studies since 1950 have been made, or are in progress, in eighteen states, namely: Alaska, Arizona, Delaware, Florida, Iowa, Michigan, Nebraska, North Carolina, Ohio, Pennsylvania, Utah, Virginia, and the New England states. These studies include use of selected sample counties, sample districts, and regional surveys.

4. Sampling methods designed or approved by the Statistical Reporting Service are used. While the methods generally are similar to those in use by the Soil Conservation Service, Forest Service, Corps of Engineers, and other public agencies, they are designed especially to supply data needed to answer economic questions.

One type of sampling is the sample cross section. Cross sections appear to provide workable means of obtaining land use data in flood plains, valleys, and other irregularly shaped areas. Areal block samples have been used in large, somewhat uniform agricultural areas. Individual farm samples have been drawn by random selection, and by taking numbers at intervals from the universe, in surveys of methods, costs and returns from land improvement and conversion. In some instances, for sample or case study townships and districts, there has been coverage of the use of all tracts of land where complete information appeared desirable.

In several studies, use of airphotos and airphoto analysis has provided data with minimum requirements of trained people and time. Topographic maps and soils maps have been important aids in making more meaningful land use estimates. Methods have been developed using airphoto interpretation to obtain data on such items as land clearing and draining, urban development on farmland, land use, and cultural development on river flood plains.

The block sample enumerative agricultural land and production surveys conducted annually by the Statistical Reporting Service are a very useful source of information for land use inventory purposes. They promise much for the cropland and pasture land use inventories of the future, especially when the sample is enlarged from the 1962 coverage for thirty states to all fifty states. A sample of counties has been picked at random to represent varying conditions in each state and region of the United States. Within each selected county, a number of blocks or segments of farmland then were chosen at random for visit by field technicians or enumerators to record detailed data on questionnaires and maps for land use and production.

In several surveys since 1957, use has been made of a sample drawn by a random statistical procedure for each county in the United States for the National Inventory of Soil and Water Conservation Needs.[2] The sample plots are located on county highway maps and airphotos. In the East, generally, a 2 percent sample of 100 acre plots has been used. In the central states, the plots are 160 acres, and in some western range and forest regions, the plots are 640 acres, or sections.

5. Methods of land use data collection include:

(a) Collection by mail and personal calls. Requests are made by letter or by personal inquiry to public land management agencies at five-year intervals for copies of annual, biennial, and other reports of ownership and use of federal, state, county, and local government land. If reports are incomplete, or not clear on agricultural and other major uses of land, specific information is requested by letter or personal call. Special effort is made to obtain coverage

[2] The samples used in the Soil and Water Conservation Needs Inventory were developed cooperatively by the U.S. Statistical Reporting Service and the statistical laboratories at Iowa State Agricultural Experiment Station, (Ames), Texas State Agricultural Experiment Station, and Cornell University.

of land used for crops and for pasture and range. A few brief tabular forms are used to record the data.

(b) Inspection of farm and ranch property units. Property units for a few detailed agricultural surveys are inspected systematically according to an approved design, and data recorded by use of airphotos, section or other maps, and simple card forms.

(c) Interviews with individuals in charge of land units. Interviews with individuals for a limited number of surveys are conducted by use of approved questionnaires prepared to meet the needs of the specific investigations. Airphotos, maps, and cards are used frequently for location, summarization, and recording purposes to supplement the questionnaires.

(d) Obtaining information from well-informed local people for land units, districts, and townships. In a few specific instances, land use estimates are obtained from selected sample or case study units, districts or townships. For example, detailed data are obtained at times from officers of drainage or other land improvement districts, townships, agricultural committeemen, officers, or members, of farm marketing and processing organizations, or businesses, and from contractors doing custom work for farmers and ranchers, such as land development and improvement. Airphotos, section maps, township, district and county maps, questionnaires and card forms are used in obtaining and recording land use data and other information pertinent to the inquiry.

6. First year of activation of land use inventories: national land use inventories, graphic summaries of agriculture, and related studies of land utilization were undertaken by Dr. O. E. Baker, about 1912, in the Office of Farm Management, Bureau of Plant Industry, of the Department of Agriculture.

In 1919 the research in land resources and utilization being done by Dr. Baker was included in the newly formed Division of Land Economics in the Office of Farm Management. The Land Economics Division became a part of the Bureau of Agricultural Economics when it was organized in 1922. Since 1922, national land use inventories and related local, state, and regional studies of land resources and land use have been made in the Bureau of Agricultural Economics and in succeeding Farm and Land Economics Divisions, in the Agricultural Research Service and Economic Research Service. In 1962, the national land use inventory and related land use projects were assigned to the new Resource Development Economics Division of the Economic Research Service.

7. Identification of questionnaires (a few selected questionnaires and other recent forms used in state surveys are listed as examples):

(1) Appraisal of Land Use in Potter County, Pennsylvania (1955).
(2) Custom Land Development Costs, Central Florida (1953).
(3) Land Use Changes, Costs and Returns from Improved Pastures, Central Florida (1953).
(4) Economic Appraisal of Farmland Drainage and Clearing in 3 Coastal Plain Counties, North Carolina (1957).

8. Examples of publications.

National Surveys

(1) Major uses of Land and Water in the United States, with Special Ref-

erence to Agriculture, Summary for 1959. Agricultural Economic Report No. 13, Farm Economics Division, Economic Research Service, U.S. Department of Agriculture, July 1962. By Hugh H. Wooten, William C. Pendleton, and Karl Gertel. (Published every five years.)

(2) A Graphic Summary of Land Utilization, 1959. A Co-operative Report, Economic Research Service, U.S. Department of Agriculture and the Bureau of the Census, U.S. Department of Commerce, Vol. V, Part 6, Chapter 1, U.S. Census of Agriculture, 1959. July 1962. By James R. Anderson and Hugh H. Wooten. (Published every five years.)

(3) Changes in Farm Production and Efficiency. A Summary Report, 1964. Statistical Bulletin No. 233, Economic Research Service, U.S. Department of Agriculture. (Published annually.)

(4) Federal and State Rural Lands, With Special Reference to Grazing. Circular No. 909, U.S. Department of Agriculture, May 1952. (This publication is listed because it indicates general sources of data on uses of public land for the land use inventory listed in 1 above.)

State Surveys

(1) An Economic Appraisal of the use of Idle Land in Potter County, Pennsylvania, for Crops, Pasture and Forest, Pennsylvania State Agricultural Experiment Station Bulletin 642. Feb. 1959. By Karl Gertel, John C. Frey, and Robert J. Marty. In Co-operation with Farm Economics Research Division, Agricultural Research Service, U.S. Department of Agriculture.

(2) Costs of Clearing Land and Establishing Improved Pasture in Central Florida. Florida Agricultural Experiment Station, Bulletin 600. In Co-operation with the Farm Economics Research Division, Agricultural Research Service, U.S. Department of Agriculture. By L. A. Reuss.

(3) Land Clearing and Drainage in Eastern North Carolina. Agricultural Research Service Publication 43–127, U.S. Department of Agriculture. Jan. 1961. By James R. Anderson and Henry W. Dill, Jr.

(4) Land Use in the Rural Urban Fringe, A Case Study of New Castle County, Delaware. Agricultural Experiment Station Bulletin 340. In Co-operation with Farm Economics Division, Economic Research Service, U.S. Department of Agriculture. July 1962. By William M. Crosswhite and Gerald F. Vaughn.

9. Agencies, sections, and personnel engaged in inquiries. Much of the work described above is done by the Land Use Investigations staff, of the Land and Water Branch, Resource Development Economics Division, (formerly part of the Farm Economics Division), Economic Research Service, in cooperation either formally or informally with other federal and state agencies, including state agricultural experiment stations, colleges, and universities.

10. Names of agencies, history, authority, and source of funds. The Report of the Congressional Hearings on the Department of Agriculture Appropriation for 1963 states in part that the research in the Resource Development Economics Division of ERS is concerned with the extent and utilization of land and water resources, adjustments in production and resource use, development of rural

areas, use of capital in adjustment and development, and alternative policies and programs.[3] The following statement is from the Report of the Hearings on the Appropriation Bill for 1963:

> The Economic Research Service was established by Secretary's Memorandum No. 1446, Supplement No. 1 of April 3, 1961, under Reorganization Plan No. 2 of 1953, and other authorities. The Service develops and carries out a program of economic research designed to benefit farmers and the general public. The findings of this are made available to farmers and others through research reports and through economic outlook and situation reports . . . .

11. Comments on results of land use inquiries:

a. Approximately 70 percent of the land use studies described in this section which were completed through 1962 were done within the agency and 30 percent cooperatively by other state and federal agencies.

b. Procedures generally included simple standard methods and not higher statistical methods.

c. An average of five processed, or printed, reports of significant contributions were published from results of the national land use inventory project in each five-year period, 1942 to 1962, inclusive. From 2,000 to 25,000 copies of these publications were distributed depending on number printed and the demand. Altogether, about 350 separate publications or contributions were made from national land utilization and cooperative state projects from 1942 to 1962.

d. Analysts generally have been credited by reviewers and users of publications as having done well with the data available to them.

e. A complaint common to nearly all data collection is that there is too long a time lag between collection of data and publication. Inquiries are frequently made for current annual data and for comparisons with former years. Impatience is expressed with variations in different land use data from different sources and with changes in definitions. These criticisms are general and not directed alone at the national land use inventory project described in this report but to estimates made by other projects as well.

f. Brief reviews of summaries of results are made by specialists in various land use fields, to determine accuracy and refinement in analysis. Additional reviews and cooperative work by well-informed land use specialists would add to better analysis and uniformity in definitions and estimates.

g. Several persons who assembled and analyzed land use data are available for suggestions in Washington or in universities and experiment stations. The land use committee includes several men acquainted with the national land use inventory.

h. Printed reports summarizing results of specified land use projects are listed in preceding section 8.

Related Land and Water Economics Research

Programs of authorized land and water economics research closely related and complementary to land use statistical studies already described in this

[3] Department of Agriculture Appropriation for 1963, Hearings Before a Subcommittee on Appropriations, House of Representatives (87th Cong. 2nd sess.), Part 3, 1962, pp. 1128 and 1130, and pp. 1143, 1144, 1147, 1148, 1159–1161.

chapter are: (a) agricultural water use and supply inventories and analyses including irrigation, drainage, flood plains, water storage areas, and watersheds; (b) development and analyses of basic land ownership and tenure information; (c) urbanization and recreational impacts on rural land and water use; and (d) land and water resource institutions and legal analyses.

Two of these projects, water use and land tenure, assemble and analyze several segments of basic data on agricultural land and water use and ownership and are described briefly below:

Water Use Inventory and Analyses: On appraisals of agricultural water use and supply, data on current and projected water supply and use are compiled, analyzed, and interpreted for their economic significance, with particular emphasis on agricultural uses and their supply sources. Major data sources are various reports of the Bureau of the Census, the U.S. Geological Survey, and the Bureau of Reclamation; all available state publications are also examined.

Recent examples of inventory-type reports include Agr. Econ. Rpt. No. 13 on "Major Uses of Land and Water," ERS-USDA, 1962; and "Land and Water Resources: A Policy Guide," USDA, 1962. A detailed guide for compiling and interpreting water statistics available from a variety of sources was also published recently. See "Water Uses, Supplies, and Projections," unnumbered, ERS-USDA, 1961. Similarly, a method for accumulating and card-filing data on flood plain land use and soil features was published in the report "Sampling, Coding, and Storing Flood Plain Data," Agr. Handbook 237, ERS-USDA, 1962.

Land Ownership: The work project dealing with development and analyses of basic land ownership information assembles economic data on the distribution of land holdings by sizes and types of owners and operators, including private and public land, conditions and trends in land tenure and use of land. The principal sources of data are programs of research in cooperation with the land grant colleges, state agricultural experiment stations, federal agencies, private organizations, and data collected by the Bureau of the Census.

Publications include "A Graphic Summary of Farm Tenure," a co-operative report published at five-year intervals by the Economic Research Service and the Bureau of the Census, and other federal and state publications which present the results of special studies of land ownership and use. The latest report in the series of Graphic Summaries of Farm Tenure is dated November 1962.

Two recent examples of landownership studies are the Great Plains States ownership survey with results published in *Land Ownership in the Great Plains, 1958, A Statistical Summary,* Stat. Bull. No. 261, 1960; and the southeastern states ownership survey with results now being published in "Rural Landownership in the Southeast" (in process). Earlier publications include *Farm Land Ownership in the United States,* Misc. Pub. No. 699, 1949.

Land Use Inventory Definitions and Explanations

Cropland. Total cropland available for crops includes cropland used for crops, cropland in soil-improvement crops, idle cropland, and cropland used only for pasture. The acreage of cropland used only for pasture may also be included with the acreage of other pasture or non-forested pasture if the acreage of all improved land used for pasture is desired.

Cropland used for crops is defined as the acreage actually used and in preparation for crops. It is made up of three components—acreage of cropland harvested (land from which one or more crops were harvested), crop failure, and cultivated summer fallow. Certain areas of newly seeded crops and soil-improvement crops not harvested or pastured are not included, as data relating to them are incomplete. Nor is idle cropland included, as the cropland-used-for-crops series is intended to measure changes in the land area in crops or in preparation for crops the following year.

Idle and fallow cropland and cropland used only for pasture are usually considered in the crop-rotation system as land that is used for crops, though not necessarily in each year. Fallow land often is cultivated to conserve moisture and kill weeds in preparation for crops. Much of the idle land is left unplanted for a year or two only, although some of it is the poorer cropland that represents abandonment for crop purposes.

The series on cropland used for crops is based on the continuous series of principal crops harvested and crop losses developed and maintained, 1909 to 1963, by the Bureau of Agricultural Economics, the Agricultural Marketing Service, The Statistical Reporting Service, and data from the Census of Agriculture. The acreages of cropland harvested were used for the eight censuses taken at five-year intervals from 1925 to 1959. Interpolations were made for the intervening years, based on the Bureau of Agricultural Economics and Statistical Reporting Service series on principal crops harvested, 1925 to 1963. For earlier years, 1909 to 1924, the Bureau of Agricultural Economics series on principal crops harvested and acreages of specified crops harvested reported by the ten-year censuses were used, and adjustments were made for crops not reported. Additions were made to the acreage of cropland harvested reported by the 1950, 1954, and 1959 censuses of agriculture to cover some of the undernumeration of cropland harvested that was indicated by postnumeration surveys. This adjustment was necessary in order to account satisfactorily for the total acreage of crops harvested, as reported by the Statistical Reporting Service.

Before the Agriculture Adjustment Administration program began in 1933, farmers usually thought in terms of "gross areas," which did not allow for land occupied by ditches, fencerows, turnrows, or building sites. In later years, their thinking has been more in terms of "net acres." No doubt this change in method of reporting has affected to some extent recent estimates of acreages of individual crops and of total cropland. It has reduced these acreages by an estimated 3 percent from what they would have been under the definitions of cropland that prevailed prior to 1933. For an estimate on changes in acreage of cropland in the South see Langsford, E. L., "Changes in Cotton Production In War and Peace—Analyses by Production Areas," U.S. Dept. of Agr., Bur. Agr. Econ. F. M. 45, 33 pp., illus., Washington, D.C., 1944. (Mimeographed.)

Acreages of crop failure as given in census reports were used for census years from 1925 to 1948 when reported, and interpolations for intervening years were based on the crop losses or differences between planted and harvested acreages of principal crops as estimated by the Bureau of Agricultural Economics. Acreages of crop failure for 1949 to 1963 are based chiefly on crop losses as reported by the Statistical Reporting Service. Reported acreages of crop losses are adjusted for the replanting of part of the acreage on which winter wheat is abandoned. Hayland that produced nothing but pasture in some dry seasons is not included in crop failure in recent years.

Estimates of acreage of cultivated summer fallow were made only for the geographic divisions that lie west of the Mississippi River. From 1945 to 1948, estimates of fallow were based chiefly on acreages seeded to wheat on summer fallow land, as estimated in the Bureau of Agricultural Economics and according to data issued by the Great Plains Council. For 1949 and subsequent years, estimates of fallow were based partly on the 1950, 1954, and 1959 censuses of agriculture, estimates of wheat seeded on summer fallow made by the Agricultural Marketing Service, the Statistical Reporting Service, and information obtained from the Great Plains Council. Estimates for years prior to 1945 were built up from fragmentary data available in the Bureau of Agricultural Economics and the Agricultural Research Service.

Pasture and range. Estimates of the acreage of all pasture and grazing land include open permanent pasture in farms, farm woodland pastured, and all land grazed not in farms. Grazing land not in farms is part grassland, part shrubs and other nonforest growth, and part brushland and woodland range.

In the land use inventory for purposes of convenience to the users of statistics, pasture and range is classified in two different ways. The first breakdown includes (1) grassland pasture and grazing and, (2) woodland and forest pastured or grazed. The second breakdown separates (1) pasture in farms from (2) grazing land not in farms.

Grassland pasture and range. Grassland pasture and grazing land includes all land used primarily for pasture and grazing, exclusive of the woodland and forest pastured or grazed. It includes the shrub and brushland types of pasture and grazing land such as sagebrush, scattered mesquite, and some other shrub types in the West, and some scattered brushland pasture in the East, and all tame, wild, or native grasses and legumes and other forage used for pasture or grazing.

Woodland and forest range. Only rough approximations can be made of the total acreage of woodland and forest not in farms which contains some areas that have forage subject to grazing, or that have value for grazing, at some time during the year. Woodland and forest land actually grazed, or useful for grazing, consists principally of open woodland or forest, scattered cleared and cutover areas, abandoned fields, brush-grown pasture, and other land within forested areas that has grass or other forage growth.

In the northern states, the woodland areas grazed, or subject to grazing, usually include woodland adjacent to farms in the corn belt, the lake states, and the northeastern states. Much forest land in the Arkansas-Missouri Ozark area is subject to grazing. The acreage of woodland grazed in New England and other sections of the Northeast includes occasional abandoned fields and brush-grown pastures.

In the southern states, the woodland and forest lands estimated to be subject to grazing, or useful for grazing, contain areas covered by switch cane, abandoned fields (not reforested), cutover land, and grass and other forage areas within forests, such as the open longleaf-slash pine belt of the coastal plain, the Arkansas Ozark area, and some semiprairie, open grassland, savanna, and marshland areas in Florida, Georgia, Louisiana, and Texas.

The chief woodland and forest areas in the western states that are subject to or useful for grazing include arid woodlands, brush and shrub lands, woodland-grasslands, open forests, such as the Ponderosa pine forests, and some cutover areas that have grass or other forage.

Land use and cover classes of land grazed and in open grassland, shrubs, woodland, and forest are not always mutually exclusive. Grassland, in places, includes spots of brushland and scattered trees, while woodland and forest includes many areas of open grass and other forage.

Pasture and range in farms. Farm pasture consists of open or nonforested pasture, grassland pasture (permanent pasture, not cropland and not woodland), and woodland pastured. (Cropland used only for pasture is included as a part of the cropland area in arriving at the total acreage of cropland available for crops.)

Improved pasture ordinarily is in tame grasses and legumes, either seeded or natural growth, but it may include native forage. All classes usually have had improvement or conservation practices applied, such as weed and brush control, seeding or reseeding, either artificial or natural, fertilization, drainage, irrigation, or other similar practices that improve yields.

Range not in farms. Grazing land not in farms comprises the open grassland and shrub grazing lands and the woodland and forest area grazed. Most of the grazing land not in farms is public land in the western states, and privately owned nonfarm woodlands and coastal prairies and savanna lands in the South.

Source of information on pasture and range acreages. The published records showing the trend in acreages of land used for pasture and grazing over a long period of time are the decennial estimates of the United States Department of Agriculture, 1880 to 1920; and the quinquennial reports of the Bureau of the Census, 1925 to 1959, for pasture in farms, supplemented by estimates of pasture and grazing land not in farms made by the Department of Agriculture. These estimates have been issued currently about every five years since 1916, although in some periods the published figures are revisions of those from previous years. Since 1900 eight special land use studies have been made which have brought together many available data on pasture and grazing lands. These studies were made for the following years: 1920, published in 1923 Yearbook of Agriculture; 1930, published in the Reports of the Land Committee, National Resources Board, in 1934 and 1935; 1945, published in the various federal and state agricultural adjustment reports, 1945 to 1950; 1958, published in Basic Statistics of the National Inventory of Soil and Water Conservation Needs, (USDA Stat. Bull. 317, Aug. 1962), and related publications, and U.S. Dept. Agr. Misc. Pub. 663, "Inventory of Major Land Uses," 1945; and 1950, 1954, and 1959 bulletins, "Major Uses of Land in the United States," (USDA Tech. Bull. 1082, Oct. 1953; AID 168, Jan. 1957; and AER 13, July 1962).

The United States Department of Agriculture does not make annual estimates of pasture and grazing land by states as is done for crops planted and harvested.

The national land use inventory depends in part upon enumerations of farm land made every ten years by the Bureau of the Census from 1880 to 1920, and every five years beginning with 1925 as part of the Census of Agriculture, and in part upon estimates from the state and federal agencies that manage public land or deal with agricultural land use, programs, and surveys. Estimates for pasture and grazing land not in farms are combined with acreages in farms reported by agricultural surveys and by census to form the totals for pasture and range. Necessary adjustments to avoid duplication in acreages are made on the basis of the agricultural census instructions and reports as to land included in farms and the records of the agencies that manage public land as to land leased out to farmers and ranchers, used by permit, or otherwise used in agriculture.

Estimates of all pasture and grazing land include open permanent pasture in farms, cropland used only for pasture, farm woodland pastured, and all land grazed not in farms. Grazing land or range not in farms is part grassland, part shrubs and other nonforest growth, and part brushland and woodland.

Forest and woodland. Forest land and woodland as defined by the U.S. Forest Service include (1) lands that are at least 10 percent stocked by trees of any size and capable of producing timber or other wood products, or of influencing the climate or the water regime; (2) land from which the trees described in (1) have been removed to less than 10 percent stocking and which have not been developed for other use; (3) afforested areas; and (4) chaparral areas. (For definitions refer to publications listed at the end of this section.)

Land that is grazed and that bears sparse forest growth—only 10 to 30 percent covered by trees—or from which the forest has been removed to less than 10-percent stocking but which has not been developed for uses other than timber production, or for pasture, may in some areas overlap the acreages reported by farmers as open pasture and grazing land in farms (grassland pasture, or pasture other than cropland and woodland).

Most of the available forest land in the East, North, and South is commercial in character, whereas about two-thirds of such forest land in the Great Plains and half of that in the West is classed as non-commercial woodland growth. Noncommercial woodland includes inaccessible alpine ranges, chaparral, mesquite, pinon-juniper, and semi-arid shrub and brush growth.

Acreages and definitions of woodland and forest presented generally are based on the following Forest Service publications: (1) "Timber Resources for America's Future," Forest Resource Report No. 14, Jan. 1958, and "Basic Forest Statistical Tables, 1960 and 1961," Mimeo; (2) "Basic Forest Statistics, 1950"; and (3) "Forests and National Prosperity," Misc. Pub. 668, Aug. 1948.

Special-use areas. The specified special uses include (1) the intensively used urban, town, and built-up areas, highway, road, and railroad rights-of-way, airports, radio stations, research facilities and factories, rural institutional sites, such as universities, hospitals, prisons, and fairgrounds; (2) the extensive areas of rural land held for parks, wildlife refuges, national defense, flood-control, and watershed protection; and (3) the agricultural areas used for farmsteads, farm roads, and lanes.

Special uses of rural land for which estimates generally are not available include those for industrial and commercial sites in rural areas, mining areas, clay, sand, and stone quarry sites, power, telephone and gaspipe line rights-of-way, drainage and irrigation ditches, cemeteries, and golf courses.

Areas in rural villages and small towns with populations of 100 to 1,000 are not included in urban and town areas. At present, much of the acreage in these small villages and towns is included in other major uses of land such as forest, grazing, farm, and other land. Separation would call for revision of accepted major land use areas of many counties and states.

Water area in large reservoirs, canals, and waterways is not included among the special uses of land as the approximate land area of the United States excludes all natural or artificial water bodies of forty acres or more.

Rural highways, roads, railroads, farmsteads, and farm roads and lanes are roughly distributed in accordance with population and numbers of farms.

Although there are parks, game refuges, and military reservations in nearly all parts of the country, the larger ones are located in the West, particularly in the Rocky Mountain states. Farmsteads, feed lots, and farm roads and lanes included here among the special-use areas are an integral part of farms and ranches and make substantial contributions to agricultural production. Certain of the special-service areas, as highways, roads, and railroads, directly or indirectly affect the productivity and efficiency of agriculture.

Miscellaneous other areas. Miscellaneous unaccounted-for areas not found among other major uses include marshes, sand dunes, bare rock areas, and deserts. There remain at present several million acres of rural land not generally used for agriculture, grazing, forests, or special uses. Most of it is classified as having low surface-use value for agriculture, except for incidental values for wildlife, watersheds, and recreation. Some have mineral and other subsurface values.

Summary

In determining major land areas used for cropland, pasture, range, forest, urban, and other purposes, the first estimates were prepared from recent federal and state government reports, maps, and other publications. The data so obtained were reviewed and checked when possible through use of current maps, aerial photographs, unpublished public records, and locally obtained land use information. Special attention was given to areas outside farms not covered by the agricultural census. Types and conditions of land use were ascertained from recent farm, settlement, land utilization, and ownership surveys, forest surveys, and grazing land studies, soil and land capability surveys, conservation needs inventories, airphotos, and by use of public records of ownership, tax assessment, topographic, and other maps.

APPENDIX F.

Utilization of Land in Farms: The Program of the Statistical Reporting Service, USDA[1]

The Statistical Reporting Service is responsible for the collection, compilation, and analysis of a large volume of basic facts depicting the current status of agriculture in the United States. These data relate to the use of, or activity on, land in farms which is approximately half of the land area of the United States, or nearly 60 percent for the forty-eight conterminous states. Numerous reports each year are regularly released to growers, dealers, processors, and others who have an interest in agricultural commodities. Generally speaking, the statistical program is oriented on a state basis. County estimates of acreage are made for several crops.

In recent years, the statistical reports and services have been expanding to meet additional needs for information. As part of a long-range program to provide more accurate data, as well as survey facilities for obtaining additional needed data, two enumerative surveys based on probability area sampling are conducted each year. These surveys offer considerable potential for the improvement of land use statistics. One is made in June to give dependable bases for estimates of numbers of farms, land in farms, acreage planted or to be planted, and livestock numbers. The second is in the late fall, for harvested acreages, production, and livestock. These surveys began developing on a pilot basis in 1954 and reached operating levels in thirty-nine states in 1965. When operational in all states there will be about 17,000 segments, area sampling units, in the sample. These segments usually contain from one to four farms, with an average of about two farms.

All land within each sample segment is accounted for by tracts, a tract being a contiguous piece of land under the same ownership or management. Within each tract all fields in which crops are grown are identified on aerial photographs and the acreages by crops are recorded. In addition, acreage devoted to "other uses" (farmsteads, woods, roads, Conservation Reserve, idle, residential, etc.) is recorded in order to have an accounting of all lands in each sample area as a control on the accuracy of the field work. At the present time the data on "other uses" of land are not tabulated.

[1] A statement prepared for this book, by the Statistical Reporting Service.

Area Sampling

Because of its importance, a brief resume of area sampling is given for those who may be unfamiliar with it. The concept is quite simple. The total land area to be sampled is divided into small areas with identifiable boundaries called segments. Rules of association are formulated which associate every "unit" of the population with one and only one segment. Thus, when a segment is selected for a sample, all units associated with it are in the sample and have the same probability of being in the sample as the segment had of being selected. Area sampling is very versatile as it can be used as a "frame" for sampling all farms, farms of a particular type, households, parcels of land, businesses, etc. The size of segments (sampling units) and the sampling design are adapted to the purposes of the survey.

The "units" of a population to be sampled might be farms as defined for census of agriculture purposes. In that case, a unique identification point, or headquarters, is defined for each farm. An entire farm regardless of its location is in the sample if its headquarters is within a sample segment. This procedure has been referred to as the open segment approach in contrast to the closed segment which requires, for example, accounting for all land and livestock within a segment. Both the open and closed segment concepts can be used in the same survey.

For a land use survey, most parcels are likely to fall entirely within segments, as segments are bounded to the extent possible by well-defined landmarks. Parcels entirely within a sample segment are clearly in the sample. Simple rules can be established for deciding whether to include or exclude an entire parcel when it overlaps a segment boundary.

Land Used for Crops

Information on acreage and production for specific crops, and statistical methods employed is provided below in excerpts from Miscellaneous Publication No. 967, Statistical Reporting Service of the U.S. Department of Agriculture.

Field and Seed Crops

Field and seed crop statistics deal with all the major crops except fruits, vegetables, and nuts; the crops covered involve approximately 80 percent of the total crop acreage in the United States (table 1).

The pattern of statistics for field crops is rather uniform. For most of them the general coverage includes (1) acreage planted, (2) acreage harvested, (3) yield per acre harvested, and (4) total production. Harvested acreage and production estimates for most field crops, particularly the major ones, go back to 1866. Estimates of planted acreage for many crops were begun in 1919 and for others in 1929; before 1919 estimates related, for the most part, to acreage of a crop actually harvested; acreage lost from any cause was excluded.

The general methods employed in estimating acreage and yield of field crops are based largely on the theory of sampling—selecting a limited number

TABLE 1.—*Statistical Coverage of Field and Seed Crops*

Crop	Acreage			Production	Production, by classes, by types	Stocks	Disposition	Monthly marketings	Prices received by farmers	Value of production	Value of sales
	Intentions	Planted	Harvested								
Field crops:											
Barley	X	X	X	X	---	X	X	X	X	X	X
Beans, dry edible	X	X	X	X	X	---	X	X	X	X	X
Broomcorn	---	X	X	X	---	---	X	---	X	X	X
Buckwheat	---	X	X	X	---	---	X	X	X	X	X
Corn, all purposes	X	X	X								
Corn for grain	---	---	X	X	---	X	X	X	X	X	X
Corn for silage	---	---	X	X	---	---	---	---	X	---	---
Corn for hogging, grazing, or forage	---	---	X								
Cotton lint	X	X	X	X	---	---	---	X	X	X	X
Cottonseed	---	---	X	X	---	---	X	---	X	X	X
Cowpeas grown alone	X	X	X	---	---	---	---	---	---	---	---
Cowpeas interplanted	---	X	X	---	---	---	---	---	---	---	---
Cowpeas, equivalent solid acres	---	X	X								
Cowpeas for peas	---	---	X	X	---	---	X	X	X	X	X
Cowpeas grazed or plowed under	---	---	X								
Flaxseed	X	X	X	X	---	X	X	X	X	X	X
Hay, all	X	---	X	X	---	X	X	X	X	X	X
Hay, wild	---	---	X	X	---	---	---	---	X	---	---
Hay, alfalfa and mixtures	---	---	X	X	---	---	---	---	X	---	---
Hay, clover, timothy, and mixtures	---	---	X	X	---	---	---	---	X	---	---
Hay, lespedeza	---	---	X	X	---	---	---	---	X	---	---
Hay, soybean	---	---	X	X	---	---	---	---	X	---	---
Hay, cowpea	---	---	X	X	---	---	---	---	X	---	---
Hay, peanut	---	---	X	X	---	---	---	---	X	---	---
Hay, grain	---	---	X	X	---	---	---	---	X	---	---
Hay, other	---	---	X	X	---	---	---	---	X	---	---
Mung beans	---	X	X	X	---	---	---	---	X	X	X
Oats	X	X	X	X	---	X	X	X	X	X	X
Peanuts grown alone	X	X	X	---	---	---	---	---	---	---	---
Peanuts interplanted	---	X	X	---	---	---	---	---	---	---	---
Peanuts, equivalent solid acres	---	X	X	---	---	---	---	---	---	---	---
Peanuts picked and threshed	---	X	X	X	---	X	X	X	X	X	X
Peas, dry field	X	X	X	X	X	---	X	X	X	X	X
Popcorn	---	X	X	X	---	---	X	---	X	X	X
Rice, rough	X	X	X	X	---	X	X	X	X	X	X
Rye	X	X	X	X	---	X	X	X	X	X	X
Sirup, maple	---	---	---	X	---	---	X	---	X	X	X
Sorghums, all purposes	X	X	X								
Sorghums for grain	---	---	X	X	---	X	X	X	X	X	X
Sorghums for silage	---	---	X	X	---	---	---	---	X	---	---
Sorghums for forage	---	---	X	X	---	---	---	---	X	X	---
Soybeans grown alone	X	X	X	---	---	---	---	---	---	---	---
Soybeans interplanted	---	X	X	---	---	---	---	---	---	---	---

TABLE 1.—*Statistical Coverage of Field and Seed Crops*—Continued

Crop	Acreage			Production	Production, by classes, by types	Stocks	Disposition	Monthly marketings	Prices received by farmers	Value of production	Value of sales
	Intentions	Planted	Harvested								
Field crops—Continued:											
Soybeans, equivalent solid acres	----	X	X	----	----	----	----	----	----	----	----
Soybeans for beans	----	----	X	X	----	X	X	X	X	X	X
Soybeans grazed or plowed under	----	----	X	----	----	----	----	----	----	----	----
Sugarcane for sugar and seed	----	----	X	X	----	----	----	----	X	X	X
Sugarcane for sirup	----	----	X	X	----	----	X	----	X	X	X
Sugarcane sugar and molasses	----	----	----	X	----	----	----	----	----	----	----
Sugar beets for sugar	X	X	X	X	----	----	----	----	X	X	X
Sugar beet sugar, pulp, and molasses	----	----	----	X	----	----	----	----	----	----	----
Tobacco, by states	X	X	X	X	----	----	----	----	X	X	X
Tobacco, by types	X	X	X	X	X	----	----	----	X	X	----
Velvetbeans, all purposes	----	X	X	X	----	----	X	----	X	X	----
Wheat, winter	X	X	X	X	----	----	----	----	X	X	----
Wheat, durum	X	X	X	X	----	X	----	----	X	X	----
Wheat, other spring	X	X	X	X	----	----	----	----	X	X	----
Wheat, all	X	X	X	X	X	X	X	X	X	X	X
Seed crops:											
Alfalfa	----	----	X	X	----	X	X	X	X	X	X
Alsike clover	----	----	X	X	----	X	X	X	X	X	X
Crimson clover	----	----	X	X	----	X	----	----	X	X	----
Red clover	----	----	X	X	----	X	X	X	X	X	X
Sweetclover	----	----	X	X	----	X	X	X	X	X	X
White clover	----	----	X	X	----	X	----	----	X	X	----
Ladino clover	----	----	X	X	----	X	----	----	X	X	----
Smooth bromegrass	----	----	X	X	----	X	----	----	X	X	----
Crested wheatgrass	----	----	X	X	----	X	----	----	X	X	----
Merion bluegrass	----	----	X	X	----	X	----	----	X	X	----
Kentucky bluegrass	----	----	----	X	----	X	----	----	X	X	----
Fescue, chewings	----	----	X	X	----	X	----	----	X	X	----
Fescue, red	----	----	X	X	----	X	----	----	X	X	----
Fescue, tall	----	----	X	X	----	X	----	----	X	X	----
Orchardgrass	----	----	X	X	----	X	----	----	X	X	----
Redtop	----	----	X	X	----	X	----	----	X	X	----
Ryegrass	----	----	X	X	----	X	----	----	X	X	----
Bentgrass	----	----	X	X	----	X	----	----	X	X	----
Sudangrass	----	----	X	X	----	X	----	----	X	X	----
Timothy	----	----	X	X	----	X	X	X	X	X	X
Lespedeza	----	----	X	X	X	X	X	X	X	X	X
Mustard	----	----	X	X	X	----	----	----	X	X	----
Vetches (3)	----	----	X	X	X	X	----	----	X	X	----
Austrian winter peas	----	----	X	X	----	X	----	----	X	X	----
Lupine	----	----	X	X	----	X	----	----	X	X	----
Seed potatoes, certified	----	----	X	X	X	----	----	----	----	----	----
Vegetable seeds	----	----	X	X	X	X	----	----	----	----	----

in the universe whose behavior is used to describe the behavior of the whole. The sampling procedures embrace both mail and enumerative survey methods. The aim is to maintain as much objectivity as possible in sample data. It would be desirable to place all surveys on a random sampling basis so that measures of reliability may be mathematically calculated. For the most part, however, samples consist of farmers who report voluntarily on operations for the farm they operate and in some instances also for their neighborhood. For some commodities, survey data actually represent close to total acreages.

The many varied inquiries that go to farmers are tailored to provide the specific information needed for estimating purposes. Locality data provided by the volunteer reporters are largely subjective; that is, reporters must exercise considerable judgment in arriving at the figures they report.

Since 1954 a supplementary estimating method based on probability sampling has been used. Basically it consists of: (1) enumerating randomly selected land areas for acreage data; and (2) making crop population and fruiting counts on randomly selected sample units to obtain information on seasonal advancement, fruiting rate, and outturn per acre.

Estimates represent the combined efforts of both field and Washington personnel. For the most part the initial work starts in the field offices. Sample data are collected, summarized, analyzed, and interpreted into recommendations for each crop by the field statistician and then sent to the Washington office. In Washington the data are again reviewed in detail by the Crop Reporting Board, with each member making his own interpretation of the data. These interpretations are then resolved into the official estimate.

Estimates of acreage that farmers intend to plant are issued first. They are followed by estimates of acreage planted and, later in the season, by acreage harvested. Estimates of prospective crop production are made during the growing season. At the end of the year final or preliminary postharvest estimates are made.

Acreage estimates and forecasts serve several fundamental purposes. Most important, for nearly all field and vegetable crops, acreage estimates are one of the two components of forecasts and preliminary estimates of production (yield per acre is the other component). Preliminary production estimates made during the growing season are the product of independently made estimates of acreage and of yield per acre. Similarly, final production estimates are the product of final estimates of acreage and yield, except for a few cash crops for which nearly complete processing or marketing data are available.

In addition, acreage estimates become a fundamental part of the Department's programs; they provide basic data for research, program planning, and administration. Forecasts and estimates of acreage help farmers plan their plantings, serve as direct measures of land utilization, and are primary indicators of the future demand for various farm production supplies and farm labor.

In general, the progression of acreage forecasts and estimates is from prospective plantings to actual plantings, acreage for harvest, and actual harvested acreage. Most spring-sown crops follow the sequence of: (1) acreage intended for planting (prospective plantings) as of March 1, released about mid-March, (2) acreages planted and acreage for harvest, released with the July Crop Production report, and (3) acreage planted and harvested, released in the December Annual Crop Production Summary. However, all spring-sown crops do not follow this exact sequence. For example popcorn acreages planted and for harvest are estimated in August rather than in July and several minor commodities are estimated annually only in the December Annual Crop Production Summary. Fall-sown grains (winter wheat and rye) depart from the sequence, as seeded acreage is estimated in December of the year preceding harvest and acreage of winter wheat for harvest is estimated in May.

Acreages based on the major acreage surveys in March and June are adjusted, if necessary, for use in computing monthly production forecasts, but these adjusted acreages are usually not published. Such adjustments are necessitated by unusual conditions (usually weather) that result in changes in growers' plans relative to the acreage to be planted or harvested. Such adjustments are based primarily on the current condition or probable yield of the crop as reported by the monthly farm reporters. In some instances, special acreage data are made available either through special surveys or acreage evaluation items on the monthly Farm Report.

The primary purpose of the report on prospective plantings issued in March is to assist growers generally in making such further changes in their acreage plans as may appear desirable. The acreages actually planted may turn out to be larger or smaller than indicated, by reason of weather conditions, agricultural programs, price changes, labor supply, financial conditions, and the effect of the report on farmers' actions. The report on prospective plantings is released sufficiently early that modification of plans is possible in most areas. The prospective acreages are used as a base to which projected yields for spring wheat on June 1 are applied, to give a production forecast before the July harvested acreage estimates are available.

Planted acreage is usually larger than the harvested acreage because of crop failure or uses for which estimates are not made. For example, acreage used for pasture, cover crop, and soil improvement is not considered as part of the harvested acreage for most crops. The total harvested acreage of many crops is broken down into utilization groups. For example, although the major use of corn and sorghums is for grain, separate estimates are also made for the acreage harvested for silage and for forage, including acreage grazed or hogged. The breakdown of soybean acreage is for beans, hay, and other uses; cowpea and peanut acreages are treated in the same way. The estimate of the acreage of each small grain (wheat, oats, barley, rye) harvested for grain excludes acreage harvested ripe and fed unthreshed as well as the acreage harvested for hay or cut green for silage or green feed. The aggregate acreage of all small grains cut for hay, including acreage cut ripe and fed unthreshed, is estimated as a single item and is published as one of the kinds of hay.

Methods

In general, acreage estimates are based on two types of information: (1) absolute acreage data for a given crop season, ordinarily obtained from the quinquennial United States Census of Agriculture, a state assessors' census, or some other complete or nearly complete enumeration; and (2) indicated changes in acreages of individual crops from one year to the next, obtained by questionnaire (either mail or personal enumeration) from samples of farmers or processors. Acreage data of the first type are called acreage bases or benchmarks, while the sample data are called acreage indications.

The United States Census of Agriculture, taken each ten years from 1850 to 1920 and each five years since, provides data on harvested acreage for most of the principal crops. These data are not always comparable from one census to another from state to state or among the crops, but in general they provide benchmarks for reviewing longtime changes in the principal crops grown in this country. Generalizations that evaluate census data are difficult because of differences among states and differences between censuses in timing, definitions, and questions asked. But it is safe to say that for most crops federal census totals represent minimum levels.

The annual state assessors' census is another valuable benchmark in thirteen states. This varies in completeness from state to state; in some states it is not complete enough to serve as an absolute benchmark. Data from the state assessors' census are available in time for either preliminary acreage estimates each December or for the revisions the following year. The federal census data, however, do not become available until a year or more after the year to which they relate. Accordingly, federal census data are used for benchmarks in future years and for "truing up" historical estimates. The changes made after each quinquennial census are shown as census revisions, since the bulk of the new evidence comes from the census, but other relevant data are also considered or reconsidered at the same time.

An almost ideal method of obtaining accurate acreage information would be to make a complete enumeration by mail, by personal interview, or by a combination of both. This would provide a means of obtaining data on both planted acreage and harvested acreage by method of utilization. This ideal is hardly approached even in the states where the assessors' censuses ask for acreages in the current rather than the preceding year, for ordinarily only one type of acreage information, either planted or harvested, is available. Furthermore, insufficient time elapses between the harvesting of late crops and the date of the yearend acreage and production estimates in December to make possible the use of current data even if the assessors' censuses were taken in the late fall after harvest.

Sources of Sample Data

The sample data are secured from two main types of surveys—mailed and enumerative. The mailed surveys are divided into two groups—one for crops that are widely grown and the other for those crops grown in specialized localities which would not be adequately represented in a general-purpose sample. The enumerative method is used only for the June acreage and the fall acreage surveys. For the general surveys of field crop acreages—March prospective plantings, June acreage, or the fall acreage—questionnaires are designed to obtain data on crops widely grown within a state. The questions for individual crops relate to the individual operations of the growers who answer the questions—being limited to the farm or ranch operated for the mailed survey and to the sample segment for the enumerative survey.

In most states, the March prospective planting and the June acreage questionnaires are mailed to large lists of general farmers, and the fall acreage survey questionnaires are distributed in October by rural mail carriers. A predetermined number of cards is allotted to each rural carrier for distribution to representative farmers on his route. Presumably this distribution is more nearly random than the distribution of questionnaires mailed to farmers on lists maintained in the state offices. In a few states, fall cards are also mailed direct to each reporter who sent in a card the previous year, in order to provide a large number of "identical" returns.

The March survey questionnaire regarding prospective plantings (mailed late in February) obtains data on the acreages of specific spring-planted crops planned for the current year (or actually planted in the far South) and the acreage planted the previous year. Information on fall-planted crops is also reported and provides a basis for preliminary estimates of acreage of these crops for harvest. The June questionnaire also asks both this year's and last year's acreages, while most of the fall acreage survey questionnaires have spaces for reporting only the current year's harvested acreages. The fall questionnaires used in areas where abandonment is frequently heavy, ask for both planted and harvested acreages of the various crops.

Special surveys are necessary to obtain acreage information on crops that are not widely grown or are grown only in localized areas. These special surveys usually ask for acreage as well as for other information on the crop; they may vary materially from state to state for the same crop. They usually ask for acreage data on the individual farm and sometimes "judgment" questions covering the acreage in the locality as a percentage of the previous year.

Basic data for the preparation of estimates of utilization of acreage of a given crop are usually obtained by means of the acreage utilization and abandonment survey questionnaires. These are usually mailed in August for small grains in central and southern states and in early November for small grains in northern states and for fall-harvested crops. These questionnaires, mailed to individual farmers, ask for information concerning utilization of planted acreages of various crops and the production obtained on the acreage harvested for each specific purpose. A few states use a combined fall acreage survey and fall acreage utilization and abandonment survey to obtain measures of the acreages planted or harvested and of the utilization of such acreages; questionnaires are distributed through a combination of rural-carrier and direct-mail methods.

Vegetables and Potatoes

Estimates for vegetables cover three major groups—fresh market vegetables, vegetables for processing, and potatoes and sweetpotatoes. Included with fresh market vegetables are cantaloupes, watermelons, and strawberries (table 2).

The first government estimate of the potato crop (of production by states) was published in the annual report of the Commissioner of Patents for the year 1841. In 1862, estimates of acreage and yield per acre were published by the Commissioner of Agriculture. The following year, publication of the condition of the crop was inaugurated. Sweetpotato estimates were started in 1868. From 1868 until 1909, potato and sweetpotato estimates included only acreage, yield per acre, production, and prices on December 1.

Estimates of farm disposition and season average prices began in 1909, and monthly forecasts of potato and sweetpotato production began in July 1912. Commercial vegetable estimates for onions and cabbage were started by the department in May 1914. By the close of 1916, releases on vegetables had been expanded to cover acreage, yield, and production of: cabbage, celery,

TABLE 2.—*Statistical Coverage of Vegetable and Related Crops*

Crop	Acreage: Intentions	Acreage: Planted	Acreage: Harvested	Production	Stocks	Disposition	Prices received by farmers [1]	Value of production	Value of sales	Semimonthly progress report
Vegetables for fresh market:[2]										
Artichokes	-----	X	X	X	-----	-----	X	X	-----	-----
Asparagus	X	X	X	X	-----	-----	X	X	-----	-----
Beans, green lima	-----	X	X	X	-----	-----	X	X	-----	-----
Beans, snap	-----	X	X	X	-----	-----	X	X	-----	-----
Beets	-----	X	X	X	-----	-----	X	X	-----	-----
Broccoli	-----	X	X	X	-----	-----	X	X	-----	-----
Brussels sprouts	-----	X	X	X	-----	-----	X	X	-----	-----
Cabbage	X	X	X	X	X	-----	X	X	-----	-----
Cantaloupes	-----	X	X	X	-----	-----	X	X	-----	-----
Carrots	-----	X	X	X	-----	-----	X	X	-----	-----
Cauliflower	-----	X	X	X	-----	-----	X	X	-----	-----
Celery	-----	X	X	X	-----	-----	X	X	-----	-----
Corn, sweet	-----	X	X	X	-----	-----	X	X	-----	-----
Cucumbers	-----	X	X	X	-----	-----	X	X	-----	-----
Eggplant	-----	X	X	X	-----	-----	X	X	-----	-----
Escarole	-----	X	X	X	-----	-----	X	X	-----	-----
Garlic	-----	X	X	X	-----	-----	X	X	-----	-----
Kale	-----	X	X	X	-----	-----	X	X	-----	-----
Lettuce	-----	X	X	X	-----	-----	X	X	-----	-----
Melons, honeydew	-----	X	X	X	-----	-----	X	X	-----	-----
Mint, for oil	-----	X	X	X	-----	-----	X	X	-----	-----
Onions	X	X	X	X	X	-----	X	X	-----	-----
Peas, green	-----	X	X	X	-----	-----	X	X	-----	-----
Peppers, green	-----	X	X	X	-----	-----	X	X	-----	-----
Shallots	-----	X	X	X	-----	-----	X	X	-----	-----
Spinach	-----	X	X	X	-----	-----	X	X	-----	-----
Strawberries	X	X	X	X	-----	-----	X	X	-----	-----
Tomatoes	-----	X	X	X	-----	-----	X	X	-----	-----
Watermelons	X	X	X	X	-----	-----	X	X	-----	-----
Vegetables for commercial processing:										
Asparagus	-----	X	X	X	-----	-----	X	X	-----	-----
Beans, green lima	X	X	X	X	-----	-----	X	X	-----	-----
Beans, snap	X	X	X	X	-----	-----	X	X	-----	X
Beets	X	X	X	X	-----	-----	X	X	-----	-----
Cabbage for sauerkraut	X	X	X	X	-----	-----	X	X	-----	-----
Corn, sweet	X	X	X	X	-----	-----	X	X	-----	X
Cucumbers for pickles	X	X	X	X	X	-----	X	X	-----	-----
Peas, green	X	X	X	X	-----	-----	X	X	-----	X
Spinach	-----	X	X	X	-----	-----	X	X	-----	-----
Tomatoes	X	X	X	X	-----	-----	X	X	-----	-----
Potatoes and sweetpotatoes:										
Potatoes [2]	X	X	X	X	X	X	X	X	X	-----
Sweetpotatoes	X	X	X	X	-----	X	X	X	X	-----

[1] Includes prices by utilization groups.

[2] For each crop, separate estimates are made for winter, spring, summer, and fall seasons, with appropriate subgroupings (early, mid, late) under each season.

onions, cantaloupes, watermelons, and strawberries for fresh market; sweet corn, peas, and tomatoes for processing; and cucumbers for pickles. Potato stocks reports were added in 1924.

In 1963, fresh market vegetables were estimated in all states except Montana, North Dakota, South Dakota, Vermont, and West Virginia. The most recent states added to the program were Alaska and Hawaii. In Hawaii, estimates for six vegetables were made starting with 1954, and four additional ones were estimated starting with 1960. Estimates were begun in 1960 on three vegetables in Alaska.

Estimates are published for twenty-seven fresh market vegetables and melons: artichokes, asparagus, green lima beans, snap beans, beets, broccoli, brussels sprouts, cabbage, carrots, cauliflower, celery, sweet corn, cucumbers, eggplant, escarole, garlic, kale, lettuce, onions, green peas, green peppers, shallots, spinach, tomatoes, cantaloupes, honeydew melons, and watermelons. In recent years, these twenty-seven crops, which are grown commercially in the more important producing states, provide statistics on about 85 percent of the national output of all vegetables and melons grown for fresh market. Once a year, an estimate for total vegetables is prepared and published. This includes an estimate for these twenty-seven crops in states not included in the regular program, as well as an allowance for many miscellaneous vegetables. Regular forecasts are also published on peppermint and spearmint for oil, and strawberries.

Commercial vegetables are harvested somewhere in the United States every month. Except for the cabbage and onions put into storage, fresh vegetables are, for the most part, extremely perishable and must be handled quickly to avoid heavy losses from spoilage. Production prospects can change rapidly during the growing season, as vegetables are generally very sensitive to weather changes. Insects and diseases can be serious problems. Because of the rapid pace of marketing and possibilities of damage to growing crops, timeliness is of utmost importance in publishing vegetable forecasts.

Most of the production of fresh market vegetables is concentrated in areas that are particularly adapted to specific crops. The plantings in these areas are often dominated by distributors or grower-shippers. However, in some areas a crop is grown by many producers, usually on general farms. This is particularly true for such crops as snap beans, cabbage, sweet corn, cucumbers, tomatoes, cantaloupes, watermelons, and strawberries.

In these areas, reports collected by mail regarding plantings on individual farms provide a suitable basis for the estimates. Names of vegetable growers are obtained from rural carrier cards, market managers, county agricultural agents, grower associations, inspection service, dealers, and others. The general methods of collecting information by mailed inquiries and analyzing information on fresh market vegetables are similar to those used with other crops.

Commercial vegetable processing is defined as canning, freezing, pickling, and other processing of vegetables by firms organized to process agricultural products and sell their output for public consumption. Home canning, home freezing, and institutional processing are thus excluded. A comprehensive program of monthly and bimonthly reports is carried on for the ten principal processing vegetable crops. Those included are: asparagus, green lima beans, snap beans, beets for canning, cabbage for kraut, sweet corn, cucumbers for pickles, green peas, spinach, and tomatoes.

While total vegetable production has kept pace with the increasing national population, the relative importance of vegetables produced for processing has increased sharply since World War II. By 1962 well over one-third of all vegetables produced were being used for freezing and canning. Utilization by canners has shown a consistent uptrend since 1945, but development and growth of the frozen food industry is the principal factor in the increasing output of the processing industry.

The program of estimates for processing vegetables covers: (1) intended acreage, (2) acreage planted, (3) in-season forecasts of production, (4) annual summary of acreage planted, acreage harvested, yield per acre, production, season average price to growers, and value, and (5) revisions.

Prospective or intended acreage reports issued before actual planting of each crop reflect early plans of processors for the coming season. These reports serve as a guide to the industry and to growers in adjusting their plans for the coming year.

Immediately after the planting season, an estimate is made of acreage actually planted. This estimate serves as the basis for estimates of acreage for harvest, which are in turn used in conjunction with anticipated yield to arrive at forecasts of production during the growing season. These production forecasts are made at the beginning of each month from June through October for most crops. Forecasts of green pea production are issued in mid-June, July 1, and mid-July. Preliminary production of cucumbers for pickles and October 1 stocks of pickles are reported in November. Acreage, yield, and production estimates for asparagus processed are reported in the annual summary.

The annual summary, published in December, is a comprehensive report covering acreage, yield, production, price, and value for all ten crops included in the processing vegetable program.

The methods used by the Statistical Reporting Service in making estimates of vegetables grown for processing are unlike those used for most other crops. Inasmuch as utilization is controlled completely by the relatively small number of companies engaged in processing vegetables, these business firms become the logical source of primary data rather than the growers. In addition, processors are the best source of basic data for a number of other reasons: (1) They maintain detailed records of quantities of raw products delivered to the plants and prices paid for them; (2) they grow on their own or on leased farms much of the raw product used in their plants; (3) to assure supplies and an orderly flow of raw materials to the plants, most processors enter into some kind of contractual agreement with growers and thus are fully informed on total acreage available to them; (4) field representatives of the processing company are in constant contact with conditions affecting the crop, yield prospects, and so on. It is also more economical to obtain primary data from the vegetable processors than to attempt to effect an equal degree of accuracy in estimates by surveying many more growers.

Fruits, Nuts, Horticultural Specialties, and Hops

The Crop Reporting Board currently estimates production for sixteen noncitrus fruits, six citrus fruits, five tree nuts, and seven bush berries. The estimates for many of the fruit crops are shown separately by important types

TABLE 3.—*Statistical Coverage of Fruit, Nut Crops, Horticultural Specialties, and Hops*

Crop	Acreage			Production	Production, by classes, by kinds	Stocks	Disposition [2]	Prices received by farmers [3]	Value of production	Value of sales
	Intentions	Planted	Harvested [1]							
Hops	-----	-----	X	X	-----	X	X	X	X	X
Horticultural specialties: [4]										
Cut flowers	-----	-----	-----	X	X	-----	-----	-----	-----	X
Nursery products	-----	-----	-----	X	X	-----	-----	-----	-----	X
Noncitrus fruits:										
Apples	-----	-----	-----	[5] X	-----	-----	X	X	X	X
Apricots	-----	-----	-----	X	-----	-----	X	X	X	X
Avocados	-----	-----	-----	X	-----	-----	[6] X	[7] X	X	X
Bush berries [8]	X	-----	X	X	X	-----	X	X	X	-----
Cherries [9]	-----	-----	-----	X	-----	-----	X	X	X	X
Cranberries	-----	-----	X	X	-----	-----	X	X	X	X
Dates	-----	-----	-----	X	-----	-----	[6] X	[7] X	X	X
Figs	-----	-----	-----	X	-----	-----	X	X	X	X
Grapes [10]	-----	-----	-----	X	-----	-----	X	X	X	X
Nectarines	-----	-----	-----	X	-----	-----	X	X	X	X
Olives	-----	-----	-----	X	-----	-----	X	X	X	X
Peaches [10]	-----	-----	-----	X	-----	-----	X	X	X	X
Pears [11]	-----	-----	-----	X	-----	-----	X	X	X	X
Persimmons	-----	-----	-----	X	-----	-----	[6] X	[7] X	X	X
Plums	-----	-----	-----	X	-----	-----	X	X	X	X
Pomegranates	-----	-----	-----	X	-----	-----	[6] X	[7] X	X	X
Prunes	-----	-----	-----	X	-----	-----	X	X	X	X
Citrus fruits:										
Grapefruit [12]	-----	-----	-----	X	-----	-----	X	X	X	X
Lemons	-----	-----	-----	X	-----	-----	X	X	X	X
Limes	-----	-----	-----	X	-----	-----	X	X	X	X
Oranges [9]	-----	-----	-----	X	-----	-----	X	X	X	X
Tangelos	-----	-----	-----	X	-----	-----	X	X	X	X
Tangerines	-----	-----	-----	X	-----	-----	X	X	X	X
Tree nuts:										
Almonds	-----	-----	-----	X	-----	-----	[6] X	[7] X	X	X
Filberts	-----	-----	-----	X	-----	-----	X	[7] X	X	X
Pecans [9]	-----	-----	-----	X	-----	-----	[6] X	[7] X	X	X
Walnuts	-----	-----	-----	X	-----	-----	X	X	X	X
Tung nuts	-----	-----	-----	X	-----	-----	[6] X	[7] X	X	X

1 Acreages for individual fruit crops other than those indicated are not available; a composite is published in the Annual Crop Summary.
2 Includes utilization of sales for fruits and tree nuts.
3 Includes prices by utilization groups.
4 California, Colorado, Florida, Illinois, Iowa, and New York.
5 Includes separate estimates for 18 important varieties.
6 Utilization estimates not available for these items.
7 Prices by utilization groups not available.
8 Washington and Oregon.
9 Includes estimates by varietal groups.
10 Includes estimates by varietal groups in California.
11 Includes estimates by varietal groups for California, Oregon, and Washington.
12 Includes estimates by varietal groups for Florida and by areas for California.

or varieties. In six selected states, annual estimates are made of production, sales, and intentions for four cut flowers and production, sales, and January 1 inventories for eight nursery products. The program also includes acreage, yield, and production estimates for hops and estimates of the stocks of hops on hand as of March 1 and September 1 each year.

In general when fruit and nut crops have reached a stage of development where prospective production can be judged, forecasts of production are started and are published each month until the crop has been harvested. Estimates of production, economic abandonment, season average price, and value are published in December (except for persimmons and pomegranates). At the end of the marketing season, estimates are made of farm disposition, utilization of sales, price, and value for all fruit and nut crops.

These disposition and utilization estimates are published in a series of four bulletins, as follows: (1) Early season noncitrus fruits, "Fruits, Noncitrus—Production, Use, and Value, by States" Part I, in early May; (2) late season noncitrus fruits, "Fruits, Noncitrus—Production, Use, and Value, by States" Part II, early July; (3) "Tree Nuts—Production, Use, and Value, by States," early August; and (4) Citrus Fruits—Production, Use, and Value, by States," early October. Except for a few tree nut crops, for which complete marketing data are not available in time, the disposition and utilization estimates for the preceding year's crop are published before the first forecast for the new crop. (See table 3.)

For all crops except cut flowers and nursery products the estimates for earlier years are reviewed and revised, if necessary, following each quinquennial Census of Agriculture. Annually, when production, farm disposition, and utilization of sales estimates are being prepared, those items for the previous year may be revised if additional check data have become available.

Beginning in 1866 condition reports during the growing season and production reports at the end of harvest, both in terms of percent of a full crop, were obtained from crop reporters for apples, pears, and grapes, but it was not until 1914 that the condition and production percentage reports were interpreted into quantitative production estimates. In 1916 historic data were compiled, and an improved basis for the forecasts was established. In general, estimates have been carried back to 1909, although apples were carried back to 1889 and peaches back to 1899. Estimates and forecasts for other crops have been added as the industry expanded and as demand for such data increased.

The first annual report of utilization estimates for fresh sales and principal processing uses was published in 1944 (for noncitrus fruits), although the data are available for earlier years for various crops. The utilization estimates were undertaken in response to the need by growers, trade organizations, and government agencies for such data, particularly at the beginning of World War II.

Primary data used in preparing estimates and forecasts are collected by state offices primarily from individual farmers (orchardists) and businessmen who cooperate on a voluntary basis. Processors, handlers, and marketing order committeemen are also important sources of information. Primary data are collected by means of mailed questionnaires, enumerative field surveys, objective fruit counts, and general field travel. The two basic sources of data obtained by mail are the monthly Farm Report questionnaire and special fruit inquiries.

APPENDIX G.

Land Use Statistical Work of the Bureau of the Census[1]

The Bureau of the Census relates every figure it publishes to some land area. This area is often the entire United States, but it may be a state, a county, or a smaller area. Within the prescribed area, the Bureau enumerates and itemizes various kinds of entities and activities. It goes even further in the agriculture statistics and shows specifically how many acres of land were used for each agricultural purpose.

For example, the Bureau has reported that Prince George's County, Maryland, covers 485 square miles, had 357,000 people, 100,000 housing units, 1,250 farms, 164 manufacturing plants, 11 mining establishments, 1,500 retail stores, 142 wholesale establishments, 900 establishments for selected services, 30 local governments, and $189.5 million in annual building construction. Of the total 310,400 acres, 124,300 were in farms: 31,600 acres were in cropland harvested, 13,100 in cropland used only for pasture, 17,900 in cropland not harvested and not pastured, 5,200 in woodland pastured, 40,500 in woodland not pastured, 3,700 in other pasture, and 12,400 in other farm land.

These are only summary figures. They are augmented by many details—in some cases multitudinous details. Moreover, the Bureau has filed the tapes and cards containing the original data and stands ready to retabulate them to fit special needs. Some of these files are available for purchase and further use on buyers' automatic data processing equipment. An inventory of machine-readable data, including specifications of content of the files and type of equipment with which compatible for use, is available on request from the Director, Bureau of the Census, Washington, D.C. 20233.

Some of the land areas are small. At the county level or below, the Bureau tabulates statistics for the following areas:

- Counties (or equivalents)
- Urban
  - Urbanized area
    - Central cities
    - Urban fringe
  - Other urban
- Rural
  - Places of 1,000 or 2,500
  - Other rural

[1] A statement prepared by the Bureau of the Census for this report.

Minor civil divisions and census county divisions
Incorporated places
Unincorporated places
Urban towns and townships
Areas annexed to urban places
Wards (or equivalents)
Census tracts
Central business districts
Major retail centers
Statistical areas in large cities (e.g., community and health areas, groups of census tracts)
Enumeration districts
City blocks

The Geography Division of the Bureau does the basic work in determining land areas. It obtains from cities, counties, and other political units their established political boundaries, and it sets up boundaries of administrative and statistical areas, such as enumeration districts and urbanized areas. It collects maps and prepares the detailed mapping materials needed to collect the data. In these activities, it is confronted by the use of the land, and it has described below its resources for making new studies of land use.

Some of the other divisions of the Bureau—Agriculture, Business, Construction, Governments, Housing, Industry, Population, Statistical Reports, and Transportation—provide statistics at the county level or below, or they have particular capacity and resources that could be called upon for new studies of land use, or they would find land use statistics useful.

A detailed listing of most of the data published by the Census Bureau for small areas is included in the *Directory of Federal Statistics for Metropolitan Areas,* recently issued by the Advisory Commission for Governmental Relations. A booklet, *Guide to Census Statistics—Subjects and Areas,* is available on request from the Director, Bureau of the Census.

Land Use and Geography Division

The principal direct sources of information on land use in the Geography Division are reference materials such as the Sanborn maps, city directories, and telephone directories arranged in address sequence. These sources indicate the types of economic activity being carried on in specified locations.

An important contribution to land use data, in fact to any area-oriented statistics, is the geographic framework, developed by the Geography Division for Bureau use, which permits the assignment of any occurrence to a unit area and the subsequent combination of unit areas to successively larger areas.

A third potential adjunct to land use studies is the area measurement abilities of the Division, especially the "map area computer" which has recently been developed and put into operation.

Reference Materials

The Sanborn maps, publications of the Sanborn Map Company of Pelham, New York, are highly detailed presentations of map information for urban areas. These maps depict each building, type of construction, story height, and lot lines. The maps identify the use to which most buildings are put, except that only the first or street floor occupancy is shown for multi-story, multi-use commercial buildings. These maps, without supplementary information, permit the ready determination of broad classification of existing land use patterns in urban areas, save for the lack of detail for the multi-story structures noted above. The Sanborn Map Company updates its maps periodically but this correction service has not been purchased by the Bureau since 1950 for the major share of this map set.

The use of directories, especially telephone directories arranged in street address sequence, permits the extension of the information on the Sanborn maps in that the names of the telephone customers in the multi-use buildings can be readily located and much information on within-structure occupancy can be compiled from the listings.

Geographic Framework

For census purposes the United States has been divided into approximately 900,000 areas in such fashion that small units can be combined in successively larger areas. By far the most numerous of the areas are the 750,000 city blocks for which population totals and housing unit characteristics were published in the 1960 census reports. With minor exceptions, individual blocks were defined and data published for all cities with 50,000 or more inhabitants and for smaller cities that contracted with the Bureau for this service.

The next larger area in the 1960 census area hierarchy is the enumeration district or ED. In areas where blocks were designated, each ED consists of a group of blocks, while beyond these "block areas" the ED is the smallest area for which separate statistics have been compiled. All larger areas for which 1960 census data have been compiled consist of groupings of complete enumeration districts.

In general terms, the next larger areas above the ED are census tracts and city wards, areas which are usually unrelated and overlapping in a random fashion. Nonetheless, ED's can be combined in one fashion to yield tract data and in another to secure ward totals.

It should be noted that not all cities are divided into wards and that no effort was made to get tabulations of ward data for small cities, generally those with fewer than 5,000 inhabitants. Similarly, the system of census tracts does not embrace all of the United States but does include more than 90 percent of the population of Standard Metropolitan Statistical Areas as well as minor areas outside SMSA's.

Further combinations of ED's (or tracts or wards) yield city, township (or equivalent area), county, congressional district, state, and U.S. totals as well as totals for such statistical areas as urbanized areas, unincorporated places, and census county divisions.

For the economic census (business, manufactures, and mineral industries) the areas mentioned above are somewhat abridged in order to minimize processing difficulties and conflicts with "disclosure" rules, i.e., rules to avoid the release of information that will permit the identification of data for individual establishments.

For agriculture census purposes, ED's are designed to permit ready tabulation of information at the county level although the schedules are so marked that information for townships or their equivalents (our general terms are minor civil division or "MCD" and census county division or "CCD") can be tabulated by a more time-consuming process for those who are willing to pay the costs.

In the economic censuses separate data can be tabulated for cities with 2,500 or more inhabitants, selected MCD's, and counties, although some information is published for only the larger areas, e.g., cities with 10,000 or more inhabitants. In addition, business data are compiled and published for central business districts (CBD's) in most cities with 100,000 or more inhabitants and for major retail centers (MRC's), i.e., shopping centers in or near these cities. CBD's are individual census tracts or combinations of census tracts; MRC's are not.

The economic censuses are not conducted by direct enumeration, as are the population, housing, and agriculture censuses, but by mail. Accordingly, specialized procedures were and are being developed to permit the assignment of a report form to the appropriate area on the basis of establishment address. Recent developments include the creation of computer tapes that can be matched to respondent-reported address information to permit allocation to area. While the geographic framework for this allocation process does not greatly exceed the needs of the economic censuses, the frame can be extended to embrace additional area detail. Further, the work now being performed in testing future census procedures may lead to the development of "address registers" for urban areas by means of which any residential address can be assigned to the smallest unit of area required for decennial census processing.

While the above comments relate to the assignment of information to small areas, the developments relate only to the ease of the performance, not to our abilities to accomplish such work. The boundary data, reference materials, and human resources of the Geography Division can be used to accomplish the assignment of the vast majority of unit census records to the block level, and, frequently, to subdivisions of blocks.

Area Measurement

The Bureau of the Census has long been recognized as the prime source of area measurements for the United States and its components. Capabilities in this field have recently been widely extended through the completion of a new "map area computer." This electronic device will record the area in square inches of a section cut from a map within a fraction of 1 percent of precision. The output can be automatically punched into cards for subsequent accounting machine or computer accomplishment of the arithmetic required for scale conversion. The device uses what is essentially a sampling method with search or test points so spaced that each observation represents 1/1000 of a square inch.

This machine is being used in the determination of the 1960 land and water areas of MCD's, CCD's and of places with 1,000 or more inhabitants. Twelve state reports presenting these data together with population totals and population densities have been published and additional reports will be issued during 1965.

Agriculture Division

About 64 percent of the total land area of the 50 states is used for agriculture, and 83 percent is used for agriculture and forestry.

For the typical county of the United States, the Census of Agriculture provides data on land in farms, classified according to use in the preceding year. Except for 200 or so metropolitan counties, and for Alaska, the Census of Agriculture provides data on the use of a large part of the land in the United States. The land use categories for which data are provided include four uses of cropland, two uses of woodland, and two uses of land other than cropland and woodland. Data on land in farms according to use are published for each county. Unpublished data, comparable to those for counties, are available in unpublished form for minor civil divisions or combinations of adjacent minor civil divisions.

To provide checking of coverage of the Census of Agriculture, it would be useful to have data for each county on:

1. Areas used for cities, towns, and suburban housing developments.
2. Areas owned by government.
3. Areas occupied by commercial forests.

Business Division

For each county and each incorporated city of 2,500 or more inhabitants information is published for retail trade and selected services on number of establishments, sales, employment, payroll, and number of proprietors. Detail by kind of business varies, depending on the number of establishments in the area. Similar information is available for wholesale trade except that data are not published for cities with fewer than 5,000 inhabitants. In New England, New Jersey, and Pennsylvania, statistics are also published for selected towns and townships.

Statistics on retail stores, hotels, and motion picture theaters are published for central business districts (defined in terms of census tracts) of 97 SMSA's (1958 census). Major retail centers located outside of central business districts in these SMSA's have also been defined and statistics are available on retail stores in about 450 such centers.

Special censuses of business tabulations relating to land use have been made on a reimbursable basis, for a number of organizations. These areas consist frequently of subdivisions of urban or urban fringe areas, often in terms of census tracts. For 1958 and prior censuses, such work consisted primarily of hand sorting of individual reports through the use of street directories supplied by the requesting organization. Other special tabulations have been made for cities or towns not included as part of the original publication program. It has even been possible to prepare a special tabulation of establishments located on a specific street within a city.

For the 1963 census some work has been undertaken on tract coding of establishment records by computer. There are, however, some inadequacies in the source material presently available for this purpose. The Bureau cannot make computer tabulations of business statistics, by tract, at a reasonable cost, unless it obtains more accurate information than is now available to assign tract codes to individual establishments.

The availability on computer tape of a reference location directory for all large and many small cities adds a great deal of flexibility to tabulation potentialities of business census records. There were some limitations; however, work now in the development phase offers bright prospects of a substantial decrease in these limitations.

One factor which should be kept in mind in planning a business land use statistics program is the effect of the Census Bureau disclosure rules. Normally, the smaller the area, the smaller the number of establishments there are in the area; and this leads to potential disclosure of operations of an individual company, resulting in suppression of data for that area.

A possible extension of land use statistics is to tabulate data for the smaller retail trade centers. This would be an expansion of the existing program for major retail centers. Another possibility is to relate population concentrations to trade centers in terms of distance, sales volume, and income grouping. This could also be related to taxing jurisdiction to see if any pattern is discernible.

Construction Statistics Division

For a representative county it is now possible to provide the following information about building permit-issuing places within that county:

1. The numbers and valuation of privately owned housing units and residential buildings authorized by building permits.
2. The information of "1," above, separately for one-family, two-family, three-and-four-family, and five-or-more-family buildings.
3. The number and valuation of publicly owned housing units authorized by contract awards.
4. The number and valuation of privately owned buildings authorized by building permits for the following categories:
   (a) Non-housekeeping residential buildings (hotels, motels, etc.).
   (b) Nonresidential buildings and structures.
      1. Amusement and recreational buildings.
      2. Churches and other religious buildings.
      3. Industrial buildings.
      4. Parking garages.
      5. Residential garages and carports.
      6. Service stations and repair garages.
      7. Hospitals and other institutional buildings.
      8. Office, bank, and professional buildings.
      9. Public works and utilities buildings.
      10. Schools and other educational buildings.
      11. Stores and other mercantile buildings.
      12. Other non-residential buildings.
      13. Structures other than buildings.
5. The number of permits and valuation of work authorized for additions and alterations to privately owned houses and apartments and to other privately owned buildings.

These data are available for each permit-issuing jurisdiction, which may be a county, city, township, village, or other type of local jurisdiction. At present, these data are collected monthly from each of about 3,000 of the more active permit-issuing places, accounting for about 88 percent of the housing units authorized by permits throughout the United States in 1963. The total number of units authorized by permits accounts for about 85 percent of all housing units built in the United States. These percentages vary considerably by geographic regions.

The valuations provided by building permits almost always understate actual construction costs by an unknown but considerable margin. In the case of public housing contract awards, the valuations are the contract values, a more reasonable measure of actual value.

Governments Division

Information Available for All County Areas

In the census of governments, which is taken for each year ending in "2" and "7," the Governments Division identifies and gathers data on the employment and finances of substantially all local governments in every county. Each unit is coded geographically in terms of its county location (or of its primary or headquarters county). Multiple-county units—a rather limited group—are specifically identified, and the names of the counties in which they operate are recorded. Except for a very limited number of special districts (such as "bridge authorities"), each local government can potentially be associated with a specifically defined territory, but the census of governments has not involved any delineation or measurement of local government areas as such. However, school districts are classified "by type of area served," and those which are coterminous with any county, township, or incorporated place are so identified.

In the census of governments also, summary figures are gathered for every county area as to assessed values of property for local general property taxation, in terms of aggregates for state-assessed property, locally assessed realty, and locally assessed personality.

Information Available for Selected Areas Only

In the quinquennial census of governments, additional information relating to taxable property values is gathered for a large sample of county areas (more than one-third of the total number, and including all of the most populous counties). This additional information includes sample-based estimates of the number and assessed value of locally assessed real property by assessed-value size and by use class (non-farm single-family houses, multi-family residential property, acreage and farms, commercial, industrial, and vacant lots); and data on the assessed value and sales price of real properties sold during a six-month period, similarly classified by size and use-class.

In regular annual surveys covering an extensive state-by-state sample, the Governments Division gathers data on the employment and finances of several thousand individual local governments.

Resources for New Studies Relating to Land Use

The sampling of taxable real properties, which is done in numerous counties for the periodic census of governments, involves reference use of local assessment records. In many instances (though not all) these record sources show more detail about the characteristics of particular properties (such as their area, kind of improvement, or particular use) than are transcribed for the census of governments. It would appear feasible for numerous areas, therefore, to develop additional land use information as an adjunct to the assessed value survey of the census.

As has been mentioned, the identification of individual governmental units in the census of governments does not include specific delineation of their boundaries or areas. If this were done, it would be possible to associate particular land areas or locations with various governments and their respective taxing, debt incurring, and service characteristics. (For counties, townships and municipalities, such boundary delineation is carried out by the Census Bureau in connection with the periodic census of population, but at a time which differs from that of the census of governments. The Census Bureau has not carried out mapping work for school districts or local special district governments.)

The comprehensive list of local governments which is maintained by the Governments Division provides a means for mail collection of land use information that may be available from local governments or officials, and has been so utilized in the past. For example, mail canvasses have been conducted to identify local governments that have building-permit systems. Similarly, the Division's research files lend themselves to the determination of the nature of local real estate assessment records, especially in states where minimum or uniform requirements apply to such records.

Desirable Program Extensions Relating to Land Use

It would be possible in the census of governments to develop considerably more detailed type-of-property information on locally assessed taxable real estate. This would require more intensive and costly enumeration work than has previously been done. However, if attention were focused mainly upon commercial, industrial, and multiple-family residential property, and especially if sample-based findings would serve the intended purposes, the additional effort would be limited by the fact that sizable properties of these kinds make up only a small fraction of the total number of taxable properties. The feasibility and possible cost of developing such more detailed information should be explored.

We believe there might also be public interest in developing another kind of geographical data as part of the census of governments, at least for major metropolitan counties. This would involve an effort to ascertain and delineate the various "total tax rate areas" that result in such counties from the diverse combinations of particular types and layers of property-taxing local governments. Potential interest in this matter arises from the possible relationship between diversity of tax burdens and trends in urban development, with particular reference to industrial and commercial concentrations. There has thus far been too little study of such an undertaking to offer any firm conclusion as to its feasibility or potential value.

APPENDIX G

Housing Division

Data Available

For counties, the Bureau published statistics from the census of housing on air conditioning, electrical appliances, automobiles, bathing facilities, condition and plumbing facilities, fuels, heating equipment, occupancy, persons in household, persons per room, rent (contract and gross), rooms, tenure, toilet, trailers, units in structure, vacant units, value, water supply, year moved into unit, and year structure was built. Statistics on sewage disposal and source of water were also provided for counties not in standard metropolitan statistical areas.

Most of these statistics were also published for urban and rural places with populations of 2,500 or more. For census tracts, more limited information was published, and for city blocks and places of 1,000 to 2,500 population, the list was still shorter. For all these types of area, however, statistics were published for condition and plumbing facilities, occupancy, persons per room, rooms, tenure, and value. Unpublished statistics are also available from the census of housing for small areas.

Resources for Studies of Land Use

The resources of the Housing Division in regard to land use studies consist of a staff of approximately ten professional survey statisticians and economists who have had experience in dealing with the collection of information and the classification of structures. The Division has conducted surveys of components of change to measure the change in usage of properties over time and has made studies of residential finance in which the concept of "properties" as well as housing units has been dealt with.

Need for Land Use Statistics

The use Housing Division could make of land use statistics would depend on the nature of the statistics themselves, i.e., the detail in which the land uses were classified, the frequency of the surveys, and the geographic coverage. Most land use surveys have been made on a 100-percent coverage basis at infrequent intervals. An example of the data provided by these surveys would be as follows: Tract 421 consists of 121.1 acres of which 62.9 are in residential use, 24.2 are in public use, 10.5 are in commercial use, 19.5 are in industrial use, and 4.0 are vacant. Data of a similar nature could be provided by blocks, by wards, by any other geographic subdivision, or for the city or SMSA as a whole. Much greater detail can also be provided for each of these broad characteristics; for instance, some cities have ten or more different zoning classifications for residential land alone. If data of this type were available, they could be used in further analysis of many types of housing data.

In the area of financial characteristics, land use information would provide the basis for more thorough analysis of housing in small areas (blocks, neighborhoods, etc.). Knowledge of land uses would (1) make for more effective determination of the reasonableness of the financial characteristics data in a particular area at a particular time; (2) facilitate analytical comparisons of the data in different areas; and (3) permit the analysis of periodic changes in the financial characteristics data of a particular area.

In dealing with vacancies it would be important to relate both the frequency and characteristics of vacant units to the land use of the neighborhood in which they occur. That is, are vacancies occurring in tracts with mixed land usage or are they only in residential areas? If vacancy rates are high, is there a different distribution of these vacants throughout tracts than if the vacancy rates are low?

An additional area of housing data with which the Division is struggling is the concept of "neighborhood quality." Obviously, land use data when related to other housing characteristics would provide many guidelines to the establishment of objective criteria for the measurement of neighborhood quality.

Land use data are currently being used by the Tri-State Transportation Committee to prepare estimates of future travel patterns within a metropolitan area. Similarly, the Bureau could relate land use information to its journey-to-work data to determine if there are geographic differences in the patterns of intra-urban travel.

Information on land use would also be a valuable adjunct to a components-of-inventory-change program. Land use data would supplement the data describing changes in the housing inventory by identifying the areas in terms of current uses of land and subsequent changes in use. Current uses would identify, for example, areas of potential development or growth based on the availability, location, and type of vacant land, and those areas which may be designated for redevelopment. Changes in land use classification would provide a basis for identifying the areas where changes in the housing inventory had occurred, that is, areas of new construction and demolition, areas undergoing changes in residential use such as from single-family to multi-family use, and areas changing from residential to nonresidential use. Location of these areas and other land use data would provide additional characteristics of the types of changes occurring in the residential inventory. Information on land use would supplement the components-of-change-statistics in conjunction with other housing data in providing an additional basis for estimating residential needs for replacement of existing housing and for additional housing.

Besides the above specific uses, land use data might be of real help in providing better stratification of housing units in sample surveys. It should also be pointed out that if a complete land use survey were made in a given SMSA, this is only a short step removed from a complete real property inventory, and a real property inventory is one of the major components in the proposed survey of wealth.

Industry Division

Data Available

Manufactures. For each city of 10,000 or more population and for each county, the Bureau publishes statistics from the quinquennial census of manufactures on number of establishments, employment, payroll, value added by manufacture, capital expenditures, etc. For incorporated places of 2,500 to 10,000, the Bureau has unpublished statistics on these subjects. In the 1963 census, these statistics can be provided for census tracts on a reimbursable basis.

In addition, the Bureau publishes industry statistics for each county in which the industry group is important. Industry statistics can also be tabulated for cities of 2,500 population or more.

For the large industrial counties of the country, the Bureau publishes statistics from the annual survey of manufacturers on employment, payrolls, value added by manufacture, and capital expenditures, by industry group.

Mineral Industries. For each county in which the mineral industry was important, the Bureau publishes information from the quinquennial census of mineral industries on number of establishments in the industry, value added in mining, employment, payroll, cost of supplies, etc., value of shipments and receipts, and capital expenditures. Information is also provided on the size of the establishments as measured by their employment.

The 1964 edition of *Guide to Industrial Statistics* was recently published. This guide contains a locator for the sources of manufacturing and mining statistics published by the Bureau of the Census and other government agencies.

Resources for Studies of Land Use

Information can be collected from manufacturing plants in the United States for other items, such as areas occupied by manufacturing establishments and the amount devoted to plant, roadways, landscaping, etc.

Population Division

The Bureau published the number of inhabitants, according to the 1960 Census of Population, for virtually all political areas, including townships. When it came to providing statistics on the characterisiics of these inhabitants, the Bureau was somewhat more selective. Even so, it published (or made available in unpublished form) the following detailed statistics for census tracts and minor civil divisions: age by sex, color or race, nativity and parentage, country of origin, residence in 1955, school enrollment by level and type of school, years of school completed, marital status by sex, household relationship, married couples, employment status by sex, class of worker of employed, occupation of employed by sex, industry of employed, place of work, means of transportation to work, and income in 1959 of families and unrelated individuals.

For counties, urbanized areas, and urban places of 10,000 or more inhabitants, the Bureau published all the above statistics plus the following: color or race by sex, nativity and parentage by color, state of birth, mother tongue, year moved into present unit, school enrollment by age, years of school completed by sex, veteran status of civilian males, families and unrelated individuals, children born by age of woman, labor force status by age and sex, weeks worked in 1959, class of worker of employed by sex, occupation of unemployed by sex, industry of employed females, income in 1959 of persons by sex, income in 1959 of persons by type, and earnings by group.

For urban places of 1,000 to 2,500, statistics were published on age by sex, color or race by sex, marital status by sex, and household relationship; for urban places of 2,500 to 10,000, somewhat more information was published.

Of course, there is a substantial amount of additional data that could be tabulated from the 1960 census for these areas. Furthermore, the Bureau of the Census is able to conduct surveys to obtain further population and household data relating to land use. For example, information on the number and characteristics of the daytime population of various areas could be obtained.

Statistical Reports Division

Two publications of the Statistical Reports Division present data for territorial units at the level of county or below, namely, the *County and City Data Book* and the *Congressional District Data Book*. Both of these books contain summary data obtained for the most part from the various censuses conducted by the Bureau, but they also include information drawn from other governmental and from private sources. Additional details about each book follow:

County and City Data Book

The 1962 edition, the sixth in the *County and City Data Book* series, presents 161 items of information for each county or county equivalent, 128 items for each SMSA, 163 items for each incorporated city of 25,000 inhabitants or more in 1960, and 67 items for each urbanized area and unincorporated urban place of 25,000 or more. All information at the level of county and below is available for sale on both standard IBM 80-column punchcards and on either IBM or Univac tape on a cost-of-reproduction basis.

Earlier editions in this series contain similar data but on a less comprehensive scale. They include the *Cities Supplement*, issued in 1944; the *County Data Book*, issued in 1947; and the *County and City Data Book*, issued in 1949, 1952, and 1956.

Congressional District Data Book

The first full-scale edition of the book, issued in 1961, contains summary statistics for districts of the 87th Congress. Data on vote cast for President and for Representatives, obtained from non-census sources, and on selected items from the 1960 Population and Housing Censuses, are presented for all congressional districts. These latter data (except for figures on total population in 1950 and 1960) are not presented on a congressional district basis in any other Census Bureau publication. In addition, some population and housing statistics relating only to the nonwhite population are presented for all districts in the Southern states and for districts in other states in which the nonwhite population represented ten percent or more of the total population in the district. Data on births, deaths, marriages, bank deposits, and selected items from agriculture, economic and governments censuses are presented for whole-county congressional districts only.

A second edition of the *Congressional District Data Book*, covering districts of the 88th Congress was published in February 1964. This edition presents 511 items of information compared with 472 items in the first edition. The data were compiled from both published and unpublished sources. The Statistical Reports Division has also published the *Procedural Report of the 1960 Censuses of Population and Housing* describing the methodology of compiling the census data. This report discusses the small areas for which data were compiled and published—the reasons for choosing these types of areas, the problems and methods of delimiting them, the particular subjects which are shown for small areas, etc. A more comprehensive procedural history of the Eighteenth Decennial Census is in preparation.

Transportation Division

The Transportation Division does not plan to collect any information of the type that is normally defined as "land use." However, both local and inter-city transportation requirements are clearly a function of land use. Transportation planners have developed elaborate analytical methods for utilizing land use data. The Division's prime interest will be as consumers rather than producers of the data.

If land use data were to be defined in an extremely broad fashion, the "traffic flow" data might be a candidate. The figures measure the service that is generated by selected types of activities in various areas and could be given locational identification. However, since the current transportation surveys are normally conducted on a relatively small sample basis, the data would be useful mostly to construct patterns for use in analytical models, rather than actual data related to specified small geographic areas.

The 1963 Census of Transportation, the first of its kind, embodies four major parts: (1) National Travel Survey, (2) Commodity Transportation Survey, (3) Truck Inventory and Use Survey, and (4) Bus and Truck Carrier Survey.

APPENDIX H.

The Housing and Home Finance Agency Interest in Land Use Statistics[1]

There are many agencies which do not have a direct role in the production of land use data but who make important use of the data originated by others. The Housing and Home Finance Agency does not *directly* "produce" comprehensive land use information but rather it "consumes" land use data. However, HHFA programs indirectly generate the production of land use data by other public agencies. For the most part, the collection of data by the housing agency is limited to statistics without reference to the consumption of land or to the other uses of land which are usually associated with housing.

In general, the interest of HHFA in land use statistics is immediate and long-term, urban-oriented, and is concerned with the total environment and not just its functional components. For utility to this agency, land use statistics, as such, must be sufficiently broad to cover these comprehensive interests.

An Urban-oriented Agency

The responsibilities of the HHFA focus upon the general area of housing and community development from a variety of perspectives. As noted earlier, the general field of housing and community development may be seen from the point of view of a single locality, a metropolitan area, a state, or an entire region. In the instance of the HHFA, the prime concern is with urban areas, the locus of national development these past fifty years.

The agency deals not only with public agencies but also with private groups and individuals. Its programs cover a variety of interrelated activities, all concerning housing in some way. "Housing" has broadened to serve varied and new and special requirements, and has become intermeshed with problems of planning, renewal, land uses, community facilities, and mass transportation which affect the fabric of our going communities, large and small. Moreover, the major programs of this agency have become rooted in our national economy and have grown into a pattern of federal assistance to states, localities and the private housing industry. Additionally, it should be noted that the HHFA relies upon local initiation—essentially, the agency provides a variety of programs which others utilize as action projects.

[1] A statement prepared by the Housing and Home Finance Agency for this report.

APPENDIX H

The Importance of Land Use Statistics

The HHFA is concerned with land problems and policies. Land use information provides the descriptive and analytic data needed to comprehend land problems and to formulate accommodating policies. In the agency programs, systematic data gathering is considered a *sine qua non;* this applies especially to localities undertaking community improvement projects.

While the main body of this book amply covers the basis for a land use inventory system it might be worthwhile for emphasis to state a few general criteria. The foremost criterion of land use inventory system should be its *utility*—a system without users is but an exercise in futility. Since the subject matter is land, another criterion would be the need to develop a simple method of *locating land* by jurisdiction as well as by geography. A third criterion would be the determination of *relevant characteristics* to be described and measured.

Another criterion, common to all information systems, is the need for *accuracy.* Accuracy would also include frequency of up-dating both in terms of comprehensive and incremental changes. A fifth criterion considers the *relationship* of the inventory system with other data.

These criteria are not exhaustive but serve to indicate, for the discussion to follow, the importance of land use statistics.

Aside from the variety of land use statistics, there are two technical considerations which are associated with the use of these data. Land use statistics may be represented *graphically* in the form of maps, charts and tables. Maps are used to illustrate the pattern, distribution, extent and structure of land uses by a variety of functional groupings of land use statistics. The *analysis* of land use statistics may take many differing forms, contingent for the most part upon the objective. Analysis may take the form of per capita utilization of certain functional categories (e.g., per capita utilization of commercial office space has been used as an index for evaluating the real estate markets), or the interrelationship of social, economic, and fiscal data with land use.

Within these two areas of application, the principal objective of compiling and analyzing land use statistics is to arrive at some decision, be it to secure a better utilization of land within a given area or to secure an equitable distribution of public services. Accurate and up-to-date land use statistics provide the basis for better decision making at various levels of government and private enterprise as well.

To illustrate the importance of land use statistics, we might take a typical development program for a community and follow its decision-making sequence.

Initially, a planning agency surveys and studies the existing physical environment to determine its condition and to arrive at some judgments as to its quality and direction of change. Land use statistics may reveal the quality, quantity, location, and identification of activities within a given area. Given certain community objectives, planning and service standards, and general development principles, the community as a whole can be evaluated and decisions reached regarding future courses of action for community improvement.

Studies in which land use statistics play an important role lead to decisions allocating land for differing uses—they provide a basis for projecting future needs. Comparative analyses with different sets of land use alternatives may be studied to evaluate public costs and contingent fiscal policies. Locational studies for public improvements and services utilize land use statistics. Through neighborhood analyses, the process of urban renewal finds practical and immediate use of land use data. In the highly technical field of market analysis, land use statistics are proving to be invaluable.

Many functional planning activities utilize land use data—for example, sewer and water system planning require the use of population equivalents, often derived from existing land use information. Another area, covered in detail within another section, is transportation planning.

Within the general area of day-to-day operations of a community, land use information is ever present in the evaluation of zoning and subdivision decisions.

At other levels of comprehensive planning—county, metropolitan and regional—land use information serves comparable functions. Land use statistics, in brief, are utilized within all levels of local development planning.

Within the field of state activities, statistics relating to the use of land are important tools in planning and general governmental operations. Land use statistics may offer the basis for population estimates for tax sharing programs (e.g., gas taxes shared state/local for streets and highways). In addition, information about the land is useful in resources development policies, park planning and development, air and water pollution policies, and the like. In each instance, land use data serve as a basic tool in the process of reaching decisions resolving physical and economic problems.

Land Use Information and HHFA Programs

When the Housing and Home Finance Agency was established in 1947, only two of the major programs it now administers were included in the scope of its operation. These were (1) the basic Federal Housing Administration mortgage insurance programs for home purchase and rental projects, and for repairs and minor improvements to existing homes; and (2) the Public Housing Administration program of federal aid to local public agencies to provide housing for low-income families.

Today these original programs have been continued in the HHFA and a number of other programs of broad scope have been established. The whole range of HHFA programs for urban renewal and redevelopment, urban and metropolitan planning, open space land, mass transportation, and community facilities have been added to HHFA's responsibilities.

In the housing field, programs have been added to support an adequate flow of mortgage financing for FHA and for Veterans Administration housing loans; to deal with the growing problem of housing for the elderly both through private and public financing; to meet many types of special housing needs, including the rehabilitation and redevelopment of blighted urban areas, the needs of moderate as well as lower income families, the support of cooperative housing, of housing and related needs in our colleges and universities, of nursing homes, of disaster housing needs, of private housing needs of military personnel; and to make financing available for major improvements and rehabilitation of existing homes.

Today the HHFA programs are carried out through five operating constituent agencies, most of them with multiple responsibilities. These are:

Federal Housing Administration
Public Housing Administration
Urban Renewal Administration
Federal National Mortgage Association
Community Facilities Administration

The HHFA responsibilities have also become more complex and far-reaching. They involve program coordination in such fields as urban renewal, housing for the elderly, and low and moderate income housing in which three or more constituent agencies are operating; coordination of planning and urban programs with those of other departments and agencies in the federal government; and development and administration of new or special programs such as the new program of loans and demonstration grants for urban mass transportation.

By and large, the HHFA program most closely associated with land use statistics is the URA Urban Planning Assistance (701) Program. The planning assistance program encourages and assists orderly development of urban areas by providing planning grants-in-aid to help solve problems of change and growth. Assistance is given to small communities, metropolitan areas and states for comprehensive planning encompassing the "preparation, as a guide for long-range development, of general physical plans with respect to the pattern and intensity of land use and the provision of public facilities, including transportation facilities, together with long-range fiscal plans for such development . . ."

Accordingly, the Urban Planning Assistance Program contributes directly to programs involving the development of land use classification and inventory systems together with the collection and analysis of primary land use statistics. In the past, the many agencies involved in the development and undertaking of land use classification systems and surveys have not related their systems to one another. The promotion and development of uniform systems of land use description have been expressed elsewhere. To reiterate, there is a need for a common language to communicate and compare land use information. No longer are we satisfied with the broad classification of land uses such as residential, commercial-industrial, public, agricultural and the like.

Recognition of this lack of comparability and uniformity is certainly not recent. Activities of the now defunct National Resources Planning Board brought out the need in 1941. The federal government, in general, is concerned with the need for promoting uniform statistical programs of national importance. A joint program to develop such a uniform classification system brought together HHFA and the Department of Commerce.

The Urban Renewal Administration and the Bureau of Public Roads joined forces to develop a standard system for identifying land use information. The collaboration of such efforts has led to the publication of the *Standard Land Use Coding Manual,* published by the U.S. Government Printing Office. Some of the broader implications of a uniform system are discussed elsewhere.

Another area within the HHFA programs which involves the use of land use data are the various urban renewal activities. In a general sequence of programming, land use information plays an important part in the Community Renewal Program, General Neighborhood Renewal Planning and the planning of specific projects.

The Community Renewal Program enables localities to receive federal assistance for attacking the problem of urban blight on a comprehensive city-wide basis, identifying and classifying the relative urgency for renewal action throughout the city.

General Neighborhood Renewal Planning permits communities to delineate a program of renewal actions covering several projects which may be extended over a period of ten years.

Specific project planning is concerned with the preparation of a detailed action plan encompassing project eligibility and feasibility, boundaries, land uses, relocation plans, land acquisition and disposition, site clearance and improvements, rehabilitation.

Other HHFA programs utilize land use information directly or indirectly. The Open Space Land Program assists localities in the acquisition of land for the purposes of providing permanent open space. The agency's community facilities programs enable local public bodies to take measures to assure minimal levels of public service. Programs cover such facilities as public housing, housing for senior citizens, college housing, a variety of public facilities, and urban mass transportation. Many of these programs have low interest loans with long repayment periods; others have grants-in-aid. These programs deal principally with the location and construction of public facilities. They involve areawide analysis including environmental studies of sites encompassing future city plans, land use policies, public transportation, public utilities, demographic characteristics, and general neighborhood land use characteristics. In most of these programs, secondary land use information provides the principal source of evaluative data.

Within the general area of housing, the HHFA has an especial interest in residential development as well as individual housing units. This interest is clearly demonstrated in the operations of the Federal Housing Administration.

The FHA provides a variety of private financing aids for new construction, home improvements and general housing rehabilitation. The financing aids come in the form of mortgage insurances and secondary mortgage operations of the Federal National Mortgage Association.

The FNMA operations channel private capital into the secondary mortgage market for homes by its purchases of or loans secured by FHA-insured and VA-guaranteed home loans. Currently the activities of FNMA extend to other areas dealing with rehabilitation or redevelopment housing, rental housing for the elderly, rental housing for moderate income families, cooperative housing, low-cost housing for families displaced by governmental actions, and other special categories of housing.

The value of land use statistics in the general field of housing has been indicated above. Current market analysis, mortgage underwriting, and subdivision analysis by the FHA operations are assisted by information revealing land use changes, direction of growth, and recent residential construction activities within the various sectors of a community. Accessibility to information describing the rate of current additions to the housing supply by geographic location aids in studies of market demand within various localities, especially when these data are presented in graphic form.

The prospects of having detailed information about housing and land development made available on a parcel-by-parcel basis opens up many avenues of utility, particularly those processes that lend themselves to computer analysis. Any of the number of ways that these processes will aid rational decision-making regarding housing and community development justifies the establishment of land use informational systems which have flexibility for diverse use and comparability.

Future Prospects

Automatic data processing including high speed computers, together with other innovative technology, are being applied by private and governmental agencies which deal with land use information. In recognition of the utility of these data processing systems, detailed and expanded land classification systems have been or are being developed. Indeed, the need for massive data inputs for transportation planning has led to a variety of systems presaging, in effect, the recognition of the need for a standard method of describing similar phenomena.

Accordingly, it is now recognized that the description of land use should be related to other information collection and inventory systems. Analytic and descriptive tools such as computer "models" created for transportation and community renewal planning have demonstrated feasibility basis and are now on a continuing basis.[2] The availability of data processing systems and the ability to introduce these systems within a practical and economic operational level provide opportunity for developing comprehensive and uniform land data systems. The HHFA has under contract a number of programs specifically dealing with this opportunity.

A co-operative project among four metropolitan planning bodies was initiated under the Agency's Urban Renewal Demonstration Grant (314) Program which can provide for grants up to two-thirds of the total cost. The program serves to test and improve techniques or methods of blight prevention and other activities associated with community improvement. It serves, at end, to provide helpful guides for renewal programs in other cities. The demonstration program being conducted at the Metropolitan Data Center, Tulsa, Oklahoma, serves to test the feasibility of establishing by use of electronic data processing equipment, a data center for the storage and analysis of information concerning land use, housing condition and occupancy, and related subjects including environmental factors. In addition, the project will attempt to explore the feasibility of maintaining a data center with up-to-date information which would be made readily available to various local agencies.

The Tulsa Metropolitan Data Center project involves five separate public agencies—Denver, Colorado; Fort Worth, Texas; Pulaski County, Arkansas; Tulsa, Oklahoma; and the City of Wichita-Sedgwick County, Kansas. Each participating agency has taken a particular area of application to develop and test. These differing applications are land use inventory, capital improvement program, community renewal program, central area planning, school facility planning. The project is to be completed during 1965.

The metropolitan data center concept is being applied in several other metropolitan areas. With its sharing of information, it should provide a system

[2] See the San Francisco Community Renewal Program and any of the number of metropolitan transportation studies.

whereby communities may better anticipate problems and better evaluate alternative solutions and courses of action. It is, in short, a management tool—its success depends upon proper and responsible management.

Another area of interest which involves the HHFA is the recently approved URA (314) demonstration grant to the District of Columbia. This project involves the development of comparable definitions and classifications of land use and housing characteristics for use by the various member jurisdictions of the Metropolitan Washington Council of Governments.

The project will attempt to develop a methodology for assembling comparable data utilized by the member local governments. This project can be viewed as a useful demonstration of a cooperative regional approach to the need for comparable quantitative information and the manner in which it can be implemented.

Another cooperative venture mentioned earlier, the *Standard Land Use Coding Manual,* provides a system for coding land use activities in such detail as to give the information considerable flexibility for meeting a variety of needs. The suggested standard code should make possible comparability of land use information among several localities within an urban area, as well as between different urban areas throughout the country.

However, each urban area must consider its present and future needs for land use information and the relative costs of different methods of information inventory systems. The proposed four-digit level of detail within the *Standard Land Use Coding Manual* is expected to be particularly useful in those urban areas where the need for detailed information has been established and where sufficient capability for utilizing such a system exists. In the evolution of this coding system, two principles were established that affected its final development.

The first was that each separate dimension or characteristic describing either a parcel of land, a structure on the parcel, or the activities within the structure, should be identified and classified separately. For example, rather than combining type of ownership and type of structure into one classification with type of activity, a separate series of classifications is necessary for each separate characteristic.

The second principle was that no rigid system for classifying land use activity is feasible for broad application to all urban areas. What is required is a coding system which will permit standardization in the coding of land use data and flexibility in the classification and use of data after coding. This can be accomplished more effectively if land use activity data are recorded and coded originally at a fairly detailed level, with summaries or classifications prepared later for application.

Over the next few years the system in the *Standard Land Use Coding Manual* is expected to be used and tested in a variety of urban development and transportation planning studies. As these field tests demonstrate the need for change, revisions of the system will be incorporated in subsequent editions of the manual.

The system uses a nine one-digit major activity classification—*residential, manufacturing, transportation, communication and utilities, trade, services, cultural, entertainment and recreational, resources production and extraction,* and *undeveloped land and water areas.* This one-digit system is further subdivided into three additional levels of progressively greater detail, with categories at the four-digit level identifying activities in detail.

In addition to the basic activity codes, this system includes a series of ten auxiliary codes. The auxiliary codes are used to identify activities which are often functionally and organizationally part of a parent operation within the urban area. For example, a warehouse operated by a retail establishment is an activity principally associated with the parent firm—it is not, in short, used for *public* storage.

The major advantage of this coding system is that it will permit a degree of standardization of both land use activity classification and code numbers. Additionally, the coding system will permit the reorganization of these detailed categories into a variety of analytic classes to individual needs. It should provide a meaningful basis for comparing land use information.

Standard Land Use Coding Manual[1]

(The following Appendix is a reproduction of the pamphlet published by the Urban Renewal Administration and the Bureau of Public Roads.)

Standard Land Use Coding Manual

A Standard System for Identifying and Coding Land Use Activities

First Edition

January 1965

Urban Renewal Administration
Housing and Home Finance Agency
and
Bureau of Public Roads
Department of Commerce

Washington, D.C.

For sale by the Superintendent of Documents, U.S. Government Printing Office
Washington, D.C., 20402 - Price 50 cents

---

[1] RFF Note: See foreword of this book for relation of this appendix to whole study.

FOREWORD

□ For the past few years the Urban Renewal Administration of the Housing and Home Finance Agency and the Bureau of Public Roads of the Department of Commerce have taken extensive steps to obtain close coordination between their programs. This follows both in spirit and letter the formal agreement reached by the Administrator of the Housing and Home Finance Agency and the Secretary of the Department of Commerce.

These coordinating relationships have been developed to a high degree in connection with the comprehensive planning programs in metropolitan areas having particular concern with transportation needs, and usually identified as land use-transportation studies. Such studies often have the joint financial support of both agencies through grants under the URA Urban Planning Assistance (701) Program and reimbursement of State and local expenditures from highway planning and research funds administered by the Bureau of Public Roads. Joint technical support also is often provided.

An outgrowth of these coordinating endeavors has been the identification of several subjects of interest to people working in the urban and transportation planning fields. One such subject that was called to our attention very early in the joint activities concerned the multiplicity of systems used in classifying land use. This publication is the result of steps taken jointly by both agencies to develop a possible standard land use coding system.

It is recognized that this edition is only the initial effort to develop a uniform coding system and that the application of this system in field operations will result in further refinements. Published under the auspices of both agencies, this is an expression of the day-to-day working relationships between the two agencies. We hope that it will further encourage State and local officials with urban development planning and transportation planning responsibilities to develop similar close working relationships.

The Urban Renewal Administration and the Bureau of Public Roads both recommend that where appropriate the detailed system of categories presented in this publication be used for the collection and coding of information describing land use activity. *However, this recommendation is not to be considered as a requirement in any programs sponsored by the two agencies.*

Communities and planning programs vary considerably as to their capacity to use and manage detailed land use data, and for this reason, it would be inappropriate to require the use of the standard coding system in all programs at this time. This coding system will be particularly useful in those urban areas where the need for *detailed* land use information has been clearly established and where the capacity exists in the form of data handling procedures and equipment for efficiently coding, preserving, and retrieving the data. However, each community must consider for its own area the existing demands and future needs for land use activity data together with the relative costs of different methods of collecting and handling the data before deciding the appropriate level of detail at which the data are to be recorded and coded (i.e. the one-, two-, three-, or four-digit level). In those urban areas where the decision has been made to collect and code the data at a grosser level of detail, i.e. at the two-or three digit level, this coding system can still provide a basis for comparability if the categories are meaningful for the objectives of the particular study.

WILLIAM L. SLAYTON,
Commissioner,
Urban Renewal Administration,
Housing and Home Finance Agency.

REX M. WHITTON,
Federal Highway Administrator,
Bureau of Public Roads,
U.S. Department of Commerce.

ACKNOWLEDGMENTS

□ The land use coding system in this publication represents the thinking and experience over many years of a large number of individuals and agencies within and outside of the Federal Government. This undertaking, the purposes of which are set forth in chapter I, Introduction, was conceived by Richard Ives, Deputy Assistant Commissioner for Urban Planning, Urban Renewal Administration, Housing and Home Finance Agency, and was directed jointly by him and Michael Lash, Chief, Urban Development Branch, Bureau of Public Roads, Department of Commerce.

The text and coding system in this publication have been developed by Harold A. Merrill, urban planner, Urban Renewal Administration, and Jacob Silver, geographer, Urban Development Branch, Bureau of Public Roads.

The study of land use classification and coding systems which provided the groundwork for this manual was conducted and developed through a Housing and Home Finance Agency contract with Barton-Aschman Associates, Inc., Evanston, Ill., under the supervision of Robert B. Teska, project administrator, and with overall direction and assistance by Rodney E. Engelen, principal associate.

Prior to the preparation of this text and coding system, the following persons reviewed copies of the preliminary study prepared by Barton-Aschman Associates, Inc., and their comments and suggestions, which are greatly appreciated, have been helpful in developing the standard land use coding system to this stage:

James R. Anderson, Department of Geography, University of Florida, Gainesville, Fla.

Kurt W. Bauer, Executive Director, Southeastern Wisconsin Regional Planning Commission, Waukesha, Wis.

C. R. Brady, Director, Valley Area Transportation Study, Tempe, Ariz.

Milton Breivogel, Director of Planning, County of Los Angeles Regional Planning Commission, Los Angeles, Calif.

E. Wilson Campbell, Director, Chicago Area Transportation Study, Chicago, Ill.

Robert D. Campbell, Department of Geography and Regional Science, George Washington University, Washington, D.C.

J. Douglas Carroll, Jr., Executive Director, Tri-State Transportation Committee, New York, N.Y.

F. Stuart Chapin, Jr., Research Director, Center for Urban and Regional Studies, University of North Carolina, Chapel Hill, N.C.

Robert C. Colwell, Director, Program Division, Federal Housing Administration, Housing and Home Finance Agency, Washington, D.C.

J. Tait Davis, Department of Geography and Regional Science, George Washington University, Washington, D.C.

Richard D. Duke, Institute for Community Development and Services, Michigan State University, East Lansing, Mich.

Henry Fagin, Department of Urban and Regional Planning, University of Wisconsin, Madison, Wis.

William L. Garrison, Department of Geography, Northwestern University, Evanston, Ill.
Douglas F. Haist, Chief of Urban and Advance Planning, Wisconsin State Highway Commission, Madison, Wis.
John R. Hamburg, Associate Director, Upstate New York Transportation Studies, Albany, N.Y.
Irving Hand, Planning Director, Metropolitan Planning Commission, Nashville, Tenn.
Britton Harris, Research Coordinator, Penn-Jersey Transportation Study, Philadelphia, Pa.
Patrick Healy, Executive Director, American Municipal Association, Washington, D.C.
Edward F. R. Hearle, The Rand Corporation, Santa Monica, Calif.
Roy D. Hockensmith, Director, Soil Survey Operations, Soil Conservation Service, U.S. Department of Agriculture, Washington, D.C.
Walter K. Johnson, Deputy Director, Wisconsin Department of Resource Development, Madison, Wis.
Stephen A. Kaufman, Deputy Director, Regional Planning Commission, Cleveland, Ohio.
Robert Kochanowski, Study Director, Pittsburgh Area Transportation Study, Pittsburgh, Pa.
Norman E. Landgren, Leader, Land Use Investigations, Economic Research Service, U.S. Department of Agriculture, Washington, D.C.
C. David Loeks, Director, Twin Cities Metropolitan Planning Commission, St. Paul, Minn.
David D. Longmaid, Executive Director, Penn-Jersey Transportation Study, Philadelphia, Pa.
John K. Mladinov, Director, Puget Sound Regional Transportation Study, Seattle, Wash.
Dennis O'Harrow, Executive Director, American Society of Planning Officials, Chicago, Ill.
Paul Oppermann, Executive Director, Northeastern Illinois Metropolitan Area Planning Commission, Chicago, Ill.
Russell H. Riley, Partner, Harland Bartholomew and Associates, St. Louis, Mo.
Victor Roterus, Economic Adviser to the Administrator, Area Redevelopment Administration, Washington, D.C.
Morton J. Schussheim, Assistant Administrator for Program Policy, Housing and Home Finance Agency, Washington, D.C.
John W. Shively, Assistant Commissioner for Technical Standards, Urban Renewal Administration, Housing and Home Finance Agency, Washington, D.C.
Herbert H. Smith, President, Herbert H. Smith Associates, West Trenton, N.J.
Oscar Sutermeister, Consultant to Division of Environmental Engineering and Food Protection, Public Health Service, Washington, D.C.
Stanley B. Tankel, Planning Director, Regional Plan Association, Inc., New York, N.Y.
Jack Urner, Acting Director, Metropolitan Planning Commission, Portland, Oreg.
Alan M. Voorhees, President, Alan M. Voorhees and Associates, Washington, D.C.
Louis B. Wetmore, Consultant, Urbana, Ill.

Sidney H. Williams, Partner, Williams and Mocine, San Francisco, Calif.

Robert L. Williams, Executive Director, American Institute of Planners, Washington, D.C.

Donald R. Woodard, Chief of Long Range Planning, Tulsa Metropolitan Area Planning Commission, Tulsa, Okla.

F. Houston Wynn, Wilbur Smith and Associates, New Haven, Conn.

In addition, the Urban Renewal Administration and the Bureau of Public Roads are indebted to the following for their comments and special counsel in the final stages of this undertaking:

Philip J. Barbato, Highway Engineer, Urban Planning Division, Bureau of Public Roads, Washington, D.C.

George F. Burks, Director, Division of Programs and Special Projects, Forest Service, U.S. Department of Agriculture, Washington, D.C.

Marion Clawson, Director, Land Use and Management Program, Resources for the Future, Inc., Washington, D.C.

Sidney Goldstein, Economic Adviser, Office of Planning, Bureau of Public Roads, Washington, D.C.

Frederick O'R. Hayes, Assistant Commissioner for Urban Planning and Community Development, Urban Renewal Administration, Housing and Home Finance Agency, Washington, D.C.

Bruce D. McDowell, Analyst, Advisory Commission on Intergovernmental Relations, Washington, D.C.

Jerome P. Pickard, Director of Research, Urban Land Institute, Washington, D.C.

Charles Stewart, Consultant to the Land Use Statistics Committee, Resources for the Future, Inc., Washington, D.C.

Hugh H. Wooton, Agricultural Economist, Economic Research Service, U.S. Department of Agriculture, Washington, D.C.

Although many different groups and persons were involved in the development of this system, the responsibility for the final product as contained herein rests with the Housing and Home Finance Agency and the Department of Commerce.□

Table of Contents

I Introduction

□ Land use statistics are required for a variety of planning purposes at the local, regional, and State levels. The need is growing for the collection of land use information in a form that will allow comparability between localities and between regions, and that will also permit the study of trends over time in individual urban areas. The lack of uniformity has led to duplication of effort in many cities. Often land use data collected for one specific purpose had little or no value for another but similar purpose, requiring a new field inventory within a short space of time. With the increasing attention being focused on urban planning and research and with the growing amounts of public funds being invested in land use inventories, the need for greater uniformity is quite plain and past due.

Amendments to section 701 of the Housing Act of 1954[1] in 1959 and in 1961, and the Federal-Aid Highway Act of 1962,[2] greatly increased the need to collect land use information that is equally useful to both urban development planning and transportation planning programs. These amendments placed a new and greater emphasis on the need to integrate urban development planning and transportation planning. Among the common denominators to both processes that allow such integration are a land use inventory and a land use forecast. A survey of existing land uses and the updating of such information, together with forecasts of the future growth and distribution of land uses, is essential in the continuous process of comprehensive planning for urban development and transportation planning.

Both the Urban Renewal Administration and the Bureau of Public Roads are aware of the important role a standard land use coding system can play in this planning process. Such a system will facilitate the interchange of statistical information and research findings between communities and public and private organizations. It would also reduce in a significant way existing obstacles to the comparison, analysis, and updating of land use data in many of our urban areas. This cooperative effort by the two agencies is a step toward advancing both these ends. □

[1] 40 U.S.C. 461.
[2] 23 U.S.C. 134.

II The Approach

A. INVESTIGATION AND CONCLUSIONS

In 1962 the Urban Renewal Administration with the cooperation of the Bureau of Public Roads and with the technical assistance of the consulting firm of Barton-Aschman Associates, Inc., of Evanston, Ill., began an investigation to determine whether a uniform and universally applicable land use classification and coding system was feasible. Besides serving the programs of the two agencies, the coding system would be such that it could be used for various types of studies and analyses in small communities with populations under 50,000 as well as in large metropolitan areas.

The study began with a review of land use classification systems already in use. Existing systems, or proposals for systems of land use classification, were gathered from over 50 different sources and reviewed in detail. Numerous persons were contacted either in person or by mail, including land use specialists from 12 of the largest urban planning and transportation planning studies then underway. In addition, valuable suggestions and help were received from the Land Use Statistics Committee of the Resources for the Future, Inc., under the chairmanship of Dr. Marion Clawson. That Committee was also seeking a solution to the problem of achieving comparability in land use statistics, and therefore, the work of the two groups was joined at several points to the mutual advantage of both.

One of the most significant conclusions of this exploration is that different characteristics or dimensions that describe land should *not* be combined into a single classification system if the system is to meet the objectives outlined above. For example, in some land use inventory projects, categories of activity have been combined with measures of intensity of use, such as the number of dwelling units in a structure, or with type of ownership, such as private and governmental. In other systems structure type, such as office building, has also been included. This mixing of characteristics restricts the use of any classification and coding scheme.

Instead of combining into one category several characteristics that can describe a piece of land, the study concluded that each separate dimension or characteristic be defined by a separate classification system. These characteristics, as illustrated in figure 1, could then be grouped as one would put together building blocks. The different characteristics that describe either a parcel of land, a structure on the parcel, or the activities on the land or within the structure are maintained separately, and they are put together in the combinations that will best fit the needs of a particular planning study. This, of course, does not mean that a variety of information cannot be collected in the same field survey. Economy of operations is possible and desirable even if a variety of different characteristics of the use of land are to be identified and recorded.

The above approach to land use description has been made possible by the very rapid changes in our technology, especially that of automatic data processing equipment. Through the use of data processing cards or electronic computer tapes, large quantities of land use information can be maintained or stored intact and in a detailed form. Through the use of electronic accounting machines or electronic computers, this detailed information can be reorganized into a variety of different classification patterns to fit the unique requirements of many types of planning studies. The computer, therefore, satisfies directly and immediately the specific requirements of a given program, and it retains the original detailed data for use in other studies. Most important of all, through the use of computers, the actual processing of detailed data can be accomplished in "machine-minutes or -hours" rather than in "man-months" or "man-years" of labor.

B. THE "ACTIVITY" CATEGORIES

Inasmuch as "activity" [3] is considered to be the most important single land use characteristic for which comparability is desired, a system of categories identifying land use activities was developed. The primary purpose was to establish an extensive system of categories that would identify each land use activity and which could also be numerically coded in order to facilitate data handling on automatic data processing equipment. This, it was felt, would provide the beginning of a standard system of identification for one specific characteristic of land use.

In developing the system of activity categories, a second major conclusion was reached, and that is that no *rigid* system for classifying land use activity is feasible for broad application to all urban areas in the United States. In the past, land use classification systems have differed one from the other for numerous reasons. However, the most frequent reason for the difference appears to have been an attempt by each city to reflect in the land use classification system its own particular economic and social composition.

For example, in Hartford, Conn., the insurance industry is an important activity and for certain planning purposes it may need to be identified not only as a separate activity, but also in more detail than, say meatpacking which is not a major Hartford industry. In Washington, D.C., governmental functions are important and would be identified in more detail than they would be, for example,

[3] The term "activity" for the purposes used here is defined as an organizational unit for performing a special function and occupying identifiable space at a fixed location.

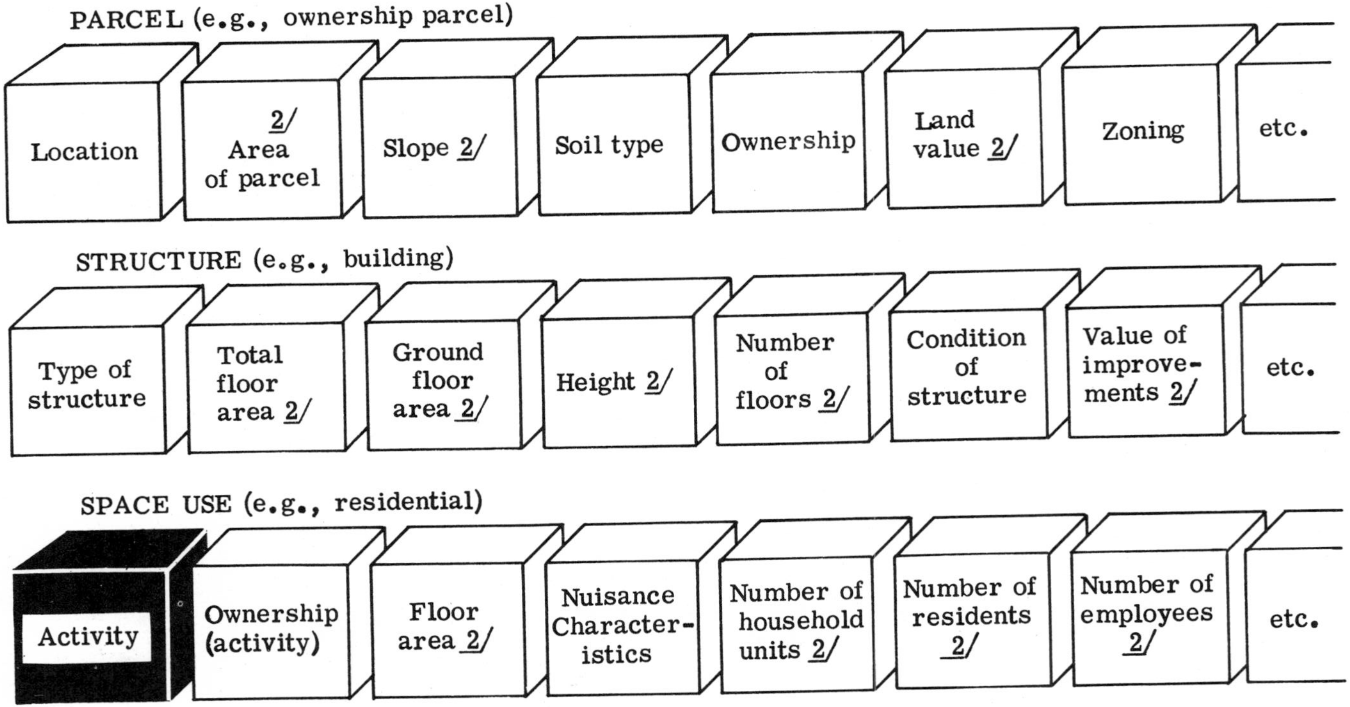

Figure 1.—An example of characteristics commonly used to describe a parcel of land [1]

[1] *This figure is neither definitive in the number of characteristics shown nor does the sequence indicate relative importance. It is presented to illustrate the type of characteristics that are considered by planning agencies when describing a parcel of land. The shaded block labeled "Activity" is the characteristic being given primary consideration in this coding system.*

[2] *These characteristics can be described by an actual figure or a range in figures representing magnitude. The other characteristics cannot be described numerically and therefore, each will need a series of "word description" categories.*

in Miami, Fla. One man's miscellaneous is another man's prime concern; no single classification structure will satisfy the needs of both.

Another frequent factor that has caused variation in past land use classification systems is the difference in the data processing methods used in different cities. Planning offices in some cities do not yet have access to automatic data processing equipment and at present use a simpler, more general system of data collection and analysis than in cities where analysis of detailed data are facilitated by such equipment.

Do these types of local factors mean then that the whole idea of developing a standard system for describing land use activity in a comparable form from city to city is a lost cause? Not at all. What it does mean is that if there is to be comparability, there must be an approach to classifying land use activity that will permit *standardization in coding land use activity data and flexibility in the use of the data once it is coded.* This only can be accomplished if land use activity is identified and coded at a fairly detailed level.

Seldom will it be necessary or even desirable in any day-to-day planning operation to work with land use activity data at the detailed level being recommended for data collection and coding (i.e., the four-digit level of detail listed in ch. IV). However, if land use activity is identified and coded using the four-digit codes, the data can then be regrouped into a variety of different classification patterns to fit the needs of special studies and analyses.

The cost of recording and coding land use information at the four-digit level of detail will usually be greater than if the data were recorded and coded at more generalized levels. This extra cost comes from the additional detail in which land uses must be identified in the field inventory and also from the additional effort required in coding the collected data. On the other hand, such extra costs often can be offset by the greater flexibility and wider utilization of the data.

As indicated in the Foreword, the question of the level of detail at which a community should inventory and record its land use information must be decided locally, giving consideration to the numerous factors involved. It should be recognized that if land use activity information is recorded and coded only at one of the more generalized levels shown in chapter IV, say at the one-, two-, or three-digit levels of detail, this will reduce many possible uses for the data. Even so, there still is an advantage in using the standard land use coding system at the more generalized levels, since these codes will still be comparable with other studies using the same system.

The list of activity categories and their numeric codes shown in chapter IV are arranged in a hierarchical order of generalization. The nine major classifications of land use recommended here are considered to be the most useful to a wide range of planning studies. However, the emphasis in this system of categories is not on the classification structure, but on the detailed identification of land use activity (i.e., the four-digit level of detail listed in ch. IV). Emphasis is also placed on the preservation of these detailed data in a form that will allow them to be conveniently and efficiently arranged into a variety of possible classifications in order to satisfy local planning requirements.

C. THE NEXT STEP

Over the next few years the proposed system of land use activity categories is expected to be used in a variety of urban development and transportation planning studies to test and refine the system. Categories may be added, changed, or reworded in order to make them more precise and operational. As field tests demonstrate the need for change, revisions of the system will be incorporated in subsequent editions of this publication.

Since this is the initial publication of the *Standard Land Use Coding Manual*, the Urban Renewal Administration and the Bureau of Public Roads invite comments, observations, and suggestions. These will be appreciated and given full consideration in future editions of this report. Please address all comments to:

Office of Urban Planning and Community Development
Urban Renewal Administration
Housing and Home Finance Agency
Washington, D.C. 20410

or

Urban Planning Division
Bureau of Public Roads
Department of Commerce
Washington, D.C. 20235

III Use of the Categories

A. DESCRIPTION AND RATIONALE

There are several facets of this coding system that should be explained to insure that the categories are properly understood and correctly applied.

1. General Structure

The standard system for coding land use activity is comprised of 9 one-digit categories (2 of which have been assigned to "manufacturing"), 67 two-digit categories, 294 three-digit categories, and 772 four-digit categories. The categories at the four-digit level identify land use activity in the greatest detail, and as the system is aggregated to the three-, two-, and one-digit levels the categories become more generalized. The structure of this classification system, therefore, permits an agency to select the level of detail considered most appropriate for analysis and presentation of its data.

The categories at the one-digit level of generalization are:

Code	*Category*	*Code*	*Category*
1	Residential.	7	Cultural, entertainment, and recreational.
2 and 3	Manufacturing.	8	Resource production and extraction.
4	Transportation, communication, and utilities.	9	Undeveloped land and water areas.
5	Trade.		
6	Services.		

In addition to the above activity categories, this system also includes a series of auxiliary codes that are used to further describe the activity identified. The use of the auxiliary categories is described in the following section of this chapter.

The reader will note that many of the categories shown in chapter IV are repeated at several levels of detail. For example, "Groceries (with or without meat)—retail" is located under code 541, and also under code 5410. A zero in the last digit position will always indicate that the code is repeated from a more general level. This was done either where it was considered unfeasible or unnecessary to identify activity in any greater detail or where it was decided that local field testing was necessary before determining more precisely the individual categories necessary at the three- and four-digit levels of generalization.

If it becomes necessary to further subdivide a category into a finer breakdown of activity than is shown, this can be done within the present system of categories and code numbers by either dropping the zeros to the right and adding digits, or where there are no zeros by adding digits to the right of the present code number. For example, a further breakdown of "Office furniture—manufacturing" (code 2520) and "Motor vehicles and motor vehicle equipment—manufacturing" (code 3441) would be as follows:

Code	*Category*	*Code*	*Category*
2520	Office furniture—manufacturing.	2521	Office furniture (wood)—manufacturing.
		2522	Office furniture (metal)—manufacturing.
3441	Motor vehicles and motor vehicle equipment—manufacturing.	34411	Motor vehicles—manufacturing.
		34412	Passenger car bodies—manufacturing.
		34413	Trucks and bus bodies—manufacturing.
		34414	Motor vehicle parts and accessories—manufacturing.
		34415	Truck trailers—manufacturing.
		34416	Etc.

This procedure permits a logical expansion of any section of the coding system, whether it be manufacturing or recreation codes, where a local planning group finds it necessary to satisfy their unique planning needs.

2. *Purpose and Use of the Auxiliary Codes*

There are certain land use activities that are generally found separated from, but are functionally and organizationally linked to other activities. For example:

a. A warehouse operated by a retail concern primarily for its own use and not for public storage;

b. A parking area operated by a manufacturing concern for use by its own employees and not for public parking;

c. An office performing management functions as part of a mining concern which has mines in several States.

These are all important space uses in themselves. However, they are also significant in their relationship to the parent activity they serve.

To illustrate this point further, consider a warehouse located separately from the parent activity it serves, which may be for example, a manufacturer of pharmaceuticals or a department store. This warehouse, during a land use inventory, may be identified and coded *only* as a warehouse. This does not permit linking the warehouse as a facility of the parent activity. It would be equally misleading if the warehouse were to be given the same code as the parent activity with no other identification. Studies of *total space use needs* or planning for the physical needs of a community are handicapped by such limited information.

To provide a link between certain significant auxiliary functions and the parent activities they serve, a series of one-digit "Auxiliary" categories are provided. These should be used with the standard system for coding land use activity. The auxiliary categories are as follows:

Code	*Auxiliary categories*	*Code*	*Auxiliary categories*
0	Not an auxiliary.	5	Automobile parking.[5]
1	Central or administrative office.[4]	6	Motor vehicle garage (maintenance and/or storage of vehicles).
2	Sales office.	7	Steam and power plant.
3	Research and development.	8–9	(Open codes).[6]
4	Warehousing and storage.		

[4] Central or administrative offices are those offices engaged in general administrative, supervisory, purchasing, accounting, or other management functions.

[5] A minimum of 5,000 square feet or approximately 17 parking spaces is necessary before the area can be identified as auxiliary parking area.

[6] Planning agencies desiring to distinguish additional types of auxiliary categories other than those defined (e.g., recreational activities that are subsidiary to or serving another activity) should use open codes 8 and 9.

Codes 1 through 7 should be used when one of the listed activities can be determined to be subsidiary to or serving another activity. For example, if a research and development laboratory of a manufacturer of pharmaceutical preparations is located down the street from the actual manufacturing plant itself, the laboratory would be considered as an auxiliary and would be coded as follows:

Basic activity code	*Auxiliary code*	*Combined activity code*
(Pharmaceutical preparations—manufacturing) 2834	(Research and development) 3	2834–3

An automobile parking area over 5,000 square feet which is an adjunct to an activity, e.g., a grocery store, and which is not used for other purposes in the same sense as a public parking area would be coded as follows:

Basic activity code	*Auxiliary code*	*Combined activity code*
(Groceries—retail) 5410	(Automobile parking) 5	5410–5

The sales office of a manufacturing concern that is separately located from the actual factory, whether it be next door in a separate building, across the street, on the other side of the town, or in another city, is considered as serving the manufacturing process. Similiarly, the permanent office of a construction company is considered as serving the construction activity. Therefore, these office activities would be coded as follows:

Basic activity code	*Auxiliary code*	*Combined activity code*
(Farm machinery and equipment—manufacturing) 3422	(Sales office) 2	3422–2
(Building construction—general contractor services) 6611	(Central or administrative office) 1	6611–1

With respect to wholesaling activity (code 51), those wholesalers *without* stock (i.e., they do not have a definite storage area set aside to maintain a volume of stock on hand) are also considered to be auxiliary, and they are identified by one of the auxiliary codes, accordingly. For example:

Basic activity code	*Auxiliary code*	*Combined activity code*
(Fruits and vegetables, fresh—wholesale) 5147	(With stock) 0	5147–0
(Fruits and vegetables, fresh—wholesale) 5147	(Sales office, without stock) 2	5147–2

On the other hand, an independent research, development, and testing laboratory would not be considered as an auxiliary activity, and it would be coded under its respective activity category, code 6391. Parking is coded in a similar way if it is public parking or parking serving more than one concern, such as the parking area of a shopping center. The following examples illustrate this:

Basic activity code	*Auxiliary code*	*Combined activity code*
(Research, development, and testing services) 6391	(Not an auxiliary) 0	6391–0
(Automobile parking) 4600	(Not an auxiliary) 0	4600–0

The preceding discussion and illustrations of the use of the auxiliary codes are centered primarily on the problem of preserving the linkage between related activities while at the same time identifying important land uses. It is recognized that for some planning studies, such as open space or recreation planning, the two open codes (8 and 9) may not provide sufficient categories for identifying recreational or open space uses which are a part of some larger activity. If it is found necessary or desirable to identify such related uses, a new and separate series of auxiliary codes should be developed to accommodate the needs of the special study, thereby preserving the original auxiliary codes for comparability over a period of time and between cities.

3. The Use of Standard Industrial Classification Nomenclature

A commonly used system for identifying economic activity is the *Standard Industrial Classification* (SIC) established and published by the U.S. Bureau of the Budget. This system developed for studying the economic characteristics of our economy is "* * * used in the classification of establishments by type of activity in which engaged; for purposes of facilitating the collection, tabulation, presentation, and analysis of data related to establishments; and for promoting uniformity and comparability in the presentation of statistical data * * *"[7] collected by various government agencies and by private organizations.

Since the SIC is a detailed classification of establishments and because of the wide acceptance of the nomenclature used in the SIC, this land use coding system uses the SIC category titles and the detailed identification of activities as far as is feasible. However, no attempt was made to identify the four-digit land use categories by the same code numbers as the comparable categories in the SIC. It was not considered practical to make the numbers the same since establishments identified by separate code numbers under the SIC have in some instances been combined into one activity description in the four-digit land use codes. In other instances different types of establishments that were grouped under one code in the SIC may have been identified separately under the land use codes, each being given a separate code number. In addition to these differences, many land use activities that need to be identified for planning purposes are not comparable to any SIC industry description, and, therefore, it would still have been necessary to establish new code numbers.

In chapter IV, the SIC codes listed in column 7 are used only as references.[8] That is, these are the codes in the SIC system that generally correspond to the four-digit land use activity listed. It should be recognized, however, *that the adoption of the same terminology does not necessarily make the land use data collected and coded under this system of categories compatible with the economic data collected using SIC specifications.* Differences often arise through the dissimilar criteria used to code activities in the two systems.

Federal agencies using the SIC in their statistical programs, such as the economic censuses of the Bureau of the Census, the Bureau of Employment Security, the Bureau of Labor Statistics, and the Bureau of Old Age and Survivors Insurance, obtain information *directly* from an "establishment" in terms of either the value of products produced, value of construction or work done, value of products sold, or value of receipts for services rendered depending upon the economic sector in which the establishment is located. The establishment is then assigned an SIC code on the basis of its *major* activity as measured by *the value of the product or services offered.* In an establishment concerned with only one product or service, there is no problem in assigning the SIC code. However, where there is a mixture of several products or services, the establishment is assigned

---

[7] *Standard Industrial Classification Manual,* prepared by Bureau of the Budget, U.S. Government Printing Office, Washington, D.C., 1957, p. 1.

[8] The SIC code numbers shown in ch. IV are from the *Standard Industrial Classification Manual* identified in footnote 7 and from the *Standard Industrial Classification Manual—Supplement to 1957 Edition,* prepared by the Bureau of the Budget, U.S. Government Printing Office, Washington, D.C., 1963.

only the code of that product or service that results in the largest percentage of total value.

The term "establishment" used by these agencies in general denotes an "economic unit which produces goods or services—for example, a farm, a mine, a factory, a store. In most instances, the establishment is at a single physical location, and it is engaged in only one, or predominantly one type of economic activity for which an industry code is applicable." [9]

In contrast to the above, in most planning studies land use activity is identified through one of three different criteria and procedures: (a) through observation, (b) through interviews, or (c) through the use of secondary data sources, e.g., insurance maps or assessors' records. Also, where there is a mixture of several activities on the same premises, the activity taking up the *greatest amount of space* is the one normally identified and coded.

Since the unit of collection in land use inventories is not based on the same "establishment" concept as defined in the SIC, and since land use activities are not classified according to the value of the product or service, the same establishment could easily be identified differently under the two systems.

As a result of these differences, economic data collected and coded using the SIC categories will not always be comparable with the land use data identified under the standard land use coding system. This will be especially true of land use activities identified at the very detailed three- and four-digit levels. Where classes of land use activity are summarized to a more generalized level, say at the two-digit level, the respective items of information can be more favorably compared. However, even at this level of generalization, a certain amount of discrepancy will still occur. If information obtained from the two systems are to be used together, the actual areas of differences should be determined, and appropriate procedures should be developed for reconciling these statistical categories.

4. Coding Ownership

The proposed system of categories identifies only the activity without regard to whether it is "publicly" or "privately" owned. If this further description of an activity is desired, a separate series of classifications should be developed. The subdivisions under ownership may simply differentiate between "public" and "private" activity, or it may have further subdivisions of these two basic categories. One such series of categories recommended for use by local communities is presented in appendix 1.

Under the system of land use activity identification proposed in this manual, the coding of governmental activities has been approached in two different ways. "Executive, legislative, and judicial functions" (code 671); "Protective functions and their related activities" (code 672); "Postal services" (code 673); "Correctional institutions" (code 674); and "Military bases and reservations" (code 675) are considered to be "Services" and, therefore, coded under this major category. As used here "Executive, legislative, and judicial functions" include only the central and administrative *office* activities of the agencies or special authorities involved in governmental functions, as well as the legislatures and the courts. On the other hand, all operational activities of government (e.g., shipbuilding, schools, or hospitals) are identified under their respective activity

[9] *Standard Industrial Classification Manual*, p. 2.

categories. In each case, if ownership of the activity is to be distinguished, it should be done through the use of a separate series of categories.

Figure 2 in part B of this chapter is a generalized example of how these two characteristics of land use (activity and ownership) could be recorded and coded. Code 20 in column 7′ identifies private activity while codes 11 and 15 indicate public activity, Federal and municipal, respectively.

5. *Coding Rural Activities*

This land use coding system has been developed primarily for use in urban area planning. However, this system is sufficiently broad and flexible enough for use in studies of the urban-rural fringe and of rural areas. Such studies would not require a new system of categories. This flexibility exists in the three- and four-digit levels of detail found under such categories as "Agriculture" and "Agricultural related activities" (codes 81 and 82) and "Commercial forestry production" (code 831). Where such three- and four-digit detail for rural land uses is not needed, these activities can be recorded in more general categories at the two-digit level.

A special series of "Farm use" categories is also provided for those who may wish to analyze agricultural activity in even greater detail, i.e., either by types of farms or by the different uses made of the area within farms. The system of "Farm use" categories and their use are explained in appendix 2.

6. *Rationale Behind Some of the Categories*

a. Household units.

The term "Household units" (code 11) is used in this coding system to prevent confusion with the types of living quarters enumerated by the Bureau of the Census. Although the definition used to identify the "Household units" is very similar to the term "Housing unit" used by the Census, the major differences between the two are in the treatment of "Residential hotels" (code 13) and "Mobile home parks or courts" (code 14). These two categories which are included in the Census term "Housing unit" are excluded from "Household units" and listed as separate categories in the coding system.

A "Household unit" identifies only one residential unit whether it be in a single family home, in an apartment house, or over a grocery store. Such descriptive characteristics as the number of "Household units" within a structure or the type of residential structure (e.g., single family detached or apartment) have not been incorporated into the basic land use activity categories since they are considered descriptions that should be recorded and coded as separate items in the information file.

As previously indicated, information about such separate characteristics can be collected at the same time that the land use inventory is made. Figure 3 in part B of this chapter is a general example illustrating a method for recording and coding (1) residential activity, (2) type of residential structure, and (3) number of "Household units."

The major advantage in following the procedure illustrated in figure 3 is the flexibility afforded in the use of the collected residential information. Instead of a limited classification system indicating a range in the number of units (i.e., 3 to 4 "Household units," 5 to 10 "Household units," etc.), there would be available a specific count of the units. Also, by using a separate series of descriptions for types of residential structures, the categories would be more precise and, therefore, more meaningful and useful. One such series of categories recommended for use by local communities is shown in appendix 3.

If a planning agency desires to incorporate a description of structure types into the basic activity coding system, the categories shown in appendix 3 can also be used to serve this purpose. Columns 1 and 2 in appendix 3 (the code number and the category) would become a series of three-digit categories under "Household units" and columns 3 and 4 would become the four-digit categories. In each case, the code numbers in the appendix would replace the zeros in the basic activity codes as follows:

		Present Codes			
Code	*Category*	*Code*	*Category*	*Code*	*Category*
11	Household units	110	Household units	1100	Household units
			After Change		
11	Household units	111	Single family structures	1111	Single units—detached
				1112	Single units—semidetached
				1113	Etc.

b. Manufacturing categories.

The number of categories and type of detail distinguished under "Manufacturing" (codes 2 and 3) exceed those of any other land use activity. The major purpose for maintaining this amount of detail is that each of the industrial activities identified under "Manufacturing" is not found in each of our urban areas as are activities such as police stations, real estate offices, or women's apparel shops.

Community "A" may contain five or six types of manufacturing industries. Community "B" may also have five or six types of manufacturing industries. However, the industries located in community "B" may be quite different than those in community "A." Since this system will be used throughout the United States, and since each community will desire to identify specifically those manufacturing activities located within its study limits, a detailed breakdown of manufacturing is necessary, recognizing, however, that not all of the detailed manufacturing categories will be used in any single community.

c. Warehousing and storage categories.

Warehousing and storage areas are handled in one of two ways. As indicated in section A2 of this chapter, a warehouse or storage area not in the same building as the parent establishment is identified with the basic code of the parent activity and the auxiliary code of 4. For example:

Basic activity code	*Auxiliary code*	*Combined activity code*
(Department stores—retail) 5310	(Warehousing and storage) 4	5310–4

On the other hand, a warehouse or storage area that is generally used by the public is coded one of the seven categories under "Warehousing and storage services" (code 637). For example:

Basic activity code	*Auxiliary code*	*Combined activity code*
(Household goods warehousing and storage) 6375	(Not an auxiliary) 0	6375–0
(Farm products warehousing and storage—excluding stockyards) 6371	(Not an auxiliary) 0	6371–0

d. Undeveloped and unused land.

"Undeveloped and unused land area—excluding noncommercial forest development" (code 9100) identifies those parcels of land that appear to be undeveloped or, if previously developed, are presently vacant and unused. This category includes such areas as vacant lands that were once farms located in the rural-urban fringe, as well as vacant parcels where structures have been demolished. "Noncommercial forest development" (code 92) was excluded from code 9100 and made a separate category because of the increasing importance of these areas to government programs concerning "open spaces" and outdoor recreation, as well as statewide planning programs.

e. Vacant floor area.

The category "Vacant floor area" (code 9400) identifies only vacated *nonresidential* floor area within a structure. No provision has been made in the activity coding system for identifying vacant residential units. However, if a distinction is needed between occupied and unoccupied "Household units," this information can be collected and coded in the same manner as total "Household units." For example:

Basic activity code	*Auxiliary code*	*Total household units*	*Total vacancies*	*Combined code description*
(Household units) 1100	(Not an auxiliary) 0	(10 units) 10	(2 vacancies) 2	1100–0–10–2

Figure 3 is an example of how vacant-nonresidential floor area within a building containing other activities would be identified and coded. The use of code 9400 alone for a parcel of land would be interpreted as a vacant building.

f. Under construction categories.

"Under construction" (code 95) is a category indicating a temporary stage of land use. The category should be changed when the land use activity information is updated or when sufficient information to identify the activity is available. "Under construction (residential)" (code 9510) is used only when the criteria for completed residential units has not been met.[10] The category of "Under construction (nonresidential)" (code 9520) is used if there is no means of determining what activities will occupy a building when it is completed.

[10] See ch. IV, footnote 5 under code 9510 for the criteria of a completed residential unit.

B. APPLICATION

1. Identifying and Coding Land Use Activities.

A series of examples have been prepared to illustrate and further clarify the application of the land use activity coding system. These examples, although very general, are intended to show at what level of detail land use activity data should be collected in order to obtain the maximum benefit of the coding system.

Figures 2, 3, 4, and 5 are examples of how activities might be identified and described in a field inventory and then coded back at the office. Section A of each figure shows the parcel and structures (marked with an X) which are being inventoried. Section B shows a schematic version of the structure(s) on each parcel with the type of activities on each floor. Section C is a portion of a field listing form on which the information will be recorded and then coded. Columns (1) through (4) on the field listing form are used to record the location of the activity, column (5) is used to describe the activity, and column (6) is used by a field lister to indicate whether or not the activity being identified is an auxiliary. An X in this column denotes that the activity is an auxiliary, and a dash denotes that it is not.

In figure 3, there are several "Household units" located at 516 Silver Lane. Where there is more than one unit in a structure, the description (Household units) need be recorded only once as shown in column 5 and the number of units listed separately as shown in column 9. Columns 8 and 8′ indicate how the type of residential structure can be recorded and coded whenever a "Household unit" is identified.

Figure 5 illustrates the treatment of a parcel of land occupied by a furniture manufacturer and its related activities. The administrative offices are located in a separate structure and, therefore, are identified as a separate but auxiliary activity. The parcel also has a defined off-street parking area that is used only by factory employees, so this too is identified as a separate but auxiliary activity.

In figures 2 through 5 each of the establishments identified is engaged in only one type of basic activity. If, however, there had been an establishment that conducted several separate activities (not auxiliary activities) within the same physical premises, e.g., a clothing manufacturer with a small retail outlet, only the activity occupying the largest floor area would be identified. Predominant floor area for activities in a structure or predominant land area for activities not in a structure will determine the activity that is coded.

With the collection, identification, and coding of the data to a four-digit level of detail (plus the use of auxiliary codes), a basic reservoir of information has been established. This information may be stored on data processing cards or on computer tapes. Where electronic data processing or computer equipment is not available, the data may remain in land use listing forms. In any case, the detailed activity data are available for use in the proposed classification system or as individual categories for regrouping into other classes.

2. Standardization and Flexibility.

Even though the nine basic activity classifications shown in chapter IV are expected to be helpful to a wide range of studies, there will be times when planning situations or preferences will call for groupings or combinations of categories differing from those proposed here. One of the best examples of

Figure 2.—Example: Describing and Coding Activities

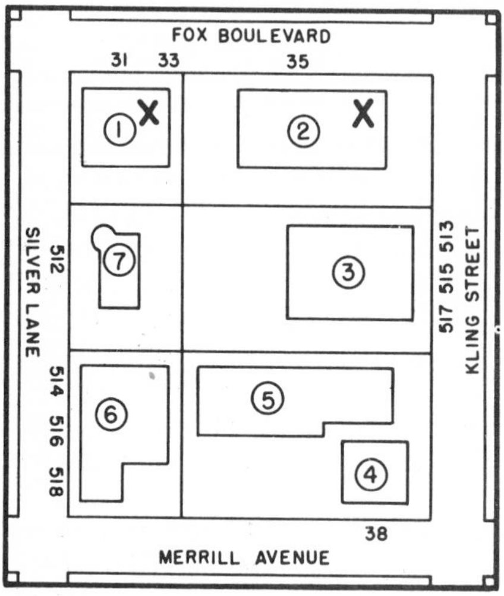

2A—Block Plan

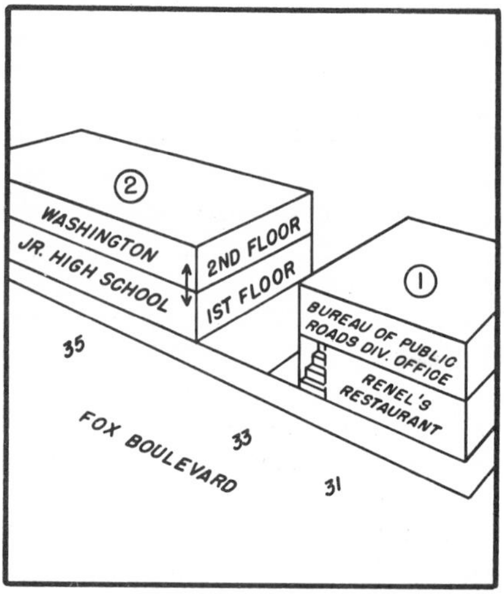

2B—Parcel Schematic

FIELD OPERATION									OFFICE OPERATION				
Street No.	Street Name	Building No.	Floor	Description of Activity	Auxiliary?	Activity Ownership	Residential Structure Type	No. of Household Units	Activity Code	Auxiliary Code	Ownership Code	Structure Code	No. of Household Units
1	2	3	4	5	6	7	8	9	5'	6'	7'	8'	9'
31	FOX BOULEVARD	1	1	RENEL'S RESTAURANT	—	PRIVATE	—	—	5810	0	20	—	—
33	FOX BOULEVARD	1	2	BUREAU OF PUBLIC ROADS, DIVISION OFFICES (ADMIN.)	X	FEDERAL	—	—	6710	1	11	—	—
35	FOX BOULEVARD	2	1+2	WASHINGTON JUNIOR HIGH SCHOOL (GRADES 7-9)	—	MUNICIPAL	—	—	6813	0	15	—	—

2C—Example of Land Use Entries on a Field Listing Form

Figure 3.—Example: Describing and Coding Activities

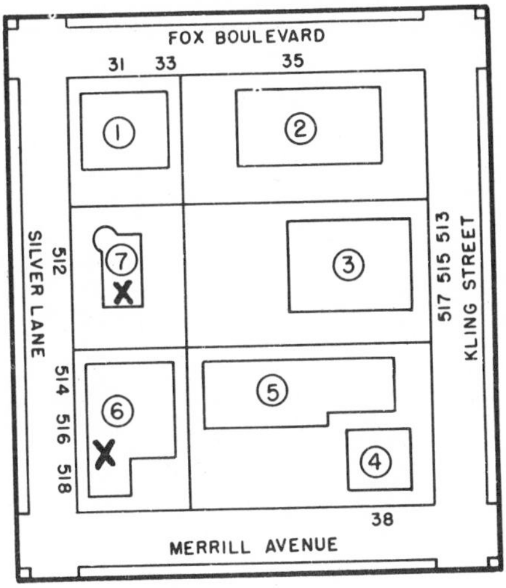

3A—Block Plan

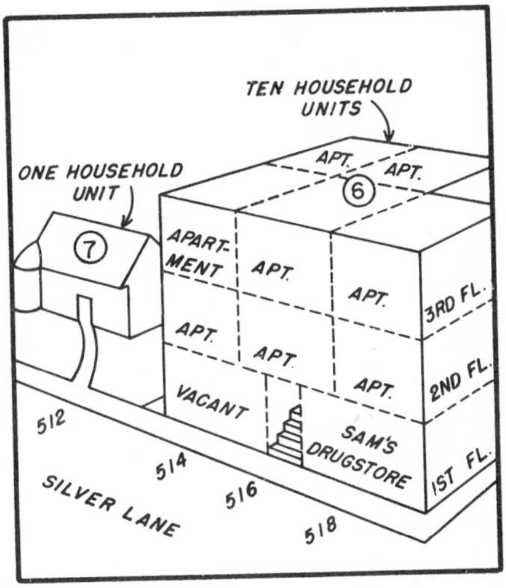

3B—Parcel Schematic

FIELD OPERATION									OFFICE OPERATION				
Street No.	Street Name	Building No.	Floor	Description of Activity	Auxiliary?	Activity Ownership	Residential Structure Type	No. of Household Units	Activity Code	Auxiliary Code	Ownership Code	Structure Code	No. of Household Units
1	2	3	4	5	6	7	8	9	5'	6'	7'	8'	9'
518	SILVER LANE	6	1	SAM'S DRUG STORE	—	PRIVATE	—	—	5910	0	20	—	—
516	SILVER LANE	6	2+3	HOUSEHOLD UNITS	—	PRIVATE	WALK-UP APART.	10	1100	0	20	31	10
514	SILVER LANE	6	1	VACANT FLOOR AREA	—	——	—	—	9400	0	—	—	—
512	SILVER LANE	7	1	HOUSEHOLD UNITS	—	PRIVATE	SINGLE UNIT—DETACHED	1	1100	0	20	11	01

3C—Example of Land Use Entries on a Field Listing Form

Figure 4.—Example: Describing and Coding Activities

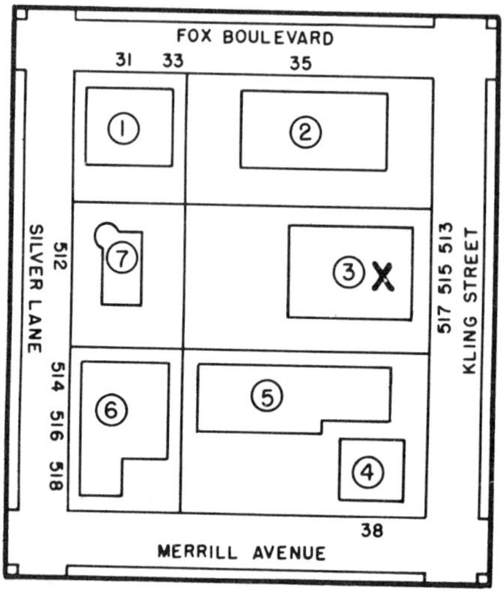

4A—Block Plan

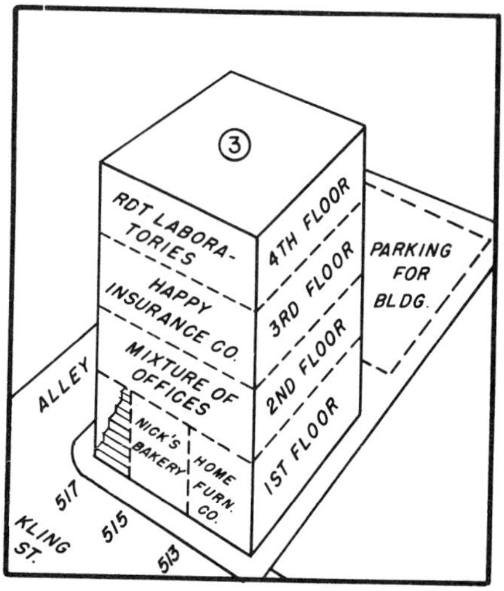

4B—Parcel Schematic

FIELD OPERATION									OFFICE OPERATION				
Street No.	Street Name	Building No.	Floor	Description of Activity	Auxiliary?	Activity Ownership	Residential Structure Type	No. of Household Units	Activity Code	Auxiliary Code	Ownership Code	Structure Code	No. of Household Units
1	2	3	4	5	6	7	8	9	5'	6'	7'	8'	9'
513	KLING ST.	3	1	HOME FURNITURE CO. (RETAIL)	—	PRIVATE	—	—	5711	0	20	—	—
515	KLING ST.	3	1	NICK'S BAKERY (WITH OVENS IN REAR)	—	PRIVATE	—	—	5461	0	20	—	—
517	KLING ST.	3	2	BIG TOWN REAL ESTATE CO. (REAL ESTATE AGENTS + BROKERS-OFFICES)	—	PRIVATE	—	—	6152	0	20	—	—
517	KLING ST.	3	2	PHYSICIAN'S OFFICE	—	PRIVATE	—	—	6511	0	20	—	—
517	KLING ST.	3	2	JONES CHEMICAL CORP. (SALES OFF. OF AGRICULTURAL FERTILIZER MFG.)	X	PRIVATE	—	—	2870	2	20	—	—
517	KLING ST.	3	2	AJAX CONSTRUCTION CO. (GENERAL OFFICES-HOME BUILDERS)	X	PRIVATE	—	—	6611	1	20	—	—
517	KLING ST.	3	2	LAW FIRM (OFFICES)	—	PRIVATE	—	—	6520	0	20	—	—
517	KLING ST.	3	3	HAPPY INSURANCE CO. (REGIONAL OFFICE OF COMPANY)	X	PRIVATE	—	—	6141	1	20	—	—
517	KLING ST.	3	4	RDT LABORATORIES (DEVELOPMENT LABORATORIES FOR RDT INDUSTRIES-RADIO TRANSMITTING EQUIPMENT MFG.)	X	PRIVATE	—	—	3436	3	20	—	—
513-517	KLING ST.	—	—	PARKING FOR VISITORS + EMPLOYEES IN THE REAR (20 SPACES)	—	PRIVATE	—	—	4600	0	20	—	—

4C—Example of Land Use Entries on a Field Listing Form

Figure 5.—Example: Describing and Coding Activities

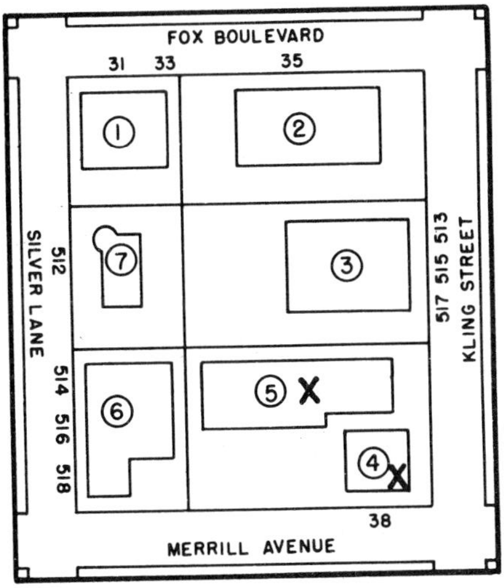

5A—Block Plan

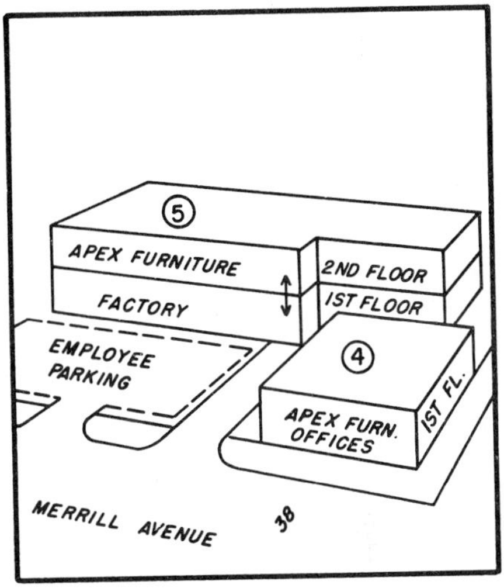

5B—Parcel Schematic

FIELD OPERATION									OFFICE OPERATION				
Street No.	Street Name	Building No.	Floor	Description of Activity	Auxiliary?	Activity Ownership	Residential Structure Type	No. of Household Units	Activity Code	Auxiliary Code	Ownership Code	Structure Code	No. of Household Units
1	2	3	4	5	6	7	8	9	5'	6'	7'	8'	9'
38	MERRILL AVE.	4	1	APEX FURNITURE FACTORY (ADMINISTRATIVE OFFICES OF FACTORY)	X	PRIVATE	—	—	2520	1	20	—	—
38	MERRILL AVE.	5	1 + 2	APEX FURNITURE FACTORY (FACTORY PRODUCING WOOD OFFICE FURNITURE	—	PRIVATE	—	—	2520	0	20	—	—
38	MERRILL AVE.	—	—	APEX FURNITURE FACTORY (EMPLOYEE PARKING-36 SPACES)	X	PRIVATE	—	—	2520	5	20	—	—

5C—Example of Land Use Entries on a Field Listing Form

this is in a metropolitan area where there are numerous local governments, many with their own planning offices. Past experience has shown that these offices have their own unique preferences concerning an activity classification system. Hence, it becomes extremely difficult to establish a compromise classification system that is acceptable to all parties concerned.

One answer to this problem is to inventory land use activity for the entire metropolitan area and to code the data using the four-digit standard land use coding system presented in chapter IV. This will establish a common base of detailed activity data that have the same standard identification and code number throughout the metropolitan area. Since each land use activity is now specifically identified, classifications of activity can be arranged to fit most analyses or special studies simply by a regrouping of the detailed categories. Hence, from this common base, each planning group within the metropolitan area can develop its own combination of categories and still maintain comparability with each of the other communities.

Thus, a major advantage of the proposed land use activity coding system is that it will permit a standardization of activity categories and code numbers, and at the same time through the use of electronic data processing equipment and electronic computers, it will also permit the reorganization of these detailed categories to classifications that may be more useful to the individual local communities. The small community of under 50,000 population and the large metropolitan area can both observe the same basic principles proposed here and have a common basis for comparing land use activity data. Tables 1 and 2 show the types of classifications that can be developed once the detailed data have been collected and coded to a common base.

Table 1 illustrates how a new classification such as "Offices" can be developed. In this example, all those activities that have been identified with an auxiliary code of 1 or 2 (central administrative offices and sales offices) have been grouped with all other "office type" activities. Since each category of activity that goes into making up the new classification of "Offices" is specified, the local community can now determine the percent that each office type category represents of the total office space identified. If this information were updated from time to time, the general trend in office space usage could be determined.

Table 2 illustrates how three different types of studies could take the same basic land use activity data (collected and coded to the four-digit level of the standard land use coding system) and recombine the categories in order to organize the data into classifications that will best fit the purposes of each study. In each case special code numbers will have to be established locally to identify the new classifications.

Throughout this report emphasis has been placed on identifying and coding to the four-digit level of detail in order to establish a common base of information. This does *not* mean that land use cannot be collected and coded to the three-, two-, or one-digit levels of generalization, if this should be desired. However, if data are collected and coded at these more general levels, it should be recognized that flexibility in the use of the data coded will also be substantially reduced.

TABLE 1.—AN EXAMPLE OF THE USE OF THE STANDARD LAND USE CODING SYSTEM FOR DEVELOPING NEW CLASSIFICATIONS

Local code no.	*New classification*	*Code*	*Categories from the standard land use coding system*
Locally determined	**Offices** This summary classification is developed by combining the following categories:		All land use activities with a 1 or 2 in the auxiliary position, plus the following categories:
		611	Banking and bank-related functions.
		6122	Agricultural, business, and personal credit services (including credit unions).
		6129	Other credit services (other than banks) NEC.
		613	Security and commodity brokers, dealers, exchanges, and services.
		614	Insurance carriers, agents, brokers, and services.
		615	Real estate and related services.
		616	Holding and investment services.
		6311	Advertising services (general).
		632	Consumer and mercantile credit reporting services; adjustment and collection services.
		6331	Direct mail advertising services.
		6339	Stenographic services and other duplicating and mailing services, NEC.
		635	News syndicate services.
		636	Employment services.
		6392	Business and management consulting services.
		6393	Detective and protective services.
		6398	Motion picture distribution and services.
		6511	Physicians' services.
		6512	Dental services.
		652	Legal services.
		659	Other professional services, NEC.
		671	Executive, legislative, and judicial functions.
		699	Other miscellaneous services, NEC.

TABLE 2.—DEVELOPING NEW CLASSIFICATIONS—THREE APPLICATIONS OF THE STANDARD LAND USE CODING SYSTEM [1]

Local code	***Central business district planning*** *(example classifications)*	*Standard code*
Locally determined	Residential:	
	Household units	11.
	Group quarters	12.
	Residential hotels	13.
	Transient lodgings	15.
	Manufacturing	2 and 3.
	Wholesale trade:	
	With storage area	51.
	Retail Trade and Services:	
	Convenience goods—retail	52, 54, 553, 591, 592, 594, 596, 598, and 599.
	Shopping goods—retail	53, 551, 552, 559, 56, 57, 593, 595, and 597.
	Personal services	62.
	Repair services	64.
	Banking services	6111.
	Offices	All land use activity with a 1 or 2 in the auxiliary code position plus those categories listed in table 1.
	Warehousing and Storage	637 plus all land use activities with an auxiliary code of 4.
	Transportation, Communication, and Utilities	4
	Public and Quasipublic Institutions:	
	Hospitals and medical clinics	6513 and 6517.
	Government protective services	672.
	Postal services	673.
	Educational services	68.
	Religious services	691.
	Welfare and charitable services	692.
	Cultural activities and nature exhibitions	71.
	Entertainment and Recreation:	
	Entertainment assembly	721.

Local code	***General transportation planning*** *(example classifications)*	*Standard code*
Locally determined	Residential:	
	Household units	11.
	Group quarters	12.
	Residential hotels	13.
	Mobile home parks or courts	14.
	Transient lodgings	15.
	Manufacturing, Communication, and Utilities:	
	Manufacturing	2 and 3.
	Communication	47.
	Utilities	48.
	Transportation:	
	Passenger terminals	4113, 4122, 4211 4212, 4213, 4312, and 4411.
	Freight terminals	4114, 4221, 4313, 4412, and 4414.
	Passenger and freight terminals.	4115, 4314, and 4413.
	Right-of-way	4111, 4112, 4121, 4311, 4391, and 45.
	Automobile parking	46 plus all land use activities with an auxiliary code of 5.
	Wholesaling and Warehousing:	
	Wholesale with storage area	51.
	Warehousing and storage	637 plus all land use activities with an auxiliary code of 4.
	Retail Trade and Services:	
	Retail trade	52, 53, 54, 55, 56, 57, 58, and 59.
	Personal services	62.
	Repair services	64.
	Offices	All land use activity with a 1 or 2 in the auxiliary code position plus those categories listed in table 1.

Local code	***General urban planning*** *(example classifications)*	*Standard code*
Locally determined	Residential:	
	Household units	11.
	Group quarters	12.
	Residential hotels	13.
	Mobile home parks or courts	14.
	Transient lodgings	15.
	Manufacturing and Nonmanufacturing Industry:	
	Light and heavy manufacturing.	2 and 3.
	Warehousing and storage	637 plus all land use activities with an auxiliary code of 4.
	Contract Construction	66.
	Transportation, Communication, and Utilities.	4.
	Commercial and Service:	
	Wholesale trade	51.
	Retail trade	52, 53, 54, 55, 56, 57, 58, and 59.
	Finance, insurance, and real estate services.	61.
	Personal services	62.
	Business services	63.
	Repair services	64.
	Professional services	65 (excluding hospital service code 6513)
	Community:	
	Hospital services	6513.
	Executive, legislative, and judicial functions.	671.
	Government protective functions.	672.
	Postal services	673.
	Educational services	68.
	Religious activities	691.
	Welfare and charitable services.	692.
	Cultural activities and nature exhibitions.	71.
	Public assembly, miscellaneous purposes.	723.
	Playgrounds and athletic areas.	742.

Public assembly, miscellaneous purposes	723.
Eating and drinking	58.
Bowling	7417.
Gymnasiums and athletic clubs	7425.
Parks (leisure and ornamental)	762.
Vacant or Unused:	
Undeveloped and unused land area	91.
Water areas	93.
Vacant floor area	94.
Under construction	95.

Public and Quasipublic:	
Hospitals and medical clinics	6513 and 6517.
Government protective services.	672.
Postal services	673.
Correctional institutions	674.
Educational services	68.
Religious activities	691.
Cultural activities	711.
Military Bases and Reservations.	675.
Entertainment and Recreation:	
Nature exhibitions	712.
Public assembly	72.
Amusements	73.
Recreational activities	74.
Parks	76.
Agricultural, Mining, and Undeveloped Areas:	
Agriculture	81.
Mining	85.
Commercial and noncommercial forested areas.	831 and 922.
Undeveloped and unused land area.	91.
Water areas	93.
Vacant floor area	94.

Leisure:	
Entertainment assembly	721.
Sports assembly and activities	722, 741, and 743.
Amusements	73.
Parks and reserves	76 and 921.
Agricultural and Open Areas:	
Agriculture	81.
Commercial forestry production and nonreserve forests (undeveloped).	831 and 922.
Undeveloped and unused land area.	91.
Water areas	93.

[1] This table is for illustration purposes only. The combination of categories under each of the 3 types of planning studies are *not* to be considered the recommended categories for these studies.

If a land use inventory records and codes data at a more generalized level of detail than the four-digit level, it will not be possible to determine whether a specific activity (which is included in the more generalized classification) is actually taking place in the study area. For example, if "Cultural, entertainment, and recreational" activities are identified and coded at the one-digit level, it will not be possible to determine from the data file whether the study area contains a planetarium, an amphitheater, or a race track.

In addition to this, if a study group decides to make planning studies calling for different classifications of the data collected, it will be restricted in the regrouping of the data to the generalized classifications already coded. While this may seem an obvious point, it is stressed here since this may be a critical decision in planning the land use inventory.

IV The Categories and Code Numbers

A. A STANDARD SYSTEM FOR IDENTIFYING AND CODING LAND USE ACTIVITIES—ONE- AND TWO-DIGIT LEVELS

Code	*Category*	*Code*	*Category*
1	Residential.	11	Household units.
		12	Group quarters.
		13	Residential hotels.
		14	Mobile home parks or courts.
		15	Transient lodgings.
		19	Other residential, NEC.[1]
2	Manufacturing.	21	Food and kindred products—manufacturing.
		22	Textile mill products—manufacturing.
		23	Apparel and other finished products made from fabrics, leather, and similar materials—manufacturing.
		24	Lumber and wood products (except furniture)—manufacturing.
		25	Furniture and fixtures—manufacturing.

[1] NEC—Not elsewhere coded.

Code	*Category*	*Code*	*Category*
2	Manufacturing.	26	Paper and allied products—manufacturing.
		27	Printing, publishing, and allied industries.
		28	Chemicals and allied products—manufacturing.
		29	Petroleum refining and related industries.
3	Manufacturing (continued).	31	Rubber and miscellaneous plastic products—manufacturing.
		32	Stone, clay, and glass products—manufacturing.
		33	Primary metal industries.
		34	Fabricated metal products—manufacturing.
		35	Professional, scientific, and controlling instruments; photographic and optical goods; watches and clocks—manufacturing.
		39	Miscellaneous manufacturing, NEC.
4	Transportation, communication, and utilities.	41	Railroad, rapid rail transit, and street railway transportation.
		42	Motor vehicle transportation.
		43	Aircraft transportation.
		44	Marine craft transportation.
		45	Highway and street right-of-way.
		46	Automobile parking.
		47	Communication.
		48	Utilities.
		49	Other transportation, communication, and utilities, NEC.
5	Trade.	51	Wholesale trade.
		52	Retail trade—building materials, hardware, and farm equipment.
		53	Retail trade—general merchandise.
		54	Retail trade—food.
		55	Retail trade—automotive, marine craft, aircraft, and accessories.
		56	Retail trade—apparel and accessories.
		57	Retail trade—furniture, home furnishings, and equipment.
		58	Retail trade—eating and drinking.
		59	Other retail trade, NEC.
6	Services.	61	Finance, insurance, and real estate services.
		62	Personal services.
		63	Business services.
		64	Repair services.
		65	Professional services.
		66	Contract construction services.
		67	Governmental services.
		68	Educational services.
		69	Miscellaneous services.
7	Cultural, entertainment, and recreational.	71	Cultural activities and nature exhibitions.
		72	Public assembly.
		73	Amusements.
		74	Recreational activities.
		75	Resorts and group camps.
		76	Parks.

Code	Category	Code	Category
7	Cultural, entertainment, and recreational—Continued.	79	Other cultural, entertainment, and recreational, NEC.
8	Resource production and extraction.	81	Agriculture.
		82	Agricultural related activities.
		83	Forestry activities and related services.
		84	Fishing activities and related services.
		85	Mining activities and related services.
		89	Other resource production and extraction, NEC.
9	Undeveloped land and water areas.	91	Undeveloped and unused land area (excluding noncommercial forest development).
		92	Noncommercial forest development.
		93	Water areas.
		94	Vacant floor area.
		95	Under construction.
		99	Other undeveloped land and water areas, NEC.

32

B. A STANDARD SYSTEM FOR IDENTIFYING AND CODING LAND USE ACTIVITIES—TWO-, THREE-, AND FOUR-DIGIT LEVELS

Code	*Category*	*Code*	*Category*	*Code*	*Category*	*SIC Reference* [1]
11	Household units.	110	Household units.	1100	Household units.[2]	—
12	Group quarters.	121	Rooming and boarding houses.	1210	Rooming and boarding houses.[3]	7021
		122	Membership lodgings.	1221	Fraternity and sorority houses.	[4] Incl. 7041
				1229	Other membership lodgings, NEC.[5]	Incl. 7041
		123	Residence halls or dormitories.	1231	Nurses' homes.	—
				1232	College dormitories.	—
				1239	Other residence halls or dormitories, NEC.	—
		124	Retirement homes and orphanages.	1241	Retirement homes.	—
				1242	Orphanages.	—
		125	Religious quarters.	1251	Convents.	—
				1252	Monasteries.	—
				1253	Rectories.	—
				1259	Other religious quarters, NEC.	—
		129	Other group quarters, NEC.	1290	Other group quarters, NEC.	—
13	Residential hotels.	130	Residential hotels.	1300	Residential hotels.[6]	Incl. 7011
14	Mobile home parks or courts.	140	Mobile home parks or courts.	1400	Mobile home parks or courts.	7031
15	Transient lodgings.	151	Hotels, tourist courts, and motels.	1510	Hotels, tourist courts, and n:otels.	7011
		159	Other transient lodgings, NEC.	1590	Other transient lodgings, NEC.[7]	—
19	Other residential, NEC.	190	Other residential, NEC.	1900	Other residential, NEC.	—

RESIDENTIAL—1

~~Conservation + Agric~~
~~Montclair, N.J~~
~~S912.C66~~

Agricultural land
in Urban Society
HD205 1982.F87

	TITLE	HRL
	THE LONELINESS OF THE LONG-DIS	
PERCY	THE AFFAIR / C. P. SNOW	
PERCY	HOMECOMING	
PERCY	THE LIGHT AND THE DARK	
PERCY	THE NEW MEN	
PERCY	STRANGERS AND BROTHERS	
PERCY	TIME OF HOPE : A NOVEL	
912	THE ANNOTATED DRACULA : ANNOT	
	TOLKIEN; A LOOK BEHIND THE LOR	
931-	TOLKIEN AND THE CRITICS; ESSAY	
REUEL	J. R. R. TOLKIEN, SCHOLAR AND	
	THE MYTHOLOGY OF MIDDLE-EARTH	
927-	THE FLOOD	
	BRIDESHEAD REVISITED	
966	CHARLES RYDER'S SCHOOLDAYS AND	
966	DECLINE AND FALL	
966	A HANDFUL OF DUST	
966	THE LOVED ONE : AN ANGLO-AMERI	
966	SCOOP	
966	SWORD OF HONOUR; THE FINAL VER	
966	THE DIARIES OF EVELYN WAUGH	
966	THE LETTERS OF EVELYN WAUGH	
	EVELYN WAUGH: A BIOGRAPHY	
1892-	HARRIET HUME, A LONDON FANTASY	
HAM G	ANGEL CAKE	
-1941	BETWEEN THE ACTS	
EN. 1	FRESHWATER : A COMEDY	
-1941	A HAUNTED HOUSE : AND OTHER SH	
-1941	NIGHT AND DAY	
-1941	TO THE LIGHTHOUSE	
THONY	TO THE LIGHTHOUSE (VIRGINIA WO	
	TWENTIETH CENTURY INTERPRETATI	
-1941	THE YEARS	
M	CRITICS ON VIRGINIA WOOLF	
	THE UNKNOWN VIRGINIA WOOLF	
	A MAN OF THE PEOPLE : A NOVEL	
	SHARDIK	
-	THREE PLAYS	
	THE NORMAN [illegible]	

FOOTNOTES

[1] The SIC codes are listed for purposes of reference. They are the codes in the SIC system that most nearly correspond to the 4-digit land use activity indicated. (See ch. III, sec. A3, "The Use of Standard Industrial Classification Nomenclature.") A dash indicates that there is no corresponding SIC code.

[2] Code 1100—"Household units" are defined as a house, an apartment, or other group of rooms, or a single room that is intended for occupancy as separate living quarters. Occupants of "Household units" do not live and eat with other persons in the structure (such as in a boarding house), and there is either (1) direct access from the outside or through a common hall, or (2) there is a kitchen or cooking equipment for the exclusive use of the occupants of the unit. The occupants may be a family, a group of unrelated persons, or a person living alone. Mobile homes not in "Mobile home parks or courts" (code 14), but resting on a permanent type of foundation (e.g., a brick or concrete block foundation) are included as well as units that are vacant or that are used on a seasonal basis. Farm homes are also included under "Household units" and should be identified separately from the remainder of the farm which is coded under "Agriculture," code 81.

[3] Code 1210—"Rooming and boarding houses" are those that have 5 or more persons renting rooms, with or without board, and not related to the head or person in charge. Where there are less than 5 roomers, the total quarters are considered as one "Household unit" and is coded 1100.

[4] "Incl. 7041" is an abbreviation which indicates that the 4-digit land use activity category is only one of several categories of establishments that are included under SIC code 7041.

[5] "NEC" is an abbreviation for "not elsewhere coded."

[6] Code 1300—"Residential hotels" are those that have 75 percent or more of the available accommodations occupied by permanent guests (i.e., persons who reside more than 30 days). Hotels with less than 75 percent are included under code 15, "Transient lodgings."

[7] Code 1590—"Other transient lodgings, NEC" includes such establishments as the YMCA, YWCA, and YMHA when 50 percent or more of the floor area is devoted to lodging and associated activities and when less than 75 percent of the accommodations are occupied by permanent guests. If 75 percent or more of the guests are permanent, use code 1300. If 50 percent or more of the floor area is devoted to recreational activity, use code 7424, "Recreation centers (general)."

B. A STANDARD SYSTEM FOR IDENTIFYING AND CODING LAND USE ACTIVITIES—TWO-, THREE-, AND FOUR-DIGIT LEVELS—Continued

Code	Category	Code	Category	Code	Category	SIC Reference [1]
21	Food and kindred products—manufacturing.	211	Meat products—manufacturing.	2111	Meat packing—manufacturing.	2011
				2112	Sausages and other prepared meat products—manufacturing.	2013
				2113	Poultry and small game dressing and packing.	2015
		212	Dairy products—manufacturing.	2121	Creamery butter—manufacturing.	2021
				2122	Cheese, natural and processed.	2022
				2123	Condensed and evaporated milk—manufacturing.	2023
				2124	Ice cream and frozen desserts—manufacturing.	2024
				2125	Fluid milk processing.	2026
		213	Canning and preserving of fruits, vegetables, and seafoods.	2131	Canning and curing seafoods.	2031
				2132	Canning specialty foods.	2032
				2133	Canning fruits, vegetables, preserves, jams, and jellies.	2033
				2134	Drying and dehydrating fruits and vegetables.	2034
				2135	Pickling fruits and vegetables; vegetable sauces and seasonings; salad dressings—manufacturing.	2035
				2136	Fresh or frozen packaged fish and seafoods.	2036
				2137	Frozen fruits, fruit juices, vegetables, and specialties.	2037
		214	Grain mill products—manufacturing.	2141	Flour and other grain mill products.	2041
				2142	Preparing feeds for animals and fowls.	2042
				2143	Cereal preparations.	2043
				2144	Rice milling.	2044

		2145	Blending and preparing flour.	2045
		2146	Wet corn milling.	2046
215	Bakery products—manufacturing.	2150	Bakery products—manufacturing.	205
216	Sugar—manufacturing.	2160	Sugar—manufacturing.	206
217	Confectionery and related products—manufacturing.	2171	Candy and other confectionery products—manufacturing.	2071
		2172	Chocolate and cocoa products—manufacturing.	2072
		2173	Chewing gum—manufacturing.	2073
218	Beverage—manufacturing.	2181	Malt liquors—manufacturing.	2082
		2182	Malt—manufacturing.	2083
		2183	Wine, brandy, and brandy spirits—manufacturing.	2084
		2184	Distilling, rectifying, and blending liquors.	2085
		2185	Bottling and canning soft drinks and carbonated waters.	2086
		2186	Flavor extracts and flavoring sirups manufacturing, NEC.	2087
219	Other food preparations and kindred products manufacturing, NEC.	2191	Cottonseed oil milling.	2091
		2192	Soybean oil milling.	2092
		2193	Vegetable oil milling (except cottonseed and soybean).	2093
		2194	Animal and marine fats and oils (including grease and tallow)—manufacturing.	2094
		2195	Roasting coffee and coffee products—manufacturing.	2095
		2196	Shortening, table oils, margarine, and other edible fats and oils—manufacturing.	2096
		2197	Ice—manufacturing.	2097
		2198	Macaroni, spaghetti, vermicelli, and noodles—manufacturing.	2098
		2199	Other food preparations and kindred products manufacturing, NEC.	2099

B. A STANDARD SYSTEM FOR IDENTIFYING AND CODING LAND USE ACTIVITIES—TWO-, THREE-, AND FOUR-DIGIT LEVELS—Continued

Code	Category	Code	Category	Code	Category	SIC Reference [1]
22	Textile mill products—manufacturing.	221	Broad and narrow woven fabrics and other smallwares (cotton, manmade fibers, silk, and wool)—manufacturing.	2210	Broad and narrow woven fabrics and other smallwares (cotton, manmade fibers, silk, and wool)—manufacturing.	221, 222, 223 and 224
		222	Knit goods—manufacturing.	2220	Knit goods—manufacturing.	225
		223	Dyeing and finishing of textiles (except wool fabrics and knit goods).	2230	Dyeing and finishing of textiles (except wool fabrics and knit goods).	226
		224	Floor coverings (rugs and carpets)—manufacturing.	2240	Floor coverings (rugs and carpets)—manufacturing.	227
		225	Yarns and threads—manufacturing.	2250	Yarns and threads—manufacturing.	228
		229	Other textile goods manufacturing, NEC.	2291	Felt goods (except woven felts and hats)—manufacturing.	2291
				2292	Lace goods—manufacturing.	2292
				2293	Padding and upholstery filling—manufacturing.	2293
				2294	Processing waste and recovering fibers and flock.	2294
				2295	Artificial leather and oil cloth manufacturing and other impregnating and coating fabrics (except rubberizing).	2295
				2296	Tire cord and fabric—manufacturing.	2296
				2297	Wool scouring, worsted combing, and towing to top.	2297
				2299	Other textile goods manufacturing, NEC.	2299

23	Apparel and other finished products made from fabrics, leather, and similar materials—manufacturing.	231	Men's, youths', and boys' suits, coats, and overcoats—manufacturing.	2310	Men's, youths', and boys' suits, coats, and overcoats—manufacturing.	231
		232	Men's, youths', and boys' furnishings, work clothing, and allied garments—manufacturing.	2320	Men's, youths', and boys' furnishings, work clothing, and allied garments—manufacturing.	232
		233	Women's, misses', juniors', girls', children's, and infants' outerwear—manufacturing.	2330	Women's, misses', juniors', girls', children's, and infants' outerwear—manufacturing.	233 and 236
		234	Women's, misses', children's, and infants' undergarments—manufacturing.	2340	Women's, misses', children's, and infants' undergarments—manufacturing.	234
		235	Hats, caps, and millinery—manufacturing.	2350	Hats, caps, and millinery—manufacturing.	235
		236	Leather and leather products—manufacturing.	2361	Leather tanning and finishing.	3111
				2362	Industrial leather belting and packing—manufacturing.	3121
				2363	Boot and shoe cut stock and findings—manufacturing.	3131
				2364	Footwear (except rubber)—manufacturing.	314
				2365	Leather gloves and mittens—manufacturing.	315
				2366	Luggage—manufacturing.	316
				2367	Handbags and other personal leather goods—manufacturing.	317
				2369	Other leather products manufacturing, NEC.	319
		237	Fur goods—manufacturing.	2370	Fur goods—manufacturing.	237

B. A STANDARD SYSTEM FOR IDENTIFYING AND CODING LAND USE ACTIVITIES—TWO-, THREE-, AND FOUR-DIGIT LEVELS—Continued

Code	*Category*	*Code*	*Category*	*Code*	*Category*	*SIC Reference* [1]
23	Apparel and other finished products made from fabrics, leather, and similar materials—manufacturing—Continued	238	Miscellaneous apparel and accessories—manufacturing.	2381	Dress and work gloves (except knit and all leather)—manufacturing.	2381
				2382	Robes and dressing gowns—manufacturing.	2384
				2383	Raincoats and other waterproof outer garments—manufacturing.	2385
				2384	Leather and sheep lined clothing—manufacturing.	2386
				2385	Apparel belts—manufacturing.	2387
				2389	Other miscellaneous apparel and accessory manufacturing, NEC.	2389
		239	Other fabricated textile products manufacturing, NEC.	2391	Curtains and draperies—manufacturing.	2391
				2392	Housefurnishings (except curtains and draperies)—manufacturing.	2392
				2393	Textile bags—manufacturing.	2393
				2394	Canvas products—manufacturing.	2394
				2395	Pleating, decorative and novelty stitching and tucking for the trade.	2395
				2396	Apparel findings and related products—manufacturing.	2396
				2399	Other fabricated textile products manufacturing, NEC.	2397 and 2399
24	Lumber and wood products (except furniture)—manufacturing.	241	Logging camps and logging contractors.	2410	Logging camps and logging contractors.	241
		242	Sawmills and planing mills.	2421	Sawmills and planing mills, general.	2421
				2422	Hardwood dimension and flooring—manufacturing.	2426

				2429	Special sawmill products manufacturing, NEC.	2429
		243	Millwork, veneer, plywood, and prefabricated structural wood products—manufacturing.	2431	Millwork.	2431
				2432	Veneer and plywood—manufacturing.	2432
				2433	Prefabricating wooden buildings and structural members—manufacturing.	2433
		244	Wooden containers—manufacturing.	2440	Wooden containers—manufacturing.	244
		249	Other lumber and wood products (except furniture) manufacturing, NEC.	2491	Wood preserving.	2491
				2499	Other lumber and wood products (except furniture) manufacturing, NEC.	2499
25	Furniture and fixtures—manufacturing.	251	Household furniture—manufacturing.	2510	Household furniture—manufacturing.	251
		252	Office furniture—manufacturing.	2520	Office furniture—manufacturing.	252
		253	Public building and related furniture—manufacturing.	2530	Public building and related furniture—manufacturing.	2531
		254	Partitions, shelving, lockers, and office and store fixtures—manufacturing.	2540	Partitions, shelving, lockers, and office and store fixtures—manufacturing.	254
		259	Other furniture and fixtures manufacturing, NEC.	2591	Venetian blinds and shades—manufacturing.	2591
				2599	Other furniture and fixtures manufacturing, NEC.	2599
26	Paper and allied products—manufacturing.	261	Pulp—manufacturing.	2610	Pulp—manufacturing.	261
		262	Paper (except building paper)—manufacturing.	2620	Paper (except building paper)—manufacturing.	262

B. A STANDARD SYSTEM FOR IDENTIFYING AND CODING LAND USE ACTIVITIES—TWO-, THREE-, AND FOUR-DIGIT LEVELS—Continued

Code	*Category*	*Code*	*Category*	*Code*	*Category*	*SIC Reference* [1]
26	Paper and allied products—manufacturing—Con.	263	Paperboard—manufacturing.	2630	Paperboard—manufacturing.	263
		264	Converted paper and paperboard products (except containers and boxes)—manufacturing.	2641	Paper coating and glazing.	2641
				2642	Envelope—manufacturing.	2642
				2643	Bags (except textile bags)—manufacturing.	2643
				2644	Wallpaper—manufacturing.	2644
				2645	Die cut paper and paperboard; and cardboard—manufacturing.	2645
				2646	Pressed and molded pulp goods—manufacturing.	2646
				2647	Sanitary paper products—manufacturing.	2647
				2649	Other converted paper and paperboard products (except containers and boxes) manufacturing, NEC.	2649
		265	Paperboard containers and boxes—manufacturing.	2650	Paperboard containers and boxes—manufacturing.	265
		266	Building paper and building board—manufacturing.	2660	Building paper and building board—manufacturing.	266
27	Printing, publishing, and allied industries.	271	Newspapers: publishing, publishing and printing.	2710	Newspapers: publishing, publishing and printing.	271
		272	Periodicals: publishing, publishing and printing.	2720	Periodicals: publishing, publishing and printing.	272
		273	Books: publishing, publishing and printing.	2730	Books: publishing, publishing and printing.	273
		274	Commercial printing.	2740	Commercial printing.	275
		275	Manifold business forms—manufacturing.	2750	Manifold business forms—manufacturing.	276

		276	Greeting card—manufacturing.	2760	Greeting card—manufacturing.	277
		277	Bookbinding and related industries—manufacturing.	2771	Blankbooks, looseleaf binders, and devices—manufacturing.	2782
				2772	Bookbinding and miscellaneous related work—manufacturing.	2789
		278	Printing trade service industries.	2781	Typesetting.	2791
				2782	Photoengraving.	2793
				2783	Electrotyping and stereotyping.	2794
				2789	Other printing trade service industries, NEC.	2799
		279	Other printing and publishing, NEC.	2790	Other printing and publishing, NEC.	274
28	Chemicals and allied products—manufacturing.	281	Industrial inorganic and organic chemicals—manufacturing.	2810	Industrial inorganic and organic chemicals—manufacturing.	281
		282	Plastics materials and synthetic resins, synthetic rubber, synthetic and other manmade fibers (except glass)—manufacturing.	2820	Plastics materials and synthetic resins, synthetic rubber, synthetic and other manmade fibers (except glass)—manufacturing.	282
		283	Drug—manufacturing.	2831	Biological products—manufacturing.	2831
				2832	Medicinal chemicals and botanical products—manufacturing.	2833
				2833	Pharmaceutical preparations—manufacturing.	2834
		284	Soap, detergents, and cleaning preparations, perfumes, cosmetics, and other toilet preparations—manufacturing.	2841	Soap and detergents (except specialty cleaners)—manufacturing.	2841
				2842	Specialty cleaning, polishing, and sanitation preparations (except soap and detergents)—manufacturing.	2842
				2843	Surface active agents, finishing agents, sulfonated oils, and assistants—manufacturing.	2843
				2844	Perfumes, cosmetics, and other toilet preparations—manufacturing.	2844

B. A STANDARD SYSTEM FOR IDENTIFYING AND CODING LAND USE ACTIVITIES—TWO-, THREE-, AND FOUR-DIGIT LEVELS—Continued

Code	Category	Code	Category	Code	Category	SIC Reference [1]
28	Chemicals and allied products—manufacturing—Continued	285	Paints, varnishes, lacquers, enamels, and allied products—manufacturing.	2850	Paints, varnishes, lacquers, enamels, and allied products—manufacturing.	285
		286	Gum and wood chemicals—manufacturing.	2860	Gum and wood chemicals—manufacturing.	286
		287	Agricultural chemicals—manufacturing.	2870	Agricultural chemicals—manufacturing.	287
		289	Other chemicals and allied products—manufacturing, NEC.	2891	Glue and gelatin—manufacturing.	2891
				2892	Explosives—manufacturing.	2892
				2893	Printing ink—manufacturing.	2893
				2894	Carbon black—manufacturing.	2895
				2899	Other chemicals and allied products manufacturing, NEC.	2899
29	Petroleum refining and related industries.	291	Petroleum refining.	2910	Petroleum refining.	291
		292	Paving and roofing materials—manufacturing.	2921	Paving mixtures and blocks—manufacturing.	2951
				2922	Asphalt felts and coatings—manufacturing.	2952
		299	Other petroleum refining and related industries, NEC.	2991	Lubricating oils and greases—manufacturing.	2992
				2999	Other petroleum and coal products manufacturing, NEC.	2999
31	Rubber and miscellaneous plastic products—manufacturing.	311	Tires and inner tubes—manufacturing.	3110	Tires and inner tubes—manufacturing.	301

		312	Rubber footwear—manufacturing.	3120	Rubber footwear—manufacturing.	302
		313	Reclaiming rubber.	3130	Reclaiming rubber.	303
		314	Miscellaneous plastic products—manufacturing.	3140	Miscellaneous plastic products—manufacturing.	307
		319	Other fabricated rubber products manufacturing, NEC.	3190	Other fabricated rubber products manufacturing, NEC.	306
32	Stone, clay, and glass products—manufacturing.	321	Flat glass—manufacturing.	3210	Flat glass—manufacturing.	3211 and incl. 3231
		322	Glass and glassware (pressed or blown)—manufacturing.	3221	Glass containers—manufacturing.	3221 and incl. 3231
				3229	Other glass and glassware (pressed or blown) manufacturing, NEC.	3229 and incl. 3231
		323	Cement (hydraulic)—manufacturing.	3230	Cement (hydraulic)—manufacturing.	324
		324	Structural clay products—manufacturing.	3241	Brick and structural clay tile—manufacturing.	3251
				3242	Ceramic wall and floor tile—manufacturing.	3253
				3243	Clay refractories—manufacturing.	3255
				3249	Other structural clay products manufacturing, NEC.	3259
		325	Pottery and related products—manufacturing.	3251	Vitreous china plumbing fixtures, china, earthenware fittings, and bathroom accessories—manufacturing.	3261
				3252	Vitreous china table and kitchen articles—manufacturing.	3262
				3253	Fine earthenware (whiteware) table and kitchen articles—manufacturing.	3263
				3254	Porcelain electrical supplies—manufacturing.	3264
				3259	Other pottery and related products manufacturing, NEC.	3269

MANUFACTURING—2 AND 3

B. A STANDARD SYSTEM FOR IDENTIFYING AND CODING LAND USE ACTIVITIES—TWO-, THREE-, AND FOUR-DIGIT LEVELS—Continued

Code	Category	Code	Category	Code	Category	SIC Reference [1]
32	Stone, clay, and glass products—manufacturing—Continued	326	Concrete, gypsum, and plaster products—manufacturing.	3261	Concrete brick and block—manufacturing.	3271
				3262	Concrete products (excluding brick and block)—manufacturing.	3272
				3263	Concrete (ready mixed)—manufacturing.	3273
				3264	Lime products—manufacturing.	3274
				3265	Gypsum products—manufacturing.	3275
		327	Cut stone and stone products—manufacturing.	3270	Cut stone and stone products—manufacturing.	328
		328	Abrasive, asbestos, and miscellaneous nonmetallic mineral products—manufacturing.	3280	Abrasive, asbestos, and miscellaneous nonmetallic mineral products—manufacturing.	329
33	Primary metal industries.	331	Blast furnaces, steel works, and the rolling and finishing of ferrous metals.	3311	Blast furnaces (including coke ovens), steel works, and the rolling of ferrous metals.	3312
				3312	Electrometallurgical products—manufacturing.	3313
				3313	Steel wire drawing and steel nails and spikes—manufacturing.	3315
				3314	Cold rolled sheet, strip, and bars—manufacturing.	3316
				3315	Steel pipe and tubes—manufacturing.	3317
		332	Iron and steel foundries.	3320	Iron and steel foundries.	332
		333	Primary smelting and refining of nonferrous metals.	3331	Primary smelting and refining of copper.	3331

				3332	Primary smelting and refining of lead.	3332
				3333	Primary smelting and refining of zinc.	3333
				3334	Primary production of aluminum.	3334
				3339	Other primary smelting and refining of nonferrous metals, NEC.	3339
		334	Secondary smelting and refining of nonferrous metals and alloys.	3340	Secondary smelting and refining of nonferrous metals and alloys.	334
		335	Rolling, drawing, and extruding of nonferrous metals.	3351	Rolling, drawing, and extruding of copper.	3351
				3352	Rolling, drawing, and extruding of aluminum.	3352
				3353	Rolling, drawing, and extruding of nonferrous metals (except copper and aluminum).	3356
				3354	Drawing and insulating of nonferrous wire.	3357
		336	Nonferrous foundries.	3360	Nonferrous foundries.	336
		339	Other primary metal industries, NEC.	3390	Other primary metal industries, NEC.	339
34	Fabricated metal products—manufacturing.	341	Ordnance and accessories.	3411	Guns, howitzers, mortars, and related equipment—manufacturing.	191
				3412	Ammunition (except small arms) manufacturing and complete assembling of guided missiles and space vehicles.	192
				3413	Tanks and tank components—manufacturing.	193
				3414	Sighting and fire control equipment—manufacturing.	194
				3415	Small arms—manufacturing.	195
				3416	Small arms ammunition—manufacturing.	196
				3419	Other ordnance and accessories manufacturing, NEC.	199

MANUFACTURING—2 AND 3

B. A STANDARD SYSTEM FOR IDENTIFYING AND CODING LAND USE ACTIVITIES—TWO-, THREE-, AND FOUR-DIGIT LEVELS—Continued

Code	*Category*	*Code*	*Category*	*Code*	*Category*	*SIC Reference* [1]
34	Fabricated metal products—manufacturing—Continued	342	Machinery (except electrical)—manufacturing.	3421	Engines and turbines—manufacturing.	351
				3422	Farm machinery and equipment—manufacturing.	352
				3423	Construction, mining, and materials handling machinery and equipment—manufacturing.	353
				3424	Metalworking machinery and equipment—manufacturing.	354
				3425	Special industry machinery (except metalworking machinery)—manufacturing.	355
				3426	General industrial machinery and equipment—manufacturing.	356
				3427	Office, computing, and accounting machines—manufacturing.	357
				3428	Service industry machines—manufacturing.	358
				3429	Other machinery manufacturing (except electrical), NEC.	359
		343	Electrical machinery, equipment, and supplies—manufacturing.	3431	Electrical transmission and distribution equipment—manufacturing.	361
				3432	Electrical industrial apparatus—manufacturing.	362
				3433	Household appliances—manufacturing.	363
				3434	Electric lighting and wiring equipment—manufacturing.	364

		3435	Radio and television receiving sets (except communication types)—manufacturing.	365
		3436	Communication equipment—manufacturing.	366
		3437	Electronic components and accessories—manufacturing.	367
		3439	Other electrical machinery, equipment, and supplies manufacturing, NEC.	369
344	Transportation equipment—manufacturing.	3441	Motor vehicles and motor vehicle equipment—manufacturing.	371
		3442	Aircraft and parts—manufacturing.	372
		3443	Ship and boat building and repairing.	373
		3444	Railroad equipment—manufacturing.	374
		3445	Motorcycles, bicycles, and parts—manufacturing.	375
		3449	Other transportation equipment manufacturing, NEC.	379
349	Other fabricated metal products manufacturing, NEC.	3491	Metal cans—manufacturing.	341
		3492	Cutlery, hand tools, and general hardware—manufacturing.	342
		3493	Heating apparatus (except electrical) and plumbing fixtures—manufacturing.	343
		3494	Fabricated structural metal products—manufacturing.	344
		3495	Screw machine products and bolts, nuts, screws, rivets, and washers—manufacturing.	345
		3496	Metal stamping—manufacturing.	346
		3497	Coating, engraving, and allied services.	347
		3498	Fabricated wire products (miscellaneous products)—manufacturing.	348
		3499	Other fabricated metal products manufacturing, NEC.	349

48

B. A STANDARD SYSTEM FOR IDENTIFYING AND CODING LAND USE ACTIVITIES—TWO-, THREE-, AND FOUR-DIGIT LEVELS—Continued

Code	*Category*	*Code*	*Category*	*Code*	*Category*	*SIC Reference* [1]
35	Professional, scientific, and controlling instruments; photographic and optical goods; watches and clocks—manufacturing.	351	Engineering, laboratory, and scientific and research instruments and associated equipment—manufacturing.	3510	Engineering, laboratory, and scientific and research instruments and associated equipment—manufacturing.	381
		352	Instruments for measuring, controlling, and indicating physical characteristics—manufacturing.	3521	Mechanical measuring and controlling instruments (except automatic temperature controls)—manufacturing.	3821
				3522	Automatic temperature controls—manufacturing.	3822
		353	Optical instruments and lenses—manufacturing.	3530	Optical instruments and lenses—manufacturing.	383
		354	Surgical, medical, and dental instruments and supplies—manufacturing.	3541	Surgical and medical instruments and apparatus—manufacturing.	3841
				3542	Orthopedic, prosthetic, and surgical appliances and supplies—manufacturing.	3842
				3543	Dental equipment and supplies—manufacturing.	3843
		355	Ophthalmic goods—manufacturing.	3550	Ophthalmic goods—manufacturing.	385
		356	Photographic equipment and supplies—manufacturing.	3560	Photographic equipment and supplies—manufacturing.	386

		357	Watches, clocks, clockwork operated devices, and parts—manufacturing.	3570	Watches, clocks, clockwork operated devices, and parts—manufacturing.	387
39	Miscellaneous manufacturing, NEC.	391	Jewelry, silverware, and plated ware—manufacturing.	3911	Jewelry and precious metals—manufacturing.	3911
				3912	Jewelers' findings and materials—manufacturing.	3912
				3913	Lapidary work.	3913
				3914	Silverware and plated ware—manufacturing.	3914
		392	Musical instruments and parts—manufacturing.	3920	Musical instruments and parts—manufacturing.	393
		393	Toys, amusement, sporting, and athletic goods—manufacturing.	3930	Toys, amusement, sporting, and athletic goods—manufacturing.	394
		394	Pens, pencils, and other office and artists' materials—manufacturing.	3940	Pens, pencils, and other office and artists' materials—manufacturing.	395
		395	Costume jewelry, costume novelties, buttons, and miscellaneous notions (except precious metals)—manufacturing.	3950	Costume jewelry, costume novelties, buttons, and miscellaneous notions (except precious metals)—manufacturing.	396
		396	Tobacco—manufacturing.	3961	Cigarettes—manufacturing.	211
				3962	Cigars—manufacturing.	212
				3963	Tobacco (chewing and smoking) and snuff—manufacturing.	213
				3964	Tobacco stemming and redrying.	214
		397	Motion picture production.	3970	Motion picture production.	7811

MANUFACTURING—2 AND 3

B. A STANDARD SYSTEM FOR IDENTIFYING AND CODING LAND USE ACTIVITIES—TWO-, THREE-, AND FOUR-DIGIT LEVELS—Continued

Code	Category	Code	Category	Code	Category	SIC Reference [1]
39	Miscellaneous manufacturing, NEC—Continued	399	Other miscellaneous manufacturing, NEC.	3991	Brooms and brushes—manufacturing.	3981
				3992	Linoleum, asphalted-felt-base, and other hard surface floor cover manufacturing, NEC.	3982
				3993	Matches—manufacturing.	3983
				3994	Lamp shades—manufacturing.	3987
				3995	Morticians' goods—manufacturing.	3988
				3996	Fur dressing and dyeing	3992
				3997	Signs and advertising displays—manufacturing.	3993
				3998	Umbrellas, parasols, and canes—manufacturing.	3995
				3999	Other miscellaneous manufacturing, NEC.	3984 and 3999

FOOTNOTES

[1] The SIC codes are listed for purposes of reference. They are the codes in the SIC system that most nearly correspond to the 4-digit land use activity indicated. (See ch. III, sec. A3, "The Use of Standard Industrial Classification Nomenclature.") A dash indicates that there is no corresponding SIC code.

Code	Category	Code	Category	Code	Category	SIC Reference[1]
41	Railroad, rapid rail transit, and street railway transportation.	411	Railroad transportation.	4111	Railroad right-of-way (excluding switching and marshaling yards).	—
				4112	Railroad switching and marshaling yards.	—
				4113	Railroad terminals (passenger).	—
				4114	Railroad terminals (freight).	—
				4115	Railroad terminals (passenger and freight).	—
				4116	Railroad equipment and maintenance.	—
				4119	Other railroad transportation, NEC.	—
		412	Rapid rail transit and street railway transportation.	4121	Rapid rail transit and street railway right-of-way.[2]	—
				4122	Rapid rail transit and street railway passenger terminals.[3]	—
				4123	Rapid rail transit and street railway equipment maintenance.	—
				4129	Other rapid rail transit and street railway transportation, NEC.	—
42	Motor vehicle transportation.	421	Bus transportation.	4211	Bus passenger terminals (intercity).[4]	—
				4212	Bus passenger terminals (local).[4]	—
				4213	Bus passenger terminals (intercity and local).[4]	—
				4214	Bus garaging and equipment maintenance.	—
				4219	Other bus transportation, NEC.	—
		422	Motor freight transportation.	4221	Motor freight terminals.	—
				4222	Motor freight garaging and equipment maintenance.	—
				4229	Other motor freight transportation, NEC.	—

B. A STANDARD SYSTEM FOR IDENTIFYING AND CODING LAND USE ACTIVITIES—TWO-, THREE-, AND FOUR-DIGIT LEVELS—Continued

Code	Category	Code	Category	Code	Category	SIC Reference [1]
42	Motor vehicle transportation—Continued	429	Other motor vehicle transportation, NEC.	4291	Taxicab transportation.	4121
				4299	Other motor vehicle transportation, NEC.	—
43	Aircraft transportation.	431	Airports and flying fields.	4311	Airport and flying field landing/takeoff fields.	—
				4312	Airport and flying field terminals (passenger).	—
				4313	Airport and flying field terminals (freight).	—
				4314	Airport and flying field terminals (passenger and freight).	—
				4315	Aircraft storage and equipment maintenance.	—
				4319	Other airports and flying fields, NEC.	—
		439	Other aircraft transportation, NEC.	4391	Heliport landing/takeoff pads.[5]	—
				4399	Other aircraft transportation, NEC.	—
44	Marine craft transportation.[6]	441	Marine terminals.[7]	4411	Marine terminals (passenger).[8]	—
				4412	Marine terminals (freight).	—
				4413	Marine terminals (passenger and freight).	—
				4414	Marine terminals (commercial fishing).	—
				4419	Other marine terminals, NEC.	—
		449	Other marine craft transportation, NEC.	4490	Other marine craft transportation, NEC.	—
45	Highway and street right-of-way.	451	Freeways.	4510	Freeways.[9]	—
		452	Expressways.	4520	Expressways.[10]	—

		453	Parkways.	4530	Parkways.[11]	—
		454	Arterial streets.	4540	Arterial streets.[12]	—
		455	Collector/distributor streets.	4550	Collector/distributor streets.[13]	—
		456	Local access streets.	4560	Local access streets.[14]	—
		457	Alleys.	4570	Alleys.[15]	—
		459	Other highway and street right-of-way, NEC.	4590	Other highway and street right-of-way, NEC.	—
46	Automobile parking.	460	Automobile parking.	4600	Automobile parking.[16]	—
47	Communication.	471	Telephone communication.	4711	Telephone exchange stations.	—
				4712	Telephone relay towers (microwave).	—
				4719	Other telephone communication, NEC.	—
		472	Telegraph communication.	4721	Telegraph message centers.	—
				4722	Telegraph transmitting and receiving stations (only).	—
				4729	Other telegraph communication, NEC.	—
		473	Radio communication.	4731	Radio broadcasting studios (only).	—
				4732	Radio transmitting stations and towers.	—
				4739	Other radio communication, NEC.	—
		474	Television communication.	4741	Television broadcasting studios (only).	—
				4742	Television transmitting stations and relay towers.	—
				4749	Other television communication, NEC.	—
		475	Radio and television communication (combined systems).	4751	Radio and television broadcasting studios, only (combined systems).	—
				4759	Other combined radio and television communication, NEC.	—
		479	Other communication, NEC.	4790	Other communication, NEC.	—

B. A STANDARD SYSTEM FOR IDENTIFYING AND CODING LAND USE ACTIVITIES—TWO-, THREE-, AND FOUR-DIGIT LEVELS—Continued

Code	Category	Code	Category	Code	Category	SIC Reference [1]
48	Utilities.	481	Electric utility.	4811	Electric transmission right-of-way.[17]	—
				4812	Electric generation plants.	—
				4813	Electricity regulating substations.	—
				4819	Other electric utility, NEC.	—
		482	Gas utility.	4821	Gas pipeline right-of-way.[17]	—
				4822	Gas production plants.	—
				4823	Natural or manufactured gas storage and distribution points.	—
				4824	Gas pressure control stations.	—
				4829	Other gas utilities, NEC.	—
		483	Water utilities and irrigation.	4831	Water pipeline right-of-way.[17]	—
				4832	Water treatment plants (purification).	—
				4833	Water storage.[18]	—
				4834	Irrigation distribution channels.	—
				4835	Water pressure control stations.	—
				4839	Other water utilities and irrigation, NEC.	—
		484	Sewage disposal.	4841	Sewage treatment plants.	—
				4842	Sewage sludge drying beds.	—
				4843	Sewage pressure control stations.	—
				4849	Other sewage disposal, NEC.	—
		485	Solid waste disposal.	4851	Refuse incineration.	—
				4852	Central garbage grinding stations.	—
				4853	Compositing plants.	—
				4854	Sanitary land fills.	—
				4855	Refuse disposals.	—

				4856	Industrial waste disposals.	—
				4857	Active slag dumps and mineral waste disposals.	—
				4859	Other solid waste disposal, NEC.	—
		489	Other utilities, NEC.	4890	Other utilities, NEC.	—
49	Other transportation, communication, and utilities, NEC.	491	Other pipeline right-of-way and pressure control stations, NEC.	4911	Petroleum pipeline right-of-way.[17]	—
				4912	Petroleum pressure control stations.	—
				4919	Other pipeline right-of-way and pressure control stations, NEC.	—
		492	Transportation services and arrangements.	4921	Freight forwarding services.	4041 and 4712
				4922	Packing and crating services.	4783
				4923	Travel arranging services.	472
				4924	Transportation ticket services.[19]	—
				4929	Other transportation services and arrangements, NEC.	—
		499	Other transportation, communication, and utilities, NEC.	4990	Other transportation, communication, and utilities, NEC.	—

FOOTNOTES

[1] The SIC codes are listed for purposes of reference. They are the codes in the SIC system that most nearly correspond to the 4-digit land use activity indicated. (See ch. III, sec. A3, "The Use of Standard Industrial Classification Nomenclature.") A dash indicates that there is no corresponding SIC code.

[2] Code 4121—"Rapid rail transit and street railway right-of-way" includes only that land which is *not* within public right-of-way (e.g., within a public street right-of-way). Railroad right-of-way used by rapid rail transit is considered to be railroad right-of-way and is coded 4111.

[3] Code 4122—"Rapid rail transit and street railway passenger terminals" identifies only those terminals that are *not* located within public right-of-way (e.g., within a public street right-of-way).

[4] Codes 4211, 4212, 4213—"Bus passenger terminals" identifies only those terminals that are *not* located on the public right-of-way (e.g., within a public street right-of-way).

[5] Code 4391—"Heliport landing/takeoff pads" are identified only when they are separate activities and not a part of code 431, "Airports and flying fields."

[6] Code 44—"Marine craft transportation." The maintenance and repair of marine craft should be coded 3443, "Ship and boat building and repairing."

[7] Code 441—"Marine terminals" include all docking facilities (e.g., wharves, piers, and docks) and associated areas that are used by commercial passenger, freight, and fishing craft. Docking facilities that primarily serve recreational type of marine craft are identified under code 744, "Marinas."

[8] Code 4411—"Marine terminals (passenger)" include ferry terminals.

[9] Code 4510—"Freeways" are divided highways for through traffic with full control of access and no cross traffic at grade.

[10] Code 4520—"Expressways" are divided highways for through traffic with full or partial control of access with grade separations at major crossroads.

Footnotes continued on following page.

B. A STANDARD SYSTEM FOR IDENTIFYING AND CODING LAND USE ACTIVITIES—TWO-, THREE-, AND FOUR-DIGIT LEVELS—Continued

[11] Code 4530—"Parkways" are highways for noncommercial traffic, with full or partial control of access. They are located within a park or within a ribbon of parklike development.

[12] Code 4540—"Arterial streets" are those streets which serve movements of traffic and are not freeways, expressways, and parkways. Generally there is no control of access.

[13] Code 4550—"Collector/distributor streets" are those streets that collect traffic from the local streets and channel it into the arterial system. These streets also provide necessary cross-connections between arterials. The collector/distributor street does not handle long through trips, and it is not continuous for any great length.

[14] Code 4560—"Local access streets" are those used primarily for access to residences, businesses, or other abutting activities.

[15] Code 4570—"Alleys" are minor narrow streets usually without sidewalks and on which building adjoin from the rear.

[16] Code 4600—"Automobile parking" includes nonresidential off-street parking that is 5,000 square feet or greater (or approximately 17 parking spaces), and that serves no other single type of activity. This code includes parking on open lots, parking within parking structures, parking within structures that also house other activities (e.g., parking area in an office building), and the parking area at shopping centers. Parking areas of less than 5,000 square feet are not identified as a separate activity.

[17] Codes 4811, 4821, 4831, 4911—These codes identify those areas where the *surface is devoted exclusively to the right-of-way* of the respective activities and is used for no other purposes.

[18] Code 4833—"Water storage" includes impounded surface water areas or water tanks used for storage. Lakes or other natural water formations are identified under code 93, "Water areas."

[19] Code 4924—"Transportation ticket services" include the ticket offices of any of the transportation systems. The ticket offices are identified only when they are a separate and distinct activity, not located within one of the transportation terminals.

Code	*Category*	*Code*	*Category*	*Code*	*Category*	*SIC Reference* [1]
51	Wholesale trade.[2]	511	Motor vehicles and automotive equipment—wholesale.	5111	Automobiles and other motor vehicles—wholesale.	5012
				5112	Automotive equipment—wholesale.	5013
				5113	Tires and tubes—wholesale.	5014
		512	Drugs, chemicals, and allied products—wholesale.	5121	Drugs, drug proprietaries and druggists' sundries—wholesale.	5022
				5122	Paints and varnishes—wholesale.	5028
				5129	Other drugs, chemicals, and allied products, wholesale, NEC.	5029
		513	Dry goods and apparel—wholesale.	5131	Dry goods, piece goods, and notions—wholesale.	5032

		5132	Apparel and accessories, hosiery, and lingerie—wholesale.	5035
		5133	Footwear—wholesale.	5039
514	Groceries and related products—wholesale.	5141	Groceries (general line)—wholesale.	5042
		5142	Dairy products—wholesale.	5043
		5143	Poultry and poultry products—wholesale.	5044
		5144	Confectionery—wholesale.	5045
		5145	Fish and seafoods—wholesale.	5046
		5146	Meat and meat products—wholesale.	5047
		5147	Fruits and vegetables (fresh)—wholesale.	5048
		5149	Other groceries and related products wholesale, NEC.	5049
515	Farm products (raw materials)—wholesale.	5151	Cotton—wholesale.	Incl. 5051
		5152	Grain—wholesale.	Incl. 5051
		5153	Hides, skins, and raw furs—wholesale.	Incl. 5051
		5154	Leaf tobacco—wholesale.	Incl. 5051
		5155	Wool and mohair—wholesale.	Incl. 5051
		5156	Livestock—wholesale.	Incl. 5051
		5157	Horses and mules—wholesale.	Incl. 5051
		5159	Other farm products wholesale, NEC.	Incl. 5051
516	Electrical goods—wholesale.	5161	Electrical apparatus and equipment, wiring supplies, and construction materials—wholesale.	5063
		5162	Electrical appliances, television, and radio sets—wholesale.	5064
		5163	Electronic parts and equipment—wholesale.	5065
517	Hardware, plumbing, heating equipment, and supplies—wholesale.	5171	Hardware—wholesale.	5072
		5172	Plumbing and heating equipment and supplies—wholesale.	5074
		5173	Air conditioning, refrigerated equipment, and supplies—wholesale.	5077

B. A STANDARD SYSTEM FOR IDENTIFYING AND CODING LAND USE ACTIVITIES—TWO-, THREE-, AND FOUR-DIGIT LEVELS—Continued

Code	Category	Code	Category	Code	Category	SIC Reference [1]
51	Wholesale trade [2]—Continued	518	Machinery, equipment, and supplies—wholesale.	5181	Commercial and industrial machinery, equipment, and supplies—wholesale.	5082
				5182	Farm machinery and equipment—wholesale.	5083
				5183	Professional equipment and supplies—wholesale.	5086
				5184	Equipment and supplies for service establishments—wholesale.	5087
				5185	Transportation equipment and supplies (except motor vehicles)—wholesale.	5088
				5189	Other machinery, equipment, and supplies wholesale, NEC.	5089
		519	Other wholesale trade, NEC.	5191	Metals and minerals (except petroleum products and scrap)—wholesale.	5091
				5192	Petroleum bulk stations and terminals—wholesale.	5092
				5193	Scrap and waste materials—wholesale.	5093
				5194	Tobacco and tobacco products—wholesale.	5094
				5195	Beer, wine, and distilled alcoholic beverages—wholesale.	5095
				5196	Paper and paper products—wholesale.	5096
				5197	Furniture and homefurnishings—wholesale.	5097

				5198	Lumber and construction materials—wholesale.	5098
				5199	Other wholesale trade, NEC.	5099
52	Retail trade—building materials, hardware, and farm equipment.	521	Lumber and other building materials—retail.	5211	Lumber yards—retail.	5211
				5212	Building materials—retail.	5212
		522	Heating and plumbing equipment—retail.	5220	Heating and plumbing equipment—retail.	522
		523	Paint, glass, and wallpaper—retail.	5230	Paint, glass, and wallpaper—retail.	523
		524	Electrical supplies—retail.	5240	Electrical supplies—retail.	524
		525	Hardware and farm equipment—retail.	5251	Hardware—retail.	5251
				5252	Farm equipment—retail.	5252
53	Retail trade—general merchandise.	531	Department stores—retail.	5310	Department stores—retail.	531
		532	Mail order houses—retail.	5320	Mail order houses—retail.	532
		533	Limited price variety stores—retail.	5330	Limited price variety stores—retail.	533
		534	Merchandise vending machine operators—retail.	5340	Merchandise vending machine operators—retail.	534
		535	Direct selling organizations—retail.	5350	Direct selling organizations—retail.	535
		539	Other retail trade—general merchandise, NEC.	5391	Dry goods and general merchandise—retail.	5392
				5392	General stores—retail.	5393
54	Retail trade—food.	541	Groceries (with or without meat)—retail.	5410	Groceries (with or without meat)—retail.	541
		542	Meats and fish—retail.	5421	Meats—retail.	5422
				5422	Fish and seafoods—retail.	5423

TRADE—5.

B. A STANDARD SYSTEM FOR IDENTIFYING AND CODING LAND USE ACTIVITIES—TWO-, THREE-, AND FOUR-DIGIT LEVELS—Continued

Code	Category	Code	Category	Code	Category	SIC Reference [1]
54	Retail trade—food—Continued	543	Fruits and vegetables—retail.	5430	Fruits and vegetables—retail.	543
		544	Candy, nut, and confectionery—retail.	5440	Candy, nut, and confectionery—retail.	544
		545	Dairy products—retail.	5450	Dairy products—retail.	545
		546	Bakeries—retail.	5461	Bakeries (manufacturing)—retail. [3]	5462
				5462	Bakeries (nonmanufacturing)—retail. [4]	5463
		549	Other retail trade—food, NEC.	5491	Egg and poultry—retail.	5491
				5499	Other retail trade—food, NEC.	5499
55	Retail trade—automotive, marine craft, aircraft, and accessories.	551	Motor vehicles—retail.	5511	Motor vehicles (new and used cars)—retail.	551
				5512	Motor vehicles (used cars only)—retail.	552
		552	Tires, batteries, and accessories—retail.	5520	Tires, batteries, and accessories—retail.	553
		553	Gasoline service stations.	5530	Gasoline service stations.	554
		559	Other retail trade—automotive, marine craft, aircraft, and accessories, NEC.	5591	Marine craft and accessories—retail.	Incl. 5599
				5592	Aircraft and accessories—retail.	Incl. 5599
				5599	Other retail trade—automotive, marine craft, aircraft, and accessories, NEC.	Incl. 5599

56	Retail trade—apparel and accessories.	561	Men's and boys' clothing and furnishings—retail.	5610	Men's and boys' clothing and furnishings—retail.	561
		562	Women's ready-to-wear—retail.	5620	Women's ready-to-wear—retail	562
		563	Women's accessories and specialties—retail.	5630	Women's accessories and specialties—retail.	563
		564	Children's and infants' wear—retail.	5640	Children's and infants' wear—retail.	564
		565	Family clothing—retail.	5650	Family clothing—retail.	565
		566	Shoes—retail.	5660	Shoes—retail.	566
		567	Custom tailoring.	5670	Custom tailoring.	567
		568	Furriers and fur apparel—retail.	5680	Furriers and fur apparel—retail.	568
		569	Other retail trade—apparel and accessories, NEC.	5690	Other retail trade—apparel and accessories, NEC.	569
57	Retail trade—furniture, homefurnishings, and equipment.	571	Furniture, homefurnishings, and equipment—retail.	5711	Furniture—retail.	5712
				5712	Floor coverings—retail.	5713
				5713	Draperies, curtains, and upholstery—retail.	5714
				5714	China, glassware, and metalware—retail.	5715
				5719	Other furniture, homefurnishings, and equipment retail, NEC.	5719
		572	Household appliances—retail.	5720	Household appliances—retail.	572
		573	Radios, televisions, and music supplies—retail.	5731	Radios and televisions—retail.	5732
				5732	Music supplies—retail.	5733
58	Retail trade—eating and drinking.	581	Eating places.	5810	Eating places.[5]	5812
		582	Drinking places (alcoholic beverages).	5820	Drinking places (alcoholic beverages).	5813

B. A STANDARD SYSTEM FOR IDENTIFYING AND CODING LAND USE ACTIVITIES—TWO-, THREE-, AND FOUR-DIGIT LEVELS—Continued

Code	*Category*	*Code*	*Category*	*Code*	*Category*	*SIC Reference* [1]
59	Other retail trade, NEC.	591	Drug and proprietary—retail.	5910	Drug and proprietary—retail.	591
		592	Liquor—retail.	5920	Liquor—retail.	592
		593	Antiques and secondhand merchandise—retail.	5931	Antiques—retail.	5932
				5932	Secondhand merchandise—retail.	5933
		594	Book and stationery—retail.	5941	Books—retail.	5942
				5942	Stationery—retail.	5943
		595	Sporting goods and bicycles—retail.	5951	Sporting goods—retail.	5952
				5952	Bicycles—retail.	5953
		596	Farm and garden supplies—retail.	5961	Hay, grains, and feeds—retail.	5962
				5969	Other farm and garden supplies retail, NEC.	5969
		597	Jewelry—retail.	5970	Jewelry—retail.	597
		598	Fuel and ice—retail.	5981	Fuel and ice dealers (except fuel oil and bottled gas dealers)—retail.	5982
				5982	Fuel oil—retail.	5983
				5983	Bottled gas—retail.	5984
		599	Other retail trade, NEC.	5991	Florists—retail.	5992
				5992	Cigars and cigarettes—retail.	5993
				5993	Newspapers and magazines—retail.	5994
				5994	Cameras and photographic supplies—retail.	5996
				5995	Gifts, novelties, and souvenirs—retail.	5997
				5996	Optical goods—retail.	5998
				5999	Other retail trade, NEC.	5999

Code	Category	Code	Category	Code	Category	SIC Reference [1]
61	Finance, insurance, and real estate services.	611	Banking and bank-related functions.	6111	Banking services.	601, 602, 603, and 604
				6112	Bank-related functions.	605
		612	Credit services (other than banks).	6121	Savings and loan associations.	612
				6122	Agricultural, business, and personal credit services (including credit unions).	613, 614, and 615
				6129	Other credit services (other than banks), NEC.	611 and 616
		613	Security and commodity brokers, dealers, exchanges, and services.	6131	Security brokers, dealers, and flotation services.	6211
				6132	Commodity contracts brokers and dealers services.	6221
				6133	Security and commodity exchanges.	623
				6134	Security and commodity allied services.	628
		614	Insurance carriers, agents, brokers, and services.	6141	Insurance carriers.	63
				6142	Insurance agents, brokers, and services.	64

FOOTNOTES

[1] The SIC codes are listed for purposes of reference. They are the codes in the SIC system that most nearly correspond to the 4-digit land use activity indicated. (See ch. III, sec. A3, "The Use of Standard Industrial Classification Nomenclature.") A dash indicates that there is no corresponding SIC code.

[2] Code 51—"Wholesale trade." A code of "0" is used in the auxiliary position for those wholesalers who maintain a definite storage area on the premises. For example, 5122–0 is a wholesaler of paints and varnishes who has a definite storage area set aside for his merchandise.

[3] Code 5461—"Bakeries (manufacturing)—retail" include only those bakeries that produce on the premises some or all of the products sold.

[4] Code 5462—"Bakeries (nonmanufacturing)—retail" include only those bakeries that do not produce on the premises the products that are sold.

[5] Code 5810--"Eating places" include both establishments serving only food as well as those serving both food and alcoholic beverages.

B. A STANDARD SYSTEM FOR IDENTIFYING AND CODING LAND USE ACTIVITIES—TWO-, THREE-, AND FOUR-DIGIT LEVELS—Continued

Code	Category	Code	Category	Code	Category	SIC Reference [1]
61	Finance, insurance, and real estate services—Continued	615	Real estate and related services.	6151	Real estate operators (except developers) and lessors.	651
				6152	Real estate agents, brokers, and management services.	653
				6153	Title abstracting services.	654
				6154	Real estate subdividing and developing services.	655
				6155	Real estate operative builders.	656
				6156	Combinations of real estate, insurance, loan, and law services.	661
				6159	Other real estate and related services, NEC.	—
		616	Holding and investment services.	6160	Holding and investment services.	67
		619	Other finance, insurance, and real estate services, NEC.	6190	Other finance, insurance, and real estate services, NEC.	—
62	Personal services.	621	Laundering, dry cleaning, and dyeing services.	6211	Laundering, dry cleaning, and dyeing services (except rugs).	7211, 7212, and 7216
				6212	Linen supply and industrial laundry services.	7213
				6213	Diaper services.	7214
				6214	Laundering and dry cleaning (self-service).	7215
				6215	Rug cleaning and repair services.	7217
		622	Photographic services (including commercial).	6220	Photographic services (including commercial).	722

		623	Beauty and barber services.	6231	Beauty services.	723
				6232	Barber services.	724
		624	Funeral and crematory services; cemeteries.	6241	Funeral and crematory services.	726
				6242	Cemeteries.	—
		625	Apparel repair, alteration and cleaning pickup services; shoe repair services.	6251	Pressing, alteration, and garment repair; laundry and dry cleaning pickup services (only).	7271
				6252	Fur repair and storage services.	7272
				6253	Shoe repair, shoe shining, and hat cleaning services.	725
		629	Other personal services, NEC.	6290	Other personal services, NEC.	729
63	Business services.	631	Advertising services.	6311	Advertising services (general).	7311
				6312	Outdoor advertising services.	7312
				6319	Other advertising services, NEC.	7319
		632	Consumer and mercantile credit reporting services; adjustment and collection services.	6320	Consumer and mercantile credit reporting services; adjustment and collection services.	7321
		633	Duplicating mailing and stenographic services.	6331	Direct mail advertising services.	7331
				6332	Blueprinting and photocopying service.	7332
				6339	Stenographic services and other duplicating and mailing services, NEC.	7339
		634	Dwelling and other building services.	6341	Window cleaning services.	7341
				6342	Disinfecting and exterminating services.	7342
				6349	Other dwelling and building services, NEC.	7349
		635	News syndicate services.	6350	News syndicate services.	735
		636	Employment services.	6360	Employment services.	736

B. A STANDARD SYSTEM FOR IDENTIFYING AND CODING LAND USE ACTIVITIES—TWO-, THREE-, AND FOUR-DIGIT LEVELS—Continued

Code	Category	Code	Category	Code	Category	SIC Reference [1]
63	Business services—Continued	637	Warehousing and storage services.[2]	6371	Farm products warehousing and storage (excluding stockyards).	4221
				6372	Stockyards.	4731
				6373	Refrigerated warehousing (except food lockers).	4222
				6374	Food lockers (with or without food preparation facilities).	4223
				6375	Household goods warehousing and storage.	4224
				6376	General warehousing and storage.	4225
				6379	Other warehousing and storage, NEC.	4226
		639	Other business services, NEC.	6391	Research, development, and testing services.	7391
				6392	Business and management consulting services.	7392
				6393	Detective and protective services.	7393
				6394	Equipment rental and leasing services.	7394
				6395	Photofinishing services.	7395
				6396	Trading stamp services.	7396
				6397	Automobile and truck rental services.	7511
				6398	Motion picture distribution and services.	7812 and 782
				6399	Other business services, NEC.	7399
64	Repair services.	641	Automobile repair and services.	6411	Automobile repair services.	753
				6412	Automobile wash services.	Incl. 7541
				6419	Other automobile services (except repair and wash), NEC.	Incl. 7541

	649 Other repair services, NEC.	6491 Electrical repair services (except radio and television).	Incl. 7621
		6492 Radio and television repair services.	7622
		6493 Watch, clock, and jewelry repair services.	763
		6494 Reupholstery and furniture repair services.	764
		6495 Armature rewinding services.	7694
		6499 Other repair services, NEC.	7699
65 Professional services.	651 Medical and other health services.	6511 Physicians' services.	801, 803, and 804
		6512 Dental services.	802
		6513 Hospital services.	806
		6514 Medical laboratory services.	8071
		6515 Dental laboratory services.	8072
		6516 Sanitariums, convalescent, and rest home services.	8092
		6517 Medical clinics—out-patient services.	—
		6519 Other medical and health services, NEC.	8099
	652 Legal services.	6520 Legal services.	811
	659 Other professional services, NEC.	6591 Engineering and architectural services.	891
		6592 Educational and scientific research services.	892
		6593 Accounting, auditing, and bookkeeping services.	893
		6594 Urban planning services.	Incl. 899
		6599 Other professional services, NEC.	Incl. 899
66 Contract construction services.	661 General contract construction services.	6611 Building construction—general contractor services.	151
		6619 Other general construction contractor services, NEC.	16

B. A STANDARD SYSTEM FOR IDENTIFYING AND CODING LAND USE ACTIVITIES—TWO-, THREE-, AND FOUR-DIGIT LEVELS—Continued

Code	*Category*	*Code*	*Category*	*Code*	*Category*	*SIC Reference* [1]
66	Contract construction services—Continued	662	Special construction trade services.	6621	Plumbing, heating, and air conditioning services.	171
				6622	Painting, paper hanging, and decorating services.	172
				6623	Electrical services.	173
				6624	Masonry, stonework, tile setting, and plastering services.	174
				6625	Carpentering and wood flooring.	175
				6626	Roofing and sheet metal services.	176
				6627	Concrete services.	177
				6628	Water well drilling services.	178
				6629	Other special construction trade services, NEC.	179
67	Governmental services.	671	Executive, legislative, and judicial functions.	6710	Executive, legislative, and judicial functions.[3]	Incl. 919, 929, and 939
		672	Protective functions and their related activities.	6721	Police protection and related activities.	Incl. 919, 929, and 939
				6722	Fire protection and related activities.	Incl. 919, 929, and 939
				6723	Civil defense and related activities.	Incl. 919, 929, and 939
				6729	Other protective functions and their related activities, NEC.	Incl. 919, 929, and 939
		673	Postal services.	6730	Postal services.	Incl. 919
		674	Correctional institutions.	6741	Prisons.	Incl. 919, 929, and 939

		6749 Other correctional institutions, NEC.	Incl. 919, 929, and 939
	675 Military bases and reservations.[4]	6751 Military training bases.	Incl. 919 and 929
		6752 Military defense installations.	Incl. 919 and 929
		6753 Military storage depots and transportation centers.	Incl. 919 and 929
		6754 Military maintenance centers.	Incl. 919 and 929
		6755 Military administration or command centers.	Incl. 919 and 929
		6756 Military communication centers.	Incl. 919 and 929
		6759 Other military bases and reservations, NEC.	Incl. 919 and 929
68 Educational services.	681 Nursery, primary, and secondary education.	6811 Nursery schools.	Incl. 821
		6812 Primary (elementary) schools.[5]	Incl. 821
		6813 Secondary schools.[6]	Incl. 821
	682 University, college, junior college, and professional school education.	6821 Universities and colleges.	Incl. 8221
		6822 Junior colleges.	Incl. 8222
		6823 Professional schools.	Incl. 8221
	683 Special training and schooling.	6831 Vocational or trade schools.	8242
		6832 Business and stenographic schools.	Incl. 8299
		6833 Barber and beauty schools.	Incl. 723 and 724
		6834 Art and music schools.	Incl. 8299
		6835 Dancing schools.	Incl. 7911
		6836 Driving schools.	Incl. 8299
		6837 Correspondence schools.	8241
		6839 Other special training and schooling, NEC.	Incl. 8299

B. A STANDARD SYSTEM FOR IDENTIFYING AND CODING LAND USE ACTIVITIES—TWO-, THREE-, AND FOUR-DIGIT LEVELS—Continued

Code	Category	Code	Category	Code	Category	SIC Reference [1]
69	Miscellaneous services.	691	Religious activities.[7]	6911	Churches, synagogues, and temples.	Incl. 866
				6919	Other religious activities, NEC.	Incl. 866
		692	Welfare and charitable services.	6920	Welfare and charitable services.	867
		699	Other miscellaneous services, NEC.	6991	Business associations.	861
				6992	Professional membership organizations.	862
				6993	Labor unions and similar labor organizations.	863
				6994	Civic, social, and fraternal associations.	864
				6999	Other miscellaneous services, NEC.	—

FOOTNOTES

[1] The SIC codes are listed for purposes of reference. They are the codes in the SIC system that most nearly correspond to the 4-digit land use activity indicated. (See ch. III, sec. A3, "The Use of Standard Industrial Classification Nomenclature.") A dash indicates that there is no corresponding SIC code.

[2] Code 637—"Warehousing and storage services" include only those facilities that are used by or are open to the public. When warehousing and storage is functionally and organizationally linked to another activity (e.g., a general contractor or an apparel manufacturer), the facilities are identified and coded the same as the parent activity and with a code of 4 (warehousing and storage) in the auxiliary position. For example, 2310–4 is a warehouse and storage area of a manufacturer of men's, youths', and boys' suits, coats, and overcoats.

[3] Code 6710—"Executive, legislative, and judicial functions" include only the central and administrative *office* activities of the agencies or special authorities involved in government functions, including the legislature and courts. All operational activities (e.g., shipbuilding, schools, or hospitals) should be identified separately under the respective activity codes.

[4] Code 675—"Military bases and reservations" include the installations used by both the active military as well as the Reserves and the National Guard.

[5] Code 6812—"Primary (elementary) schools" may or may not include a kindergarten, but they do include grades 1 through 6.

[6] Code 6813—"Secondary schools" are schools that include grades 7 through 12, popularly known as junior and senior high schools.

[7] Code 691—"Religious activities" include only those places operated for worship or for the promotion of religious activities. Activities maintained by the religious organizations (e.g., schools, hospitals, publishing houses, etc.) should be identified separately under the respective activity codes.

Code	Category	Code	Category	Code	Category	SIC Reference [1]
71	Cultural activities and nature exhibitions.	711	Cultural activities.	7111	Libraries.	823
				7112	Museums.	Incl. 841
				7113	Art galleries.[2]	Incl. 841
				7119	Other cultural activities, NEC.	—
		712	Nature exhibitions.	7121	Planetaria.	—
				7122	Aquariums.	Incl. 8421
				7123	Botanical gardens and arboretums.	Incl. 842
				7124	Zoos.	—
				7129	Other nature exhibitions, NEC.	—
		719	Other cultural activities and nature exhibitions, NEC.	7191	Historic and monument sites.[3]	—
				7199	Other cultural activities and nature exhibitions, NEC.	—
72	Public assembly.	721	Entertainment assembly.	7211	Amphitheaters.	—
				7212	Motion picture theaters.	Incl. 7831
				7213	Drive-in movies.	Incl. 7831
				7214	Legitimate theaters.	—
				7219	Other entertainment assembly, NEC.	—
		722	Sports assembly.[4]	7221	Stadiums.[5]	Incl. 7941
				7222	Arenas and field houses.	—
				7223	Race tracks.[6]	Incl. 7948
				7229	Other sports assembly, NEC.	—
		723	Public assembly, miscellaneous purposes.	7231	Auditoriums.	—
				7232	Exhibition halls.	—
				7239	Other miscellaneous assembly, NEC.	—
		729	Other public assembly, NEC.	7290	Other public assembly, NEC.	—
73	Amusements.*	731	Fairgrounds and amusement parks.	7311	Fairgrounds.	Incl. 7949
				7312	Amusement parks.	Incl. 7949

B. A STANDARD SYSTEM FOR IDENTIFYING AND CODING LAND USE ACTIVITIES—TWO-, THREE-, AND FOUR-DIGIT LEVELS—Continued

Code	Category	Code	Category	Code	Category	SIC Reference [1]
73	Amusements—Continued	739	Other amusements, NEC.	7391	Penny arcades.	Incl. 7949
				7392	Miniature golf.	Incl. 7949
				7393	Golf driving ranges.	Incl. 7949
				7394	Go-cart tracks.	Incl. 7949
				7399	Other amusements, NEC.	Incl. 7949
74	Recreational activities.*	741	Sports activities.	7411	Golf courses (without country club).	7942
				7412	Golf courses (with country club).	7947
				7413	Tennis courts.	—
				7414	Ice skating.	Incl. 7945
				7415	Roller skating.	Incl. 7945
				7416	Riding stables.	—
				7417	Bowling.	Incl. 7931
				7418	Skiing and tobogganing.	—
				7419	Other sports activities, NEC.	—
		742	Playgrounds and athletic areas.	7421	Play lots or tot lots.[7]	—
				7422	Playgrounds.[8]	—
				7423	Playfields or athletic fields.[9]	—
				7424	Recreation centers (general).[10]	—
				7425	Gymnasiums and athletic clubs.	Incl. 7949
				7429	Other playground and athletic areas, NEC.	—
		743	Swimming areas.	7431	Swimming beaches.[11]	—
				7432	Swimming pools.[12]	7944
		744	Marinas.[13]	7441	Yachting clubs.	Incl. 7949
				7442	Boat rentals and boat access sites.	—
				7449	Other marinas, NEC.	—
		749	Other recreation, NEC.	7491	Camping and picnicking areas.[14]	—
				7499	Other recreation, NEC.	—

75	Resorts and group camps.	751	Resorts.	7511	General resorts.[15]	—
				7512	Dude ranches.	Incl. 7032
				7513	Health resorts.	Incl. 8092
				7514	Ski resorts.	—
				7515	Hunting and fishing clubs.[16]	Incl. 7032
				7519	Other resorts, NEC.	—
		752	Group or organized camps.	7520	Group or organized camps.[17]	Incl. 7032
76	Parks.*	761	Parks—general recreation.	7610	Parks—general recreation.[18]	—
		762	Parks—leisure and ornamental.	7620	Parks—leisure and ornamental.[19]	—
		769	Other parks, NEC.	7690	Other parks, NEC.	—
79	Other cultural, entertainment, and recreational activities, NEC.	790	Other cultural, entertainment, and recreational activities, NEC.	7900	Other cultural, entertainment, and recreational activities, NEC.	—

FOOTNOTES

[1] The SIC codes are listed for purposes of reference. They are the codes in the SIC system that most nearly correspond to the 4-digit land use activity indicated. (See ch. III, sec. A3, "The Use of Standard Industrial Classification Nomenclature.") A dash indicates that there is no corresponding SIC code.

[2] Code 7113—"Art galleries" do not include those galleries that sell art objects commercially. Commercial sales are coded 5999, "Other retail trade, NEC."

[3] Code 7191—"Historic and monument sites" include those locations set aside for no other purpose than to commemorate an historical event, activity, or person.

[4] Code 722—"Sports assembly" includes only the public assembly areas used for nonparticipating sports.

[5] Code 7221—"Stadiums" include those used for individual sports, e.g., baseball or football, as well as those used for several sports activities.

[6] Code 7223—"Race tracks" include those used for individual racing activities, e.g., horse racing and automobile racing, as well as those used for several racing activities.

[7] Code 7421—"Play lots or tot lots" are small areas developed especially for preschool or elementary school aged children. They may contain such facilities as sand boxes, slides, teeters, swings, climbing apparatus, etc. They are identified and coded only when found as a separate activity and not subsidiary to or serving another activity (e.g. apartment house or playground).

[8] Code 7422—"Playgrounds" are areas that have been developed for active play and recreation. They are identified and coded only when found as a separate activity and not subsidiary to or serving another activity (e.g., a school).

[9] Code 7423—"Playfields or athletic fields" contain a playground as well as a field(s) or court(s) for competitive sports (e.g., baseball, football, or tennis). Bleachers or grandstands may be provided. They are identified and coded only when found as a separate activity and not subsidiary to or serving another activity (e.g., a school).

[10] Code 7424—"Recreation centers (general)" include diversified recreation for a wide variety of activities for all ages and interests. The recreation centers may contain, but are not limited to a gymnasium, social or play rooms, game rooms, arts and craft shops, etc.

[11] Code 7431—"Swimming beaches" are beach areas that have been set aside specifically for the purpose of swimming. They are identified only when they are not a part of a larger activity (e.g., a park).

[12] Code 7432—"Swimming pools" are separately identified if they are

Footnotes continued on following page.

B. A STANDARD SYSTEM FOR IDENTIFYING AND CODING LAND USE ACTIVITIES—TWO-, THREE-, AND FOUR-DIGIT LEVELS—Continued

independent of other functions (e.g., code 72, "Public assembly" or code 11, "Household units"). They may be indoor or outdoor pools.

[13] Code 744—"Marinas" include marine terminals and associated areas that are primarily for recreational marine craft. The sale and repair of recreational marine craft is coded 5591, "Marine craft and accessories—retail" and code 3443, "Ship and boat building and repairing," respectively.

[14] Code 7491—"Camping and picnicking areas" are separately identified if they are not a part of a larger activity (e.g., a park)

[15] Code 7511—"General resorts" have rooms for 20 or more persons and have provision for at least 2 types of recreational activities, excluding lawn games, children's playgrounds, and swimming pools.

*RFF Note: See text, pp. 127-28 for further discussion of these groups.

[16] Code 7515—"Hunting and fishing clubs" include areas on which artificially propagated game or fish are released for purposes of hunting or fishing. If there are other uses made of the property (e.g., agricultural use), these "other" uses should take priority in identifying the activity of the parcel.

[17] Code 7520—"Group or organized camps" include general camps for children, as well as Boy Scout and Girl Scout camps.

[18] Code 7610—"Parks—general recreation" may include, but are not limited to, picnic areas, bathing beaches, playfields, hiking trails, camping grounds, and other manmade recreation facilities.

[19] Code 7620—"Parks—leisure and ornamental" are largely for scenic or leisure purposes. They may contain beaches, children's play facilities, monuments, or statues.

Code	*Category*	*Code*	*Category*	*Code*	*Category*	*SIC Reference* [1]
81	Agriculture.[2]**	811	Farms (predominant crop, fibers).[3]	8111	Farms (predominant crop, cotton).	—
				8119	Farms (other type fiber crops).	—
		812	Farms (predominant crop, cash grains).[3]	8120	Farms (predominant crop, cash grains).	—
		813	Farms (field crops other than fiber or cash grain crops).[3]	8130	Farms (field crops other than fiber or cash grain crops).	—
		814	Farms (predominant crop, fruits, tree nuts, or vegetables).[3]	8141	Farms (predominant crop, fruits).	—
				8142	Farms (predominant crop, tree nuts).	—
				8143	Farms (predominant crop, vegetables).	—
		815	Farms (predominantly dairy products).[3]	8150	Farms (predominantly dairy products).	—

		816	Farms and ranches (livestock other than dairy).[3]	8161	Farms and ranches (predominantly cattle).	—
				8162	Farms and ranches (predominantly hog).	—
				8163	Farms and ranches (predominantly sheep).	—
				8164	Farms and ranches (predominantly goat).	—
				8169	Farms and ranches (other livestock), NEC.	—
		817	Farms (predominantly poultry).[3]	8170	Farms (predominantly poultry).	—
		818	Farms (general—no predominance).[3]	8180	Farms (general—no predominance).	—
		819	Other agriculture and related activities, NEC.	8191	Range and grassland pastures (not farm or ranch).[4]	—
				8192	Horticultural specialties.	0192
				8193	Apiary farms.	Incl. 0193
				8194	Farms or ranches (predominantly horse raising).	Incl. 0193
				8199	Other agriculture and related activities, NEC.	—
82	Agricultural related activities.	821	Agricultural processing.[5]	8211	Cotton ginning and compressing.	0712
				8212	Grist milling services.	0713
				8213	Corn shelling, hay baling, and threshing services.	0714
				8214	Contract sorting, grading, and packaging services (fruits and vegetables).	0715
				8219	Other agricultural processing services, NEC.	0719
		822	Animal husbandry services.	8221	Veterinarian services.	Incl. 0722
				8222	Animal hospital services.	Incl. 0722
				8223	Poultry hatchery services.	0723
				8229	Other animal husbandry services, NEC.	0729

RESOURCE PRODUCTION AND EXTRACTION—8

B. A STANDARD SYSTEM FOR IDENTIFYING AND CODING LAND USE ACTIVITIES—TWO-, THREE-, AND FOUR-DIGIT LEVELS—Continued

Code	Category	Code	Category	Code	Category	SIC Reference[1]
82	Agricultural related activities—Continued	829	Other agricultural related activities, NEC.	8291	Horticultural services.	0731
				8299	Other agricultural related activities, NEC.	—
83	Forestry activities and related services.[6***]	831	Commercial forestry production.[7]	8311	Timber production—predominantly for pulp wood.	—
				8312	Timber production—predominantly for saw logs.	—
				8313	Timber production—predominantly for veneer logs.	—
				8314	Timber production—mixed uses.	—
				8315	Tree products production—predominantly gum extracting (except pine gum) and bark.	0842
				8316	Tree products production—predominantly pine gum extraction.	0843
				8317	Timber and tree products production—mixed uses.	—
				8319	Other commercial forestry production, NEC.	—
		832	Forestry services.	8321	Forest nurseries.	0822
				8329	Other forestry services, NEC.	0851
		839	Other forestry activities and related services, NEC.	8390	Other forestry activities and related services, NEC.	—
84	Fishing activities and related services.	841	Fisheries and marine products.[8]	8411	Finfish fisheries.	0912
				8412	Shellfish fisheries.	0913
				8419	Other fisheries and marine products, NEC.	0914 and 0919

		842	Fishery services.	8421	Fish hatcheries.	Incl. 0989
				8429	Other fishery services, NEC.	Incl. 0989
		849	Other fishery activities and related services, NEC.	8490	Other fishery activities and related services, NEC.	—
85	Mining activities and related services.[9]	851	Metal ore mining.	8511	Iron ore-mining.	101
				8512	Copper ore-mining.	102
				8513	Lead and zinc ore-mining.	103
				8514	Gold and silver ore-mining.	104
				8515	Bauxite and other aluminum ore-mining.	105
				8516	Ferroalloy ore (except vanadium)—mining.	106
				8519	Other metal ore mining, NEC.	109
		852	Coal mining.	8521	Anthracite coal-mining.	111
				8522	Bituminous coal-mining.	1211
				8523	Lignite coal-mining.	1212
		853	Crude petroleum and natural gas.	8530	Crude petroleum and natural gas.	131
		854	Mining and quarrying of nonmetallic minerals (except fuels).	8541	Dimension stone.	141
				8542	Crushed and broken stone (including riprap)—quarrying.	142
				8543	Sand and gravel—quarrying.	144
				8544	Clay, ceramic, and refractory minerals—mining.	145
				8545	Chemical and fertilizers (mineral)—mining.	147
				8549	Other mining and quarrying of nonmetallic minerals (except fuels), NEC.	148
		855	Mining services.	8551	Metal mining-services.	108
				8552	Coal mining-services.	1112 and 1213
				8553	Crude petroleum and gas field-services.	138
				8554	Nonmetallic mining (except fuel)—services.	148
				8559	Other mining services, NEC.	—
89	Other resource production and extraction, NEC.	890	Other resource production and extraction, NEC.	8900	Other resource production and extraction, NEC.	—

B. A STANDARD SYSTEM FOR IDENTIFYING AND CODING LAND USE ACTIVITIES—TWO-, THREE-, AND FOUR-DIGIT LEVELS—Continued

FOOTNOTES

[1] The SIC codes are listed for purposes of reference. They are the codes in the SIC system that most nearly correspond to the 4-digit land use activity indicated. (See ch. III, sec. A3, "The Use of Standard Industrial Classification Nomenclature.") A dash indicates that there is no corresponding SIC code.

[2] Code 81—"Agriculture." A parcel of land is considered to be in agricultural use if 10 or more acres are under cultivation, in tree or bush crops, or are used for livestock or poultry purposes. The 10 acres may include the area of the residence, if there is one, and the immediate associated area surrounding the residence.

[3] A farm may consist of several ownership or rented parcels of land that are noncontiguous. However, each parcel should be linked together as one "farm management unit," and identified by only one 3- or 4-digit category, e.g., code 8120, "Farms (predominant crops, cash grains)."

Using the "Farm use" categories in app. 2 of this report, farm (i.e., the farm management units) are to be classified by the most predominant use made of the land (the farm use taking up the greatest percentage of farm area) excluding the areas used by farm residences and associated buildings, nonresident farm buildings, areas in feed crops, and grazed and nongrazed forested areas. Exceptions to this rule are:

a. If 50 percent or more of the value of the farm products sold in the previous year came from the sale of dairy products, or the sale of cows and calves, the farm is identified as "Farm (predominantly dairy products)," code 8150.

b. If 50 percent or more of the value of the farm products sold in the previous year came from the sale of livestock, wool, or mohair, the farm is identified as "Farms and ranches (livestock, other than dairy)," code 816.

c. If 50 percent or more of the value of the farm products sold in the previous year came from the sale of poultry and eggs, the farm is identified as "Farms (predominantly poultry)," code 8170.

d. If the percentage of dairy, livestock, and poultry products, each came to less than 50 percent of the value of the farm products sold in the previous years, and if there are 3 or more "Farm uses" (e.g., corn crop, cotton crop, etc.) within a farm, none of which takes up 25 percent of the total farm area (excluding those areas referred to above), the farm is identified as "Farms (general—no predominance)," code 8180.

[4] Code 8191—"Range and grass land pastures (not farm or ranch)" include grasslands used for grazing purposes that are not a part of a farm or ranch. These areas are usually part of the public domain in which grazing has been permitted.

[5] Code 821—"Agricultural processing" includes only preliminary processing of agricultural products. Any extensive processing, packing, canning, or manufacturing is coded 21, "Food and kindred products—manufacturing."

[6] Code 83—"Forestry activities and related services." The categories in this classification are based upon primary use of the land. It is recognized that other activities, e.g., recreation or the grazing of livestock may also be taking place within these forested areas. However, these types of activities are considered secondary in nature and not coded. Activities such as mining (code 85), permanent camping areas (code 7491), and logging camps (code 2410), located within the forested areas should be separately identified.

[7] Code 831—"Commercial forestry production" includes those forested areas not on the farms or ranches that are being managed or have been set aside to grow tree crops for "industrial wood" or to obtain tree products such as sap, bark, or seeds. "Industrial wood" includes commercial roundwood products, such as saw logs and pulpwood, but excludes fuel wood and fence posts. "Forest reserves," i.e., areas withdrawn from any commercial use of the trees, are coded 921. "Parks," e.g., national or State parks, are also a type of forest reserve, but because of their designation for recreational activity, they should be identified as "Parks" under code 76. Forested areas not on farms, ranches, or estates with no commercial use made of the trees are coded 922, "Nonreserve forests (undeveloped)."

[8] Code 841—"Fisheries and marine products" include those establishments primarily engaged in commercial fishing, the catching or taking of shellfish, or the gathering of seaweed, sponges, turtles, frogs, etc. These activities may include some preliminary processing, e.g., salting. However, any extensive processing, packing, canning, or manufacturing of these products should be coded under "Food and kindred products—manufacturing," code 21. These categories also include the docking facilities and their associated areas when these facilities are an integral part of a *single* fishery operation. When docking facilities serve several separate fishery establishments, they are coded 4414, "Marine terminals (predominantly fishing vessels)."

[9] Code 85—"Mining activities and related services" include those surface areas being used for mining or drilling purposes. The process may be tunnel excavation, strip mining, quarrying, or by drilling. These categories also include those areas where preliminary processing of raw materials (e.g., washing, crushing, screening, etc.) are taking place if these processes are an integral part of the mining operation.

**RFF Note: See text, pp. 131-37 for further discussion of relation of this classification system to existing data series on agriculture.

Code	Category	Code	Category	Code	Category	SIC Reference[1]
91	Undeveloped and unused land area (excluding noncommercial forest development).	910	Undeveloped and unused land area (excluding noncommercial forest development).	9100	Undeveloped and unused land area (excluding noncommercial forest development).[2]	—
92	Noncommercial forest development.	921	Forest reserves.[3]	9211	Forest reserves (wilderness areas).	—
				9212	Forest reserves (wildlife refuges).	—
				9219	Other forest reserves, NEC.	—
		922	Nonreserve forests (undeveloped).	9220	Nonreserve forests (undeveloped).[4]	—
93	Water areas.	931	Rivers, streams, or creeks.	9310	Rivers, streams, or creeks.	—
		932	Lakes.	9320	Lakes.[5]	—
		933	Bays or lagoons.	9330	Bays or lagoons.	—
		934	Oceans and seas.	9340	Oceans and seas.	—
		939	Other water areas, NEC.	9390	Other water areas, NEC.	—
94	Vacant floor area.	940	Vacant floor area.	9400	Vacant floor area.	—
95	Under construction.	951	Under construction (residential).	9510	Under construction (residential).[6]	—
		952	Under construction (nonresidential).	9520	Under construction (nonresidential).[7]	—
99	Other undeveloped land and water areas, NEC.	990	Other undeveloped land and water areas, NEC.	9900	Other undeveloped land and water areas, NEC.	—

See footnotes on following page.

B. A STANDARD SYSTEM FOR IDENTIFYING AND CODING LAND USE ACTIVITIES—TWO-, THREE-, AND FOUR-DIGIT LEVELS—Continued

FOOTNOTES

[1] The SIC codes are listed for purposes of reference. They are the codes in the SIC system that most nearly correspond to the 4-digit land use activity indicated. (See ch. III, sec. A3, "The Use of Standard Industrial Classification Nomenclature.") A dash indicates that there is no corresponding SIC code.

[2] Code 9100—"Undeveloped and unused land area (excluding noncommercial forest development)" identifies those parcels of land that appear to be undeveloped or if previously developed, are presently vacant and unused. This category includes such areas as vacant lands that once were farms, as well as vacant parcels where structures have been demolished. Vacant nonresidential buildings are coded 9400, "Vacant floor area."

[3] Code 921—"Forest reserves" are forested areas withdrawn from commercial utilization, and which are reserved through statute or administrative regulation for specific conservation purposes. Forested areas designated as park sites may also be restricted from commercial forestry production, but because of their designation for recreational activity they should be identified and coded as "Parks" (code 76).

[4] Code 9220—"Nonreserve forests (undeveloped)" are major forested areas not on a farm, ranch, or large estate with no commercial use made of the trees. It is recognized that other activities such as recreation or the grazing of livestock may also be taking place within these forested areas. However, these types of activities are considered secondary in nature and not coded. Activities such as mining (code 85), permanent camping areas (code 7491), and logging camps (code 2410), located within these forested areas should be separately identified.

[5] Code 9320—"Lakes" include permanent lakes (natural or manmade) with a minimum size of 1 acre. Impounded surface water areas used for storage should be identified as "Water storage," code 4833.

[6] Code 9510—Residential facilities under construction are considered to be completed when all exterior windows and doors are installed and the usable floors are in place. If construction has not reached this point, the parcel should be identified as "Under construction (residential)," code 9510.

[7] Code 9520—"Under construction (nonresidential)" is used only if there is no means of identifying the activity or activities that will occupy the structure when it is completed.

C. ALPHABETIC INDEX OF LAND USE ACTIVITIES

A

328	Abrasive, asbestos, and miscellaneous nonmetallic mineral products—manufacturing
3280	Abrasive, asbestos, and miscellaneous nonmetallic mineral products—manufacturing
6593	Accounting, auditing, and bookkeeping services
4857	Active slag dumps and mineral waste disposals
631	Advertising services
6311	Advertising services (general)
6122	Agricultural, business, and personal credit services (including credit unions)
287	Agricultural chemicals—manufacturing
2870	Agricultural chemicals—manufacturing
821	Agricultural processing
82	Agricultural related activities
81	Agriculture
5173	Air conditioning, refrigerated equipment, and supplies—wholesale
5592	Aircraft and accessories—retail
3442	Aircraft and parts—manufacturing
4315	Aircraft storage and equipment maintenance
43	Aircraft transportation
4311	Airport and flying field landing/takeoff fields
4313	Airport and flying field terminals (freight)
4312	Airport and flying field terminals (passenger)
4314	Airport and flying field terminals (passenger and freight)
431	Airports and flying fields
457	Alleys
4570	Alleys
3412	Ammunition (except small arms) manufacturing and complete assembling of guided missiles and space vehicles
7211	Amphitheaters
7312	Amusement parks
73	Amusements
2194	Animal and marine fats and oils (including grease and tallow)—manufacturing
8222	Animal hospital services
822	Animal husbandry services
8521	Anthracite coal—mining
593	Antiques and secondhand merchandise—retail
5931	Antiques—retail
8193	Apiary farms
5132	Apparel and accessories, hosiery and lingerie—wholesale
23	Apparel and other finished products made from fabrics, leather, and similar materials—manufacturing
2385	Apparel belts—manufacturing
2396	Apparel findings and related products—manufacturing

625 Apparel repair, alteration, and cleaning pickup services; shoe repair services
7122 Aquariums
7222 Arenas and field houses
6495 Armature rewinding services
6834 Art and music schools
454 Arterial streets
4540 Arterial streets
7113 Art galleries
2295 Artificial leather and oilcloth manufacturing and other impregnating and coating fabrics (except rubberizing)
2922 Asphalt felts and coatings—manufacturing
7231 Auditoriums
3522 Automatic temperature controls—manufacturing
6397 Automobile and truck rental services
46 Automobile parking
460 Automobile parking
4600 Automobile parking
641 Automobile repair and services
6411 Automobile repair services
5111 Automobiles and other motor vehicles—wholesale
6412 Automobile wash services
5112 Automotive equipment—wholesale

B

2643 Bags (except textile bags)—manufacturing
5461 Bakeries (manufacturing)—retail
5462 Bakeries (nonmanufacturing)—retail
546 Bakeries—retail
215 Bakery products—manufacturing
2150 Bakery products—manufacturing
611 Banking and bank-related functions
6111 Banking services
6112 Bank-related functions
6833 Barber and beauty schools
6232 Barber services
8515 Bauxite and other aluminum ore—mining
933 Bays or lagoons
9330 Bays or lagoons
623 Beauty and barber services
6231 Beauty services
5195 Beer, wine, and distilled alcoholic beverages—wholesale
218 Beverage—manufacturing
5952 Bicycles—retail
2831 Biological products—manufacturing
8522 Bituminous coal—mining
2771 Blankbooks, looseleaf binders, and devices—manufacturing

3311 Blast furnaces (including coke ovens), steel works, and the rolling of ferrous metals
331 Blast furnaces, steel works, and the rolling and finishing of ferrous metals
2145 Blending and preparing flour
6332 Blueprinting and photocopying services
7442 Boat rentals and boat access sites
594 Book and stationery—retail
2772 Bookbinding and miscellaneous related work—manufacturing
277 Bookbinding and related industries—manufacturing
273 Books—publishing, publishing and printing
2730 Books—publishing, publishing and printing
5941 Books—retail
2363 Boot and shoe cut stock and findings—manufacturing
7123 Botanical gardens and arboretums
5983 Bottled gas—retail
2185 Bottling and canning soft drinks and carbonated waters
7417 Bowling
3241 Brick and structural clay tile—manufacturing
221 Broad and narrow woven fabrics and other smallwares (cotton, manmade fibers, silk, and wool)—manufacturing
2210 Broad and narrow woven fabrics and other smallwares (cotton, manmade fibers, silk, and wool)—manufacturing
3991 Brooms and brushes—manufacturing
6611 Building construction—general contractor services
5212 Building materials—retail
266 Building paper and building board—manufacturing
2660 Building paper and building board—manufacturing
4214 Bus garaging and equipment maintenance
6392 Business and management consulting services
6832 Business and stenographic schools
6991 Business associations
63 Business services
4211 Bus passenger terminals (intercity)
4213 Bus passenger terminals (intercity and local)
4212 Bus passenger terminals (local)
421 Bus transportation

C

5994 Cameras and photographic supplies—retail
7491 Camping and picnicking areas
2171 Candy and other confectionery products—manufacturing
544 Candy, nut, and confectionery—retail
5440 Candy, nut, and confectionery—retail
2131 Canning and curing seafoods
213 Canning and preserving of fruits, vegetables, and seafoods
2133 Canning fruits, vegetables, preserves, jams, and jellies
2132 Canning specialty foods
2394 Canvas products—manufacturing

2894 Carbon black—manufacturing
6625 Carpentering and wood flooring
323 Cement (hydraulic)—manufacturing
3230 Cement (hydraulic)—manufacturing
6242 Cemeteries
4852 Central garbage grinding stations
3242 Ceramic wall and floor tile—manufacturing
2143 Cereal preparations
2122 Cheese (natural and processed)
8545 Chemical and fertilizers (mineral)—mining
28 Chemicals and allied products—manufacturing
2173 Chewing gum—manufacturing
564 Children's and infants' wear—retail
5640 Children's and infants' wear—retail
5714 China, glassware, and metalware—retail
2172 Chocolate and cocoa products—manufacturing
6911 Churches, synagogues, and temples
3961 Cigarettes—manufacturing
5992 Cigars and cigarettes—retail
3962 Cigars—manufacturing
6994 Civic, social, and fraternal associations
6723 Civil Defense and related activities
8544 Clay, ceramic, and refractory minerals—mining
3243 Clay refractories—manufacturing
852 Coal mining
8552 Coal mining—services
3497 Coating, engraving, and allied services
3314 Cold rolled sheet, strip, and bars—manufacturing
455 Collector/distributor streets
4550 Collector/distributor streets
1232 College dormitories
6156 Combinations of real estate, insurance, loan, and law services
5181 Commercial and industrial machinery, equipment, and supplies—wholesale
831 Commercial forestry production
274 Commercial printing
2740 Commercial printing
6132 Commodity contracts brokers and dealers services
47 Communication
3436 Communication equipment—manufacturing
4853 Compositing plants
3261 Concrete brick and block—manufacturing
326 Concrete, gypsum, and plaster products—manufacturing
3262 Concrete products (excluding brick and block)—manufacturing
3263 Concrete (ready mixed)—manufacturing
6627 Concrete services
2123 Condensed and evaporated milk—manufacturing
217 Confectionery and related products—manufacturing

5144 Confectionery—wholesale
3423 Construction, mining and materials handling machinery, and equipment—manufacturing
632 Consumer and mercantile credit reporting services; adjustment and collection services
6320 Consumer and mercantile credit reporting services; adjustment and collection services
66 Contract construction services
8214 Contract sorting, grading, and packaging services (fruits and vegetables)
1251 Convents
264 Converted paper and paperboard products (except containers and boxes)—manufacturing
8512 Copper ore—mining
8213 Corn shelling, hay baling, and threshing services
674 Correctional institutions
6837 Correspondence schools
395 Costume jewelry, costume novelties, buttons, and miscellaneous notions (except precious metals)—manufacturing
3950 Costume jewelry, costume novelties, buttons, and miscellaneous notions (except precious metals)—manufacturing
8211 Cotton ginning and compressing
2191 Cottonseed oil milling
5151 Cotton—wholesale
2121 Creamery butter—manufacturing
612 Credit services (other than banks)
8553 Crude petroleum and gas field—services
853 Crude petroleum and natural gas
8530 Crude petroleum and natural gas
8542 Crushed and broken stone (including riprap)—quarrying
711 Cultural activities
71 Cultural activities and nature exhibitions
7 Cultural, entertainment, and recreational
2391 Curtains and draperies—manufacturing
567 Custom tailoring
5670 Custom tailoring
3492 Cutlery, hand tools, and general hardware—manufacturing
327 Cut stone and stone products—manufacturing
3270 Cut stone and stone products—manufacturing

D

212 Dairy products—manufacturing
545 Dairy products—retail
5450 Dairy products—retail
5142 Dairy products—wholesale
3835 Dancing schools
3543 Dental equipment and supplies—manufacturing
6515 Dental laboratory services
6512 Dental services

531 Department stores—retail
5310 Department stores—retail
6393 Detective and protective services
6213 Diaper services
2645 Die cut paper and paperboard and cardboard—manufacturing
8541 Dimension stone—quarrying
6331 Direct mail advertising services
535 Direct selling organizations—retail
5350 Direct selling organizations—retail
6342 Disinfecting and exterminating services
2184 Distilling, rectifying, and blending liquors
5713 Draperies, curtains, and upholstery—retail
3354 Drawing and insulating of nonferrous wire
2381 Dress and work gloves (except knit and all leather)—manufacturing
582 Drinking places (alcoholic beverages)
5820 Drinking places (alcoholic beverages)
7213 Drive-in movies
6836 Driving schools
591 Drug and proprietary—retail
5910 Drug and proprietary—retail
283 Drug—manufacturing
512 Drugs, chemicals, and allied products—wholesale
5121 Drugs, drug proprietaries, and druggists' sundries—wholesale
513 Dry goods and apparel—wholesale
5391 Dry goods and general merchandise—retail
5131 Dry goods, piece goods, and notions—wholesale
2134 Drying and dehydrating fruits and vegetables
7512 Dude ranches
633 Duplicating, mailing, and stenographic services
634 Dwelling and other building services
223 Dyeing and finishing of textiles (except wool fabrics and knit goods)
2230 Dyeing and finishing of textiles (except wool fabrics and knit goods)

E

581 Eating places
5810 Eating places
6592 Educational and scientific research services
68 Educational services
5491 Egg and poultry—retail
5161 Electrical apparatus and equipment, wiring supplies, and construction materials—wholesale
5162 Electrical appliances, television, and radio sets—wholesale
516 Electrical goods—wholesale
3432 Electrical industrial apparatus—manufacturing
343 Electrical machinery, equipment, and supplies—manufacturing
6491 Electrical repair services (except radio and television)
6623 Electrical services
524 Electrical supplies—retail

5240 Electrical supplies—retail
3431 Electrical transmission and distribution equipment—manufacturing
4812 Electric generation plants
4813 Electricity regulating substations
3434 Electric lighting and wiring equipment—manufacturing
4811 Electric transmission right-of-way
481 Electric utility
3312 Electrometallurgical products—manufacturing
3437 Electronic components and accessories—manufacturing
5163 Electronic parts and equipment—wholesale
2783 Electrotyping and sterotyping
636 Employment services
6360 Employment services
6591 Engineering and architectural services
351 Engineering, laboratory, and scientific and research instruments and associated equipment—manufacturing
3510 Engineering, laboratory, and scientific and research instruments and associated equipment—manufacturing
3421 Engines and turbines—manufacturing
721 Entertainment assembly
2642 Envelope—manufacturing
5184 Equipment and supplies for service establishments—wholesale
6394 Equipment rental and leasing services
671 Executive, legislative, and judicial functions
6710 Executive, legislative, and judicial functions
7232 Exhibition halls
2892 Explosives—manufacturing
452 Expressways
4520 Expressways

F

34 Fabricated metal products—manufacturing
3494 Fabricated structural metal products—manufacturing
3498 Fabricated wire products (miscellaneous products)—manufacturing
7311 Fairgrounds
731 Fairgrounds and amusement parks
565 Family clothing—retail
5650 Family clothing—retail
596 Farm and garden supplies—retail
5252 Farm equipment—retail
3422 Farm machinery and equipment—manufacturing
5182 Farm machinery and equipment—wholesale
515 Farm products (raw materials)—wholesale
6371 Farm products warehousing and storage (excluding stockyards)
816 Farms and ranches (livestock other than dairy)
8169 Farms and ranches (other livestock), NEC
8161 Farms and ranches (predominately cattle)
8164 Farms and ranches (predominately goat)

8162 Farms and ranches (predominantly hog)
8163 Farms and ranches (predominately sheep)
813 Farms (field crops other than fiber or cash grain crops)
8130 Farms (field crops other than fiber or cash grain crops)
818 Farms (general—no predominance)
8180 Farms (general—no predominance)
8194 Farms or ranches (predominantly horse raising)
8119 Farms (other type fiber crops)
812 Farms (predominant crop, cash grains)
8120 Farms (predominant crop, cash grains)
8111 Farms (predominant crop, cotton)
811 Farms (predominant crop, fibers)
8141 Farms (predominant crop, fruits)
814 Farms (predominant crop, fruits, tree nuts, or vegetables)
8142 Farms (predominant crop, tree nuts)
8143 Farms (predominant crop, vegetables)
815 Farms (predominantly dairy products)
8150 Farms (predominantly dairy products)
817 Farms (predominantly poultry)
8170 Farms (predominantly poultry)
2291 Felt goods (except woven felts and hats)—manufacturing
8516 Ferroalloy ore (except vanadium)—mining
61 Finance, insurance, and real estate services
3253 Fine earthenware (whiteware) table and kitchen articles—manufacturing
8411 Finfish fisheries
6722 Fire protection and related activities
5422 Fish and seafoods—retail
5145 Fish and seafoods—wholesale
8421 Fish hatcheries
841 Fisheries and marine products
842 Fishery services
84 Fishing activities and related services
321 Flat glass—manufacturing
3210 Flat glass—manufacturing
2186 Flavor extracts and flavoring sirups manufacturing, NEC
5712 Floor coverings—retail
224 Floor coverings (rugs and carpets)—manufacturing
2240 Floor coverings (rugs and carpets)—manufacturing
5991 Florists—retail
2141 Flour and other grain mill products
2125 Fluid milk processing
21 Food and kindred products—manufacturing
6374 Food lockers (with or without food preparation facilities)
2364 Footwear (except rubber)—manufacturing
5133 Footwear—wholesale
8321 Forest nurseries
921 Forest reserves
9211 Forest reserves (wilderness areas)

9212 Forest reserves (wildlife refuges)
83 Forestry activities and related services
832 Forestry services
1221 Fraternity and sorority houses
451 Freeways
4510 Freeways
4921 Freight forwarding services
2136 Fresh or frozen packaged fish and seafoods
2137 Frozen fruits, fruit juices, vegetables, and specialties
5147 Fruits and vegetables (fresh)—wholesale
543 Fruits and vegetables—retail
5430 Fruits and vegetables—retail
5981 Fuel and ice dealers (except fuel oil and bottled gas dealers)—retail
598 Fuel and ice—retail
5982 Fuel oil—retail
6241 Funeral and crematory services
624 Funeral and crematory services; cemeteries
3996 Fur dressing and dyeing
237 Fur goods—manufacturing
2370 Fur goods—manufacturing
25 Furniture and fixtures—manufacturing
5197 Furniture and homefurnishings—wholesale
571 Furniture, homefurnishings, and equipment—retail
5711 Furniture—retail
6252 Fur repair and storage services
568 Furriers and fur apparel—retail
5680 Furriers and fur apparel—retail

G

553 Gasoline service stations
5530 Gasoline service stations
4821 Gas pipeline right-of-way
4824 Gas pressure control stations
4822 Gas production plants
482 Gas utility
661 General contract construction services
3426 General industrial machinery and equipment—manufacturing
7511 General resorts
5392 General stores—retail
6376 General warehousing and storage
5995 Gifts, novelties, and souvenirs
322 Glass and glassware (pressed or blown)—manufacturing
3221 Glass containers—manufacturing
2891 Glue and gelatin—manufacturing
7394 Go-cart tracks
8514 Gold and silver ore—mining
7412 Golf courses (with country club)
7411 Golf courses (without country club)

7393 Golf driving ranges
67 Governmental services
214 Grain mill products—manufacturing
5152 Grain—wholesale
276 Greeting card—manufacturing
2760 Greeting card—manufacturing
8212 Grist milling services
514 Groceries and related products—wholesale
5141 Groceries (general line)—wholesale
541 Groceries (with or without meat)—retail
5410 Groceries (with or without meat)—retail
752 Group or organized camps
7520 Group or organized camps
12 Group quarters
286 Gum and wood chemicals—manufacturing
2860 Gum and wood chemicals—manufacturing
3411 Guns, howitzers, mortars, and related equipment—manufacturing
7425 Gymnasiums and athletic clubs
3265 Gypsum products—manufacturing

H

2367 Handbags and other personal leather goods—manufacturing
525 Hardware and farm equipment—retail
517 Hardware, plumbing, heating equipment, and supplies—wholesale
5251 Hardware—retail
5171 Hardware—wholesale
2422 Hardwood dimension and flooring—manufacturing
235 Hats, caps, and millinery—manufacturing
2350 Hats, caps, and millinery—manufacturing
5961 Hay, grains, and feeds—retail
7513 Health resorts
522 Heating and plumbing equipment—retail
5220 Heating and plumbing equipment—retail
3493 Heating apparatus (except electrical) and plumbing fixtures—manufacturing
4391 Heliport landing/takeoff pads
5153 Hides, skins, and raw furs—wholesale
45 Highway and street right-of-way
7191 Historic and monument sites
616 Holding and investment services
6160 Holding and investment services
5157 Horses and mules—wholesale
8291 Horticultural services
8192 Horticultural specialities
6513 Hospital services
151 Hotels, tourist courts, and motels
1510 Hotels, tourist courts, and motels
2392 Housefurnishings (except curtains and draperies)—manufacturing

3433 Household appliances—manufacturing
572 Household appliances—retail
5720 Household appliances—retail
251 Household furniture—manufacturing
2510 Household furniture—manufacturing
6375 Household goods warehousing and storage
11 Household units
110 Household units
1100 Household units
7515 Hunting and fishing camps

I

2124 Ice cream and frozen desserts—manufacturing
2197 Ice—manufacturing
7414 Ice skating
281 Industrial inorganic and organic chemicals—manufacturing
2810 Industrial inorganic and organic chemicals—manufacturing
2362 Industrial leather belting and packing—manufacturing
4856 Industrial waste disposals
352 Instruments for measuring, controlling, and indicating physical characteristics—manufacturing
6142 Insurance agents, brokers, and services
6141 Insurance carriers
614 Insurance carriers, agents, brokers, and services
332 Iron and steel foundries
3320 Iron and steel foundries
8511 Iron ore—mining
4834 Irrigation distribution channels

J

3912 Jewelers' findings and materials—manufacturing
3911 Jewelry and precious metals—manufacturing
597 Jewelry—retail
5970 Jewelry—retail
391 Jewelry, silverware, and plated ware—manufacturing
6822 Junior colleges

K

222 Knit goods—manufacturing
2220 Knit goods—manufacturing

L

6993 Labor unions and similar labor organizations
2292 Lace goods—manufacturing
932 Lakes
9320 Lakes

3994 Lamp shades—manufacturing
3913 Lapidary work
6214 Laundering and dry cleaning (self-service)
621 Laundering, dry cleaning, and dyeing services
6211 Laundering, dry cleaning, and dyeing services (except rugs)
8513 Lead and zinc ore—mining
5154 Leaf tobacco—wholesale
236 Leather and leather products—manufacturing
2384 Leather and sheep lined clothing—manufacturing
2365 Leather gloves and mittens
2361 Leather tanning and finishing
652 Legal services
6520 Legal services
7214 Legitimate theaters
7111 Libraries
8523 Lignite coal—mining
3264 Lime products—manufacturing
533 Limited price variety stores—retail
5330 Limited price variety stores—retail
6212 Linen supply and industrial laundry services
3992 Linoleum, asphalted-felt-base, and other hard surface floor cover manufacturing, NEC
592 Liquor—retail
5920 Liquor—retail
5156 Livestock—wholesale
456 Local access streets
4560 Local access streets
241 Logging camps and logging contractors
2410 Logging camps and logging contractors
2991 Lubricating oils and greases—manufacturing
2366 Luggage—manufacturing
5198 Lumber and construction materials—wholesale
521 Lumber and other building materials—retail
24 Lumber and wood products (except furniture)—manufacturing
5211 Lumber yards—retail

M

2198 Macaroni, spaghetti, vermicelli, and noodles—manufacturing
518 Machinery, equipment, and supplies—wholesale
342 Machinery (except electrical)—manufacturing
532 Mail order houses—retail
5320 Mail order houses—retail
2181 Malt liquors—manufacturing
2182 Malt—manufacturing
275 Manifold business forms—manufacturing
2750 Manifold business forms—manufacturing
2 Manufacturing
3 Manufacturing

744 Marinas
5591 Marine craft and accessories—retail
44 Marine craft transportation
441 Marine terminals
4414 Marine terminals (commercial fishing)
4412 Marine terminals (freight)
4411 Marine terminals (passenger)
4413 Marine terminals (passenger and freight)
6624 Masonry, stonework, tile setting, and plastering services
3993 Matches—manufacturing
5146 Meat and meat products—wholesale
2111 Meat packing—manufacturing
211 Meat products—manufacturing
542 Meats and fish—retail
5421 Meats—retail
3521 Mechanical measuring and controlling instruments (except automatic temperature controls)—manufacturing
651 Medical and other health services
6517 Medical clinics out-patient services
6514 Medical laboratory services
2832 Medicinal chemicals and botanical products—manufacturing
122 Membership lodgings
561 Men's and boys' clothing and furnishings—retail
5610 Men's and boys' clothing and furnishings—retail
232 Men's, youths', and boys' furnishings, work clothing, and allied garments—manufacturing
2320 Men's, youths', and boys' furnishings, work clothing, and allied garments—manufacturing
231 Men's, youths', and boys' suits, coats, and overcoats—manufacturing
2310 Men's, youths', and boys' suits, coats, and overcoats—manufacturing
534 Merchandise vending machine operators—retail
5340 Merchandise vending machine operators—retail
3491 Metal cans—manufacturing
8551 Metal mining—services
851 Metal ore mining
5191 Metals and minerals (except petroleum products and scrap)—wholesale
3496 Metal stamping—manufacturing
3424 Metalworking machinery and equipment—manufacturing
6755 Military administration or command centers
675 Military bases and reservations
6756 Military communication centers
6752 Military defense installations
6754 Military maintenance centers
6753 Military storage depots and transportation centers
6751 Military training bases
2431 Millwork
243 Millwork, veneer, plywood, and prefabricated structural wood products—manufacturing

7392 Miniature golf
85 Mining activities and related services
854 Mining and quarrying of nonmetallic minerals (except fuels)
855 Mining services
238 Miscellaneous apparel and accessories—manufacturing
39 Miscellaneous manufacturing, NEC
314 Miscellaneous plastic products—manufacturing
3140 Miscellaneous plastic products—manufacturing
69 Miscellaneous services
14 Mobile home parks or courts
140 Mobile home parks or courts
1400 Mobile home parks or courts
1252 Monasteries
3995 Morticians' goods—manufacturing
6398 Motion picture distribution and services
397 Motion picture production
3970 Motion picture production
7212 Motion picture theaters
3445 Motorcycles, bicycles, and parts—manufacturing
4222 Motor freight garaging and equipment maintenance
4221 Motor freight terminals
422 Motor freight transportation
511 Motor vehicles and automotive equipment—wholesale
3441 Motor vehicles and motor vehicle equipment—manufacturing
5511 Motor vehicles (new and used cars)—retail
551 Motor vehicles—retail
42 Motor vehicles transportation
5512 Motor vehicles (used cars only)—retail
7112 Museums
392 Musical instruments and parts—manufacturing
3920 Musical instruments and parts—manufacturing
5732 Music supplies—retail

N

4823 Natural or manufactured gas storage and distribution points
712 Nature exhibitions
5993 Newspapers and magazines—retail
271 Newspapers: publishing, publishing and printing
2710 Newspapers: publishing, publishing and printing
635 News syndicate services
6350 News syndicate services
92 Noncommercial forest development
336 Nonferrous foundries
3360 Nonferrous foundries
8554 Nonmetallic mining (except fuel)—services
922 Nonreserve forests (undeveloped)
9220 Nonreserve forests (undeveloped)
681 Nursery, primary, and secondary education

6811 Nursery schools
1231 Nurses' homes

O

934 Oceans and seas
9340 Oceans and seas
3427 Office, computing, and accounting machines—manufacturing
252 Office furniture—manufacturing
2520 Office furniture—manufacturing
355 Ophthalmic goods—manufacturing
3550 Ophthalmic goods—manufacturing
5996 Optical goods—retail
353 Optical instruments and lenses—manufacturing
3530 Optical instruments and lenses—manufacturing
341 Ordnance and accessories
1242 Orphanages
3542 Orthopedic, prosthetic, and surgical appliances and supplies—manufacturing
6319 Other advertising services, NEC
8219 Other agricultural processing services, NEC
829 Other agricultural related activities, NEC
8299 Other agricultural related activities, NEC
819 Other agriculture and related activities, NEC
8199 Other agriculture and related activities, NEC
439 Other aircraft transportation, NEC
4399 Other aircraft transportation, NEC
4319 Other airports and flying fields, NEC
739 Other amusements, NEC
7399 Other amusements, NEC
8229 Other animal husbandry services, NEC
6419 Other automobile services (except repair and wash), NEC
639 Other business services, NEC
6399 Other business services, NEC
4219 Other bus transportation, NEC
289 Other chemicals and allied products manufacturing, NEC
2899 Other chemicals and allied products manufacturing, NEC
4759 Other combined radio and television communication, NEC
8319 Other commercial forestry production, NEC
479 Other communication, NEC
4790 Other communication, NEC
2649 Other converted paper and paperboard products (except containers and boxes) manufacturing, NEC
6749 Other correctional institutions, NEC
6129 Other credit services (other than banks), NEC
719 Other cultural activities and nature exhibitions, NEC
7199 Other cultural activities and nature exhibitions, NEC
7119 Other cultural activities, NEC
79 Other cultural, entertainment, and recreational activities, NEC

790 Other cultural, entertainment, and recreational activities, NEC
7900 Other cultural, entertainment, and recreational activities, NEC
5129 Other drugs, chemicals, and allied products wholesale, NEC
6349 Other dwelling and building services, NEC
3439 Other electrical machinery, equipment, and supplies manufacturing, NEC
4819 Other electric utility, NEC
7219 Other entertainment assembly, NEC
349 Other fabricated metal products manufacturing, NEC
3499 Other fabricated metal products manufacturing, NEC
319 Other fabricated rubber products manufacturing, NEC
3190 Other fabricated rubber products manufacturing, NEC
239 Other fabricated textile products manufacturing, NEC
2399 Other fabricated textile products manufacturing, NEC
5969 Other farm and garden supplies retail, NEC
5159 Other farm products wholesale, NEC
619 Other finance, insurance, and real estate services, NEC
6190 Other finance, insurance, and real estate services, NEC
8419 Other fisheries and marine products, NEC
849 Other fishery activities and related services, NEC
8490 Other fishery activities and related services, NEC
8429 Other fishery services, NEC
219 Other food preparations and kindred products manufacturing, NEC
2199 Other food preparations and kindred products manufacturing, NEC
9219 Other forest reserves, NEC
839 Other forestry activities and related services, NEC
8390 Other forestry activities and related services, NEC
8329 Other forestry services, NEC
259 Other furniture and fixtures manufacturing, NEC
2599 Other furniture and fixtures manufacturing, NEC
5719 Other furniture, homefurnishings, and equipment retail, NEC
4829 Other gas utilities, NEC
6619 Other general construction contractor services, NEC
3229 Other glass and glassware (pressed or blown) manufacturing, NEC
5149 Other groceries and related products wholesale, NEC
129 Other group quarters, NEC
1290 Other group quarters, NEC
459 Other highway and street right-of-way, NEC
4590 Other highway and street right-of-way, NEC
2369 Other leather products manufacturing, NEC
249 Other lumber and wood products (except furniture) manufacturing, NEC
2499 Other lumber and wood products (except furniture) manufacturing, NEC
5189 Other machinery, equipment, and supplies wholesale, NEC
3429 Other machinery manufacturing (except electrical), NEC
449 Other marine craft transportation, NEC
4490 Other marine craft transportation, NEC
7449 Other marinas, NEC
4419 Other marine terminals, NEC
6519 Other medical and health services, NEC

1229 Other membership lodgings, NEC
8519 Other metal ore mining, NEC
6759 Other military bases and reservations, NEC
8549 Other mining and quarrying of nonmetallic minerals (except fuels), NEC
8559 Other mining services, NEC
2389 Other miscellaneous apparel and accessory manufacturing, NEC
7239 Other miscellaneous assembly, NEC
399 Other miscellaneous manufacturing, NEC
3999 Other miscellaneous manufacturing, NEC
699 Other miscellaneous services, NEC
6999 Other miscellaneous services, NEC
4229 Other motor freight transportation, NEC
429 Other motor vehicle transportation, NEC
4299 Other motor vehicle transportation, NEC
7129 Other nature exhibitions, NEC
3419 Other ordnance and accessories manufacturing, NEC
769 Other parks, NEC
7690 Other parks, NEC
629 Other personal services, NEC
6290 Other personal services, NEC
2999 Other petroleum and coal products manufacturing, NEC
299 Other petroleum refining and related industries, NEC
491 Other pipeline right-of-way and pressure control stations, NEC
4919 Other pipeline right-of-way and pressure control stations, NEC
7429 Other playground and athletic areas, NEC
3259 Other pottery and related products manufacturing, NEC
339 Other primary metal industries, NEC
3390 Other primary metal industries, NEC
3339 Other primary smelting and refining of nonferrous metals, NEC
279 Other printing and publishing, NEC
2790 Other printing and publishing, NEC
2789 Other printing trade service industries, NEC
659 Other professional services, NEC
6599 Other professional services, NEC
6729 Other protective functions and their related activities, NEC
729 Other public assembly, NEC
7290 Other public assembly, NEC
4739 Other radio communication, NEC
4119 Other railroad transportation, NEC
4129 Other rapid rail transit and street railway transportation, NEC
6159 Other real estate and related services, NEC
749 Other recreation, NEC
7499 Other recreation, NEC
6919 Other religious activities, NEC
1259 Other religious quarters, NEC
649 Other repair services, NEC
6499 Other repair services, NEC
1239 Other residence halls or dormitories, NEC

19 Other residential, NEC
190 Other residential, NEC
1900 Other residential, NEC
7519 Other resorts, NEC
89 Other resource production and extraction, NEC
890 Other resource production and extraction, NEC
8900 Other resource production and extraction, NEC
569 Other retail trade—apparel and accessories, NEC
5690 Other retail trade—apparel and accessories, NEC
559 Other retail trade—automotive, marine craft, aircraft, and accessories, NEC
5599 Other retail trade—automotive, marine craft, aircraft, and accessories, NEC
549 Other retail trade—food, NEC
5499 Other retail trade—food, NEC
539 Other retail trade—general merchandise, NEC
59 Other retail trade, NEC
599 Other retail trade, NEC
5999 Other retail trade, NEC
4849 Other sewage disposal, NEC
4859 Other solid waste disposal, NEC
6629 Other special construction trade services, NEC
6839 Other special training and schooling, NEC
7419 Other sports activities, NEC
7229 Other sports assembly, NEC
3249 Other structural clay products manufacturing, NEC
4729 Other telegraph communication, NEC
4719 Other telephone communication, NEC
4749 Other television communication, NEC
229 Other textile goods manufacturing, NEC
2299 Other textile goods manufacturing, NEC
159 Other transient lodgings, NEC
1590 Other transient lodgings, NEC
49 Other transportation, communication, and utilities, NEC
499 Other transportation, communication, and utilities, NEC
4990 Other transportation, communication, and utilities, NEC
3449 Other transportation equipment manufacturing, NEC
4929 Other transportation services and arrangements, NEC
99 Other undeveloped land and water areas, NEC
990 Other undeveloped land and water areas, NEC
9900 Other undeveloped land and water areas, NEC
489 Other utilities, NEC
4890 Other utilities, NEC
6379 Other warehousing and storage, NEC
939 Other water areas, NEC
9390 Other water areas, NEC
4839 Other water utilities and irrigation, NEC
519 Other wholesale trade, NEC

5199 Other wholesale trade, NEC
6312 Outdoor advertising services

P

4922 Packing and crating services
2293 Padding and upholstery filling—manufacturing
523 Paint, glass, and wallpaper—retail
5230 Paint, glass, and wallpaper—retail
6622 Painting, paperhanging, and decorating services
285 Paints, varnishes, lacquers, enamels, and allied products—manufacturing
2850 Paints, varnishes, lacquers, enamels, and allied products—manufacturing
26 Paper and allied products—manufacturing
5196 Paper and paper products—wholesale
265 Paperboard containers and boxes—manufacturing
2650 Paperboard containers and boxes—manufacturing
263 Paperboard—manufacturing
2630 Paperboard—manufacturing
2641 Paper coating and glazing
262 Paper (except building paper)—manufacturing
2620 Paper (except building paper)—manufacturing
76 Parks
761 Parks—general recreation
7610 Parks—general recreation
762 Parks—leisure and ornamental
7620 Parks—leisure and ornamental
453 Parkways
4530 Parkways
254 Partitions, shelving, lockers, and office and store fixtures—manufacturing
2540 Partitions, shelving, lockers, and office and store fixtures—manufacturing
292 Paving and roofing materials—manufacturing
2921 Paving mixtures and blocks—manufacturing
7391 Penny arcades
394 Pens, pencils, and other office and artists' materials—manufacturing
3940 Pens, pencils, and other office and artists' materials—manufacturing
2844 Perfumes, cosmetics and other toilet preparations—manufacturing
272 Periodicals: publishing, publishing and printing
2720 Periodicals: publishing, publishing and printing
62 Personal services
5192 Petroleum bulk stations and terminals—wholesale
4911 Petroleum pipeline right-of-way
4912 Petroleum pressure control stations
291 Petroleum refining
2910 Petroleum refining
29 Petroleum refining and related industries
2833 Pharmaceutical preparations—manufacturing
2782 Photoengraving
6395 Photofinishing services
356 Photographic equipment and supplies—manufacturing

3560 Photographic equipment and supplies—manufacturing

622 Photographic services (including commercial)

6220 Photographic services (including commercial)

6511 Physicians' services

2135 Pickling fruits and vegetables, vegetable sauces and seasonings, salad dressings—manufacturing

7121 Planetaria

282 Plastics materials and synthetic resins, synthetic rubber, synthetic and other manmade fibers (except glass)—manufacturing

2820 Plastics materials and synthetic resins, synthetic rubber, synthetic and other manmade fibers (except glass)—manufacturing

7423 Playfield or athletic field

7422 Playgrounds

742 Playgrounds and athletic areas

7421 Play lot or tot lot

2395 Pleating, decorative and novelty stitching, and tucking for the trade

5172 Plumbing and heating equipment and supplies—wholesale

6621 Plumbing, heating, and air conditioning services

6721 Police protection and related activities

3254 Porcelain electrical supplies—manufacturing

673 Postal services

6730 Postal services

325 Pottery and related products—manufacturing

5143 Poultry and poultry products—wholesale

2113 Poultry and small game dressing and packing

8223 Poultry hatchery services

2433 Prefabricating wooden buildings and structural members—manufacturing

2142 Preparing feeds for animals and fowls

2646 Pressed and molded pulp goods—manufacturing

6251 Pressing, alteration and garment repair; laundry and dry cleaning pickup services (only)

6812 Primary (elementary) schools

33 Primary metal industries

3334 Primary production of aluminum

3331 Primary smelting and refining of copper

3332 Primary smelting and refining of lead

333 Primary smelting and refining of nonferrous metals

3333 Primary smelting and refining of zinc

2893 Printing ink—manufacturing

27 Printing, publishing, and allied industries

278 Printing trade service industries

6741 Prisons

2294 Processing waste and recovering fibers and flock

5183 Professional equipment and supplies—wholesale

6992 Professional membership organizations

6823 Professional schools

35 Professional, scientific, and controlling instruments; photographic and optical goods; watches and clocks—manufacturing

65 Professional services
672 Protective functions and their related activities
72 Public assembly
723 Public assembly, miscellaneous purposes
253 Public building and related furniture—manufacturing
2530 Public building and related furniture—manufacturing
261 Pulp—manufacturing
2610 Pulp—manufacturing

Q

R

7223 Race tracks
4751 Radio and television broadcasting studios, only (combined systems)
475 Radio and television communication (combined systems)
3435 Radio and television receiving sets (except communication types)—manufacturing
6492 Radio and television repair services
4731 Radio broadcasting studios (only)
473 Radio communication
5731 Radios and televisions—retail
573 Radios, televisions, and music supplies—retail
4732 Radio transmitting stations and towers
4116 Railroad equipment and maintenance
3444 Railroad equipment—manufacturing
41 Railroad, rapid rail transit, and street railway transportation
4111 Railroad right-of-way (excluding switching and marshaling yards)
4112 Railroad switching and marshaling yards
4114 Railroad terminals (freight)
4113 Railroad terminals (passenger)
4115 Railroad terminals (passenger and freight)
411 Railroad transportation
2383 Raincoats and other waterproof outer garments—manufacturing
8191 Range and grassland pastures (not farm or ranch)
4123 Rapid rail transit and street railway equipment maintenance
4122 Rapid rail transit and street railway passenger terminals
4121 Rapid rail transit and street railway right-of-way
412 Rapid rail transit and street railway transportation
6152 Real estate agents, brokers, and management services
615 Real estate and related services
6155 Real estate operative builders
6151 Real estate operators (except developers) and lessors
6154 Real estate subdividing and developing services
313 Reclaiming rubber
3130 Reclaiming rubber
74 Recreational activities
7424 Recreation centers (general)
1253 Rectories
6373 Refrigerated warehousing (except food lockers)
4855 Refuse disposals

4851 Refuse incineration
691 Religious activities
125 Religious quarters
64 Repair services
6391 Research, development, and testing services
123 Residence halls or dormitories
1 Residential
13 Residential hotels
130 Residential hotels
1300 Residential hotels
751 Resorts
75 Resorts and group camps
8 Resource production and extraction
56 Retail trade—apparel and accessories
55 Retail trade—automotive, marine craft, aircraft, and accessories
52 Retail trade—building materials, hardware, and farm equipment
58 Retail trade—eating and drinking
54 Retail trade—food
57 Retail trade—furniture, homefurnishings, and equipment
53 Retail trade—general merchandise
1241 Retirement homes
124 Retirements homes and orphanages
6494 Reupholstery and furniture repair services
2144 Rice milling
7416 Riding stables
931 Rivers, streams, or creeks
9310 Rivers, streams, or creeks
2195 Roasting coffee and coffee products—manufacturing
2382 Robes and dressing gowns—manufacturing
7415 Roller skating
3352 Rolling, drawing, and extruding of aluminum
3351 Rolling, drawing, and extruding of copper
335 Rolling, drawing, and extruding of nonferrous metals
3353 Rolling, drawing, and extruding of nonferrous metals (except copper and aluminum)
6626 Roofing and sheet metal services
121 Rooming and boarding houses
1210 Rooming and boarding houses
31 Rubber and miscellaneous plastic products—manufacturing
312 Rubber footwear—manufacturing
3120 Rubber footwear—manufacturing
6215 Rug cleaning and repair services

S

8543 Sand and gravel—quarrying
6516 Sanitariums, convalescent, and rest home services
4854 Sanitary land fills
2647 Sanitary paper products—manufacturing

2112 Sausages and other prepared meat products—manufacturing
6121 Savings and loan associations
242 Sawmills and planing mills
2421 Sawmills and planing mills, general
5193 Scrap and waste materials—wholesale
3495 Screw machine products and bolts, nuts, screws, rivets, and washers—manufacturing
6813 Secondary schools
334 Secondary smelting and refining of nonferrous metals and alloys
3340 Secondary smelting and refining of nonferrous metals and alloys
5932 Secondhand merchandise—retail
6134 Security and commodity allied services
613 Security and commodity brokers, dealers, exchanges, and services
6133 Security and commodity exchanges
6131 Security brokers, dealers, and flotation services
3428 Service industry machines—manufacturing
6 Services
484 Sewage disposal
4843 Sewage pressure control stations
4842 Sewage sludge drying beds
4841 Sewage treatment plants
8412 Shellfish fisheries
3443 Ship and boat building and repairing
6253 Shoe repair, shoe shining, and hat cleaning services
566 Shoes—retail
5660 Shoes—retail
2196 Shortening, table oils, margarine, and other edible fats and oils—manufacturing
3414 Sighting and fire control equipment—manufacturing
3997 Signs and advertising displays—manufacturing
3914 Silverware and plated ware—manufacturing
7418 Skiing and tobogganing
7514 Ski resorts
3416 Small arms ammunition—manufacturing
3415 Small arms—manufacturing
2841 Soap and detergents (except specialty cleaners)—manufacturing
284 Soap, detergents and cleaning preparations, perfumes, cosmetics, and other toilet preparations—manufacturing
485 Solid waste disposal
2192 Soybean oil milling
662 Special construction trade services
3425 Special industry machinery (except metalworking machinery)—manufacturing
2842 Specialty cleaning, polishing, and sanitation preparations (except soap and detergents)—manufacturing
2429 Special sawmill products manufacturing, NEC
683 Special training and schooling
595 Sporting goods and bicycles—retail

5951 Sporting goods—retail
741 Sports activities
722 Sports assembly
7221 Stadia
5942 Stationery—retail
3315 Steel pipe and tubes—manufacturing
3313 Steel wire drawing and steel nails and spikes—manufacturing
6339 Stenographic services and other duplicating and mailing services, NEC
6372 Stockyards
32 Stone, clay, and glass products—manufacturing
324 Structural clay products—manufacturing
216 Sugar—manufacturing
2160 Sugar—manufacturing
2843 Surface active agents, finishing agents, sulfonated oils and assistants—manufacturing
3541 Surgical and medical instruments and apparatus—manufacturing
354 Surgical, medical, and dental instruments and supplies—manufacturing
743 Swimming areas
7431 Swimming beaches
7432 Swimming pools

T

3413 Tanks and tank components—manufacturing
4291 Taxicab transportation
472 Telegraph communication
4721 Telegraph message centers
4722 Telegraph transmitting and receiving stations (only)
471 Telephone communication
4711 Telephone exchange stations
4712 Telephone relay towers (microwave)
4741 Television broadcasting studios (only)
474 Television communication
4742 Television transmitting stations and relay towers
7413 Tennis courts
2393 Textile bags—manufacturing
22 Textile mill products—manufacturing
8317 Timber and tree products production (mixed uses)
8314 Timber production—mixed uses
8311 Timber production—predominantly for pulp wood
8312 Timber production—predominantly for saw logs
8313 Timber production—predominantly for veneer logs
2296 Tire cord and fabric—manufacturing
311 Tires and inner tubes—manufacturing
552 Tires, batteries, and accessories—retail
5520 Tires, batteries, and accessories—retail
3110 Tires and inner tubes—manufacturing
5113 Tires and tubes—wholesale
6153 Title abstracting services

5194 Tobacco and tobacco products—wholesale
3963 Tobacco (chewing and smoking) and snuff—manufacturing
396 Tobacco—manufacturing
3964 Tobacco stemming and redrying
393 Toys, amusement, sporting, and athletic goods—manufacturing
3930 Toys, amusement, sporting, and athletic goods—manufacturing
5 Trade
6396 Trading stamp services
15 Transient lodgings
4 Transportation, communication, and utilities
5185 Transportation equipment and supplies (except motor vehicles)—wholesale
344 Transportation equipment—manufacturing
492 Transportation services and arrangements
4924 Transportation ticket services
4923 Travel arranging services
8315 Tree products production—predominantly gum extracting (except pine gum) and bark
8316 Tree products production—predominantly pine gum extraction
2781 Typesetting

U

3998 Umbrellas, parasols, and canes—manufacturing
95 Under construction
952 Under construction (nonresidential)
9520 Under construction (nonresidential)
951 Under construction (residential)
9510 Under construction (residential)
91 Undeveloped and unused land area (excluding noncommercial forest development)
910 Undeveloped and unused land area (excluding noncommercial forest development)
9100 Undeveloped and unused land area (excluding noncommercial forest development)
9 Undeveloped land and water areas
6821 Universities and colleges
682 University, college, junior college, and professional school education
6594 Urban planning services
48 Utilities

V

94 Vacant floor area
940 Vacant floor area
9400 Vacant floor area
2193 Vegetable oil milling (except cottonseed and soybean)
2432 Veneer and plywood—manufacturing
2591 Venetian blinds and shades—manufacturing
8221 Veterinarian services

W

X

Y

Z

Appendixes

APPENDIX 1—CODING SYSTEM FOR IDENTIFYING OWNERSHIP

Code	*Category*	*Code*	*Category* [1]
1	Public.	11	Federal.
		12	State.
		13	County.
		14	Township.
		15	Municipal.
		16	Special district.
		19	Other public, NEC.
2	Private.	20	Private.

[1] If it becomes necessary to further subdivide a category into a finer breakdown of ownership, this can be done by adding digits to the right of the present code numbers.

APPENDIX 2—CODING SYSTEM FOR IDENTIFYING FARMS AND FARM USES

A. Description of System

Due to the dichotomy of demands for data concerning agricultural land (i.e., by farms as a total management unit and also by the uses made of the individual areas within a farm or farm uses as they will be referred to), a system was devised to meet both of these demands. In order to accomplish this, however, and still maintain the basic system of land use activity categories, only those categories identifying the types of farms were incorporated at the three- and four-digit levels of generalization. The farm uses, on the other hand, were developed into a special series of codes and they are shown in part B of this appendix.

In order to identify and code the types of farms in an agricultural area, the farm uses on each farm must be inventoried and the predominant use determined in accordance with footnotes 1 and 2 under "Resource production and extraction" (code 8). The criteria set forth in these footnotes indicate that "predominant land area" cannot be determined by field observation alone nor will "predominant land area" measures necessarily identify dairy, livestock, and poultry farms. If these types of farms are to be distinguished, it will be necessary to determine whether the dairy, livestock, or poultry products comprised 50 percent or more of the total farm products sold in the previous year.

Figure 6 is a schematic outline of a farm and an example of how a farm might be described and coded on a field listing form. Columns 6, 7, 6′, and 7′ indicate two ways the same data might be coded depending upon the use to which the data will be put. In columns 6 and 7, both the farm uses and the farm type are coded; in columns 6′ and 7′, only the farm uses are coded.

Figure 6.—An Example of How Farm Types and Farm Uses Can Be Identified and Coded

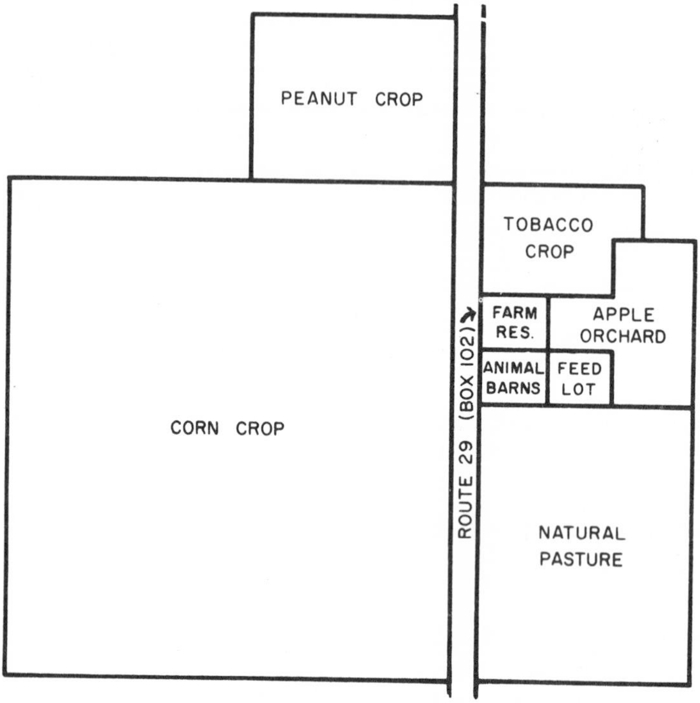

6A.—Outline of Farm

Coding to: ← Farm Types ↓ Farm Uses

FIELD OPERATION					OFFICE OPERATION	
Street No.	Street Name	Description of Activity	Farm Use Description	No. of Acres	Basic Activity Code	Farm Use Code
1	2	3	4	5	6	7
BOX 102	RTE. 29	FARMING	PEANUT CROP	10	—	165
—	—	—	CORN CROP (CASH GRAIN)	75	—	112
—	—	—	TOBACCO CROP	5	—	163
—	—	—	FARM RESIDENCE	1	—	260
—	—	—	APPLE ORCHARD	7	—	191
—	—	—	ANIMAL BARNS	1	—	250
—	—	—	FEED LOT	1	—	240
—	—	—	NATURAL PASTURE	20	—	181
BOX 102	RTE. 29	TOTAL	FARM	120	8120	112

					OFFICE OPERATION	
					Basic Activity Code	Farm Use Code
					6'	7'
					81	165
					81	112
					81	163
					81	260
					81	191
					81	250
					81	240
					81	181
BOX 102	RTE. 29	TOTAL	FARM	120	00	000

6B.—Example of Land Use Entries on a Field Listing Form

B. "Farm Use" Codes

The following is a system of codes to be used to identify the uses made of individual areas within a farm.

Code	*Category* [1]	*Code*	*Category* [2]
11	Grain crops (cash).	111	Barley crop (cash).
		112	Corn crop (cash).
		113	Oats crop (cash).
		114	Rice crop (cash).
		115	Wheat crop (cash).
		119	Other grain crops (cash), NEC.
12	Grain crops (feed).	121	Barley crop (feed).
		122	Corn crop (feed).
		123	Oats crop (feed).
		124	Rice crop (feed).
		125	Wheat crop (feed).
		129	Other grain crops (feed), NEC.
13	Fiber crops.	131	Cotton crop.
		132	Flax crop.
		133	Hemp crop.
		139	Other fiber crops, NEC.
14	Hay and alfalfa crops.	141	Hay crop.
		142	Alfalfa crop.
15	Vegetable crops.	151	Tomato crop.
		152	Strawberry crop.
		153	Celery crop.
		154	Onion crop.
		155	Bean crop.
		156	Carrot crop.
		157	Watermelon crop.
		158	Lettuce crop.
		159	Other vegetable crops, NEC.
16	Other row crops.	161	Sugar beet crop.
		162	Sugar cane crop.
		163	Tobacco crop.
		164	Soybean crop.
		165	Peanut crop.
		169	Other row crops, NEC.
17	Fallow crop land.	170	Fallow crop land.
18	Pasture land.	181	Natural pasture or range.
		182	Rotation pasture or crop land/pasture.
		189	Other pasture land, NEC.
19	Deciduous tree fruit crops.	191	Apple crop.
		192	Peach crop.
		193	Pear crop.
		194	Apricot crop.
		195	Cherry crop.
		196	Plum crop.
		197	Nectarine crop.
		199	Other deciduous tree fruit crops, NEC.

See footnotes at end of table.

Code	*Category* [1]	*Code*	*Category* [2]
20	Citrus tree fruit crops.	201	Orange crop
		202	Lemon crop.
		203	Lime crop.
		204	Grapefruit crop.
		209	Other citrus tree fruit crops, NEC.
21	Tree nut crop.	211	Pecan crop.
		212	Walnut crop.
		213	Filbert crop.
		214	Almond crop.
		219	Other tree nut crops, NEC.
22	Vine crops.	221	Grape crop.
		229	Other vine crops, NEC.
23	Bush fruits.	231	Raspberry crop.
		232	Blackberry crop.
		233	Currant crop.
		239	Other bush fruit crops, NEC.
24	Feed lot area.	240	Feed lot area.
25	Nonresident farm building area.	250	Nonresident farm building area.
26	Farm residence and associated building area.	260	Farm residence and associated building area.
27	Forests.	271	Forests (nongrazing).
		272	Forests (grazing).
28	Idle agricultural land.	280	Idle agricultural land.[3]
99	Other farm uses, NEC.	990	Other farm uses, NEC.

[1] Crop failures would be shown under the crop planted.

[2] If it becomes necessary to further subdivide a category into a finer breakdown of farm uses, this can be done by adding digits to the right of the present code number.

[3] Code 280—"Idle agricultural land" includes land once in agricultural activity and still available for such use, but is presently not being used for any purpose. This includes agricultural land being taken out of production due to Federal agricultural programs.

APPENDIX 3—CODING SYSTEM FOR IDENTIFYING STRUCTURES CONTAINING "HOUSEHOLD UNITS"

Code	*Category*	*Code*	*Category* [1]
1.	Single family structures.[2]	11	Single units—detached.[3]
		12	Single units—semiattached.[4]
		13	Single units—attached row.[5]
2	Two family structures.[6]	21	Two units—side-by-side.
		22	Two units—one above the other.
3	Multifamily structures.[7]	31	Apartments—walk up.
		32	Apartments—elevator.
4	Converted structures.[8]	41	Converted from—detached.
		42	Converted from—semidetached.
		43	Converted from—attached row.

See footnotes at end of table.

Code	Category	Code	Category
5	Mobile homes.	51	Mobile homes—on permanent foundation.
		52	Mobile homes—not on permanent foundation.
9	Nonresidential structures.	90	Nonresidential structures.[9]

[1] If it becomes necessary to further subdivide a category into a finer breakdown of structure type, this can be done by adding digits to the right of the present code number.

[2] Code 1—"Single family structures" include structures containing one "Household unit" in combination with space for business or professional use provided the buildings are primarily for residential use.

[3] Code 11—"Single units—detached" are single "Household units" whose construction is characterized by no common wall or ceiling with any other similar units.

[4] Code 12—"Single units—semiattached" are single or "Household units" whose construction is characterized by a common party wall (ground to roof) with a second "Household unit" on an adjoining lot. Where three or more units are connected in this manner (i.e., a common party wall from ground to roof), the structure is coded 13 (Single units—attached row).

[5] Code 13—"Single units—attached row" are single "Household units" whose construction is characterized by a common party wall (ground to roof) between similar units on one or both adjoining lots. There must be a minimum of three such units connected in series. If there are only two, the units should be coded 12 (Single units—semiattached).

[6] Code 2—"Two family structures" contain two "Household units" which may be one above the other or side-by-side. If built side-by-side, they do not have a common party wall (ground to roof), and they usually have a common attic, basement, heating plant, as well as other common features. This classification includes structures containing two "Household units" in combination with space for business or professional use provided the buildings are primarily residential buildings.

[7] Code 3—"Multifamily structures" contain three or more "Household units" within one structure and are characterized by having a common basement, heating plant, stairs, or entrance. Construction is characterized by both horizontal as well as vertical attachment of "Household units." This classification includes structures containing three or more housing units in combination with space for business or professional use provided the buildings are primarily for residential purposes.

[8] Code 4—"Converted Structures" include structures originally constructed for single family use. They have since been converted for use by two or more families.

[9] Code 90—"Nonresidential structures" include those built and used primarily for nonresidential purposes but may contain one or more "Household units."

U.S. GOVERNMENT PRINTING OFFICE : 1965 O—737–852

APPENDIX J.

Selected Bibliography: Land Use Statistics and Related Information[1]

Bibliographies:

BESTOR, GEORGE C., and JONES, HALWAY R. *City Planning: A Basic Bibliography of Sources and Trends.* Sacramento: California Council of Civil Engineers and Land Surveyors, 1962.

POWERS, WILLIAM F. *Significant Publications on Urban Land, 1958–1963.* Exchange Bibliography 25. Oakland: Council of Planning Libraries, 1963.

U.S. Department of Agriculture, Library and ARS. *Urbanization and Changing Land Uses: A Bibliography of Selected References.* Washington, 1960.

U.S. Department of Commerce, Bureau of the Census. *Bureau of the Census Catalog.* Washington, published quarterly; cumulative index to the annual issue. (Includes an index showing the subjects for which data are published for various kinds of geographic areas—cities, counties, standard metropolitan statistical areas, states, census regions and divisions, and outlying areas of the United States.)

———. *Guide to Census Bureau Statistics—Subjects and Areas.* Washington, 1964.

U.S. Department of the Interior, Bureau of Land Management. *Public Lands Bibliography.* Washington, 1962.

Concepts and Methodology, including Data Processing:

ABRAMS, CHARLES. *Revolution in Land.* New York: Harper and Co., 1939.

American Institute of Planners. "Symbols for Mapping Land Use: A Proposal for Standardization." New England Chapter, March 28, 1960.

AMIDON, ELLIOT L. *A Computer-Oriented System for Assembling and Displaying Land Management Information.* U.S. Forest Service Research Paper PSW-17. Berkeley: Pacific Southwest Forest and Range Experiment Station, 1964.

Baltimore Regional Planning Council (Consultants: ALAN M. VOORHEES and Associates; WILBUR SMITH and Associates). *A Regional Data System.* Technical Report No. 10. Maryland State Planning Department, June 1963.

BLUMENFELD, HANS. "The Conceptual Framework of Land Use." Paper presented to the Canadian Association of Geographers, annual meeting, McMaster University, 1962.

CHAPIN, FRANCIS STUART, JR., and WEISS, SHIRLEY F. *Factors Influencing Land Development: Evaluation of Inputs for a Forecast Model.* Authored in collaboration with THOMAS G. DONNELLY. Chapel Hill: Institute for Research in Social Science,

[1] This list is less complete for the period preceding 1958. Where distinctions such as rural, urban, domestic, foreign, etc., are used, it may be assumed that the treatment is so emphasized.

University of North Carolina in co-operation with Bureau of Public Roads, U.S. Department of Commerce, 1962.
DUKE, RICHARD D. (ed.). *Automatic Data Processing: Its Application to Urban Planning*. East Lansing: Institute for Community Development and Services, Michigan State University, 1961.
Food and Agriculture Organization of the United Nations (FAO). *Census Methodology*. (Vol. 2 of the Report on the 1950 World Census of Agriculture.) Rome: FAO, 1958.
———. *Land Utilization*. Study 3, World Agricultural Structure. Rome: FAO, 1961.
FREEMAN, T. W. *Geography and Planning*. London: University Library, 1958.
GUTTENBERG, ALBERT E. "A Multiple Land Use Classification System," *Journal of the American Institute of Planners*, XXV, 3 (August 1959), 143–50.
HARRIS, B. "Experiments in Projection of Transportation and Land Use," *Traffic Quarterly*, XVI, 2 (April 1962), 305–19.
HEARLE, EDWARD F. R. "A Data Processing System for State and Local Governments," *Public Administration Review*, XXII (September 1962), 146–52.
———, and MASON, RAYMOND J. *A Data Processing System for State and Local Governments*. Englewood Cliffs: The RAND Corporation, Prentice-Hall, Inc., 1963.
ISARD, WALTER. *Methods of Regional Analysis. An Introduction to Regional Science*. Jointly with DAVID F. BRAMHALL, and others. Cambridge: Technology Press, 1960.
LAKSHMANAN, TIRUVARUR R. *An Approach to the Analysis of Interurban Location Applied to the Baltimore Region*. Research Document No. 10. Washington: ALAN M. VOORHEES and Associates, Inc., undated.
MILLER, ROBERT W. "How to Plan and Control with PERT," *Harvard Business Review*, XLI (September-October 1963), 93.
NIEDERCORN, JOHN H. *An Econometric Model of Metropolitan Employment and Population Growth*. Memorandum RM-3758-RC. Santa Monica: The RAND Corporation, October 1963, mimeographed.
SPARKS, ROBERT M. "The Case for a Uniform Land-Use Classification," *Journal of the American Institute of Planners*, XXIV, 3 (1958), 174–78.
Vermont Central Planning Office. *Methods and Procedures for Conducting Multi-Purpose Planning. Surveys Using Electronic Data Processing Techniques*. Montpelier, 1963.
VOORHEES, ALAN M., and Associates, Inc. *Erie Transportation Study—Calibration of Traffic Estimating Model*. Pennsylvania Department of Highways, December 1963.
———. *Manual for Data Inventory*. Baltimore: Prepared for the State Planning Commission, 1962.
WOODBURY, COLEMAN. *A Framework for Urban Studies: An Analysis of Urban-Metropolitan Development and Research Needs*. Report to the Committee on Urban Research, National Research Council, Highway Research Board. Washington, 1959.

Non-governmental Publications, Rural:

ACKERMAN, JOSEPH, CLAWSON, MARION, and HARRIS, MARSHALL (eds.). *Land Economics Research*. Washington: Resources for the Future, Inc., 1962.
ANDERSON, JAMES R. "The Dilemma of Idle Land in Mapping Land Use," *The Professional Geographer*, XIV, 3 (May 1962), 15–18.
———. "Toward More Effective Methods of Obtaining Land Use Data in Geographic Research," *The Professional Geographer*, XIII, 6 (November 1961), 15–18.
BARLOWE, RALEIGH. "What Do We Want of Land?" Governor's Conference on Rural Land Use in an Urban Environment. Amherst: University of Massachusetts, April 19, 1963, mimeographed.
———. *Land Resource Economics: The Political Economy of Rural and Urban Land Resource Use*. Englewood Cliffs: Prentice-Hall, Inc., 1958.

BENEDICT, MURRAY R., CLAWSON, MARION, and others. *Forest Credit in the United States: a Survey of Needs and Facilities.* Washington: Resources for the Future, Inc., 1958.

BERTRAND, ALVIN LEE, and CORTY, FLOYD L. (eds.). *Rural Land Tenure in the United States: A Socio-Economic Approach to Problems, Programs and Trends.* Baton Rouge: Louisiana State University Press, 1962.

BEUSCHER, JACOB H. *Land Use Controls—Cases and Materials.* Madison: College Typing Co., 1962, mimeographed.

CARSTENSEN, VERNON ROSCO. *Farms or Forests: Evolution of a State Land Policy for Northern Wisconsin, 1850–1932.* Madison: College of Agriculture, University of Wisconsin, 1958.

———. "Our Fundamental Cultural Attitudes Toward Land," Governor's Conference on Rural Land Use in an Urban Environment. Amherst: University of Massachusetts, 1963, mimeographed.

——— (ed.). *The Public Lands: Studies in the History of the Public Domain.* Madison: University of Wisconsin Press, 1963.

CLAWSON, MARION. "A Positive Approach to Open Space Preservation," *Journal of the American Institute of Planners,* XXVIII, 2 (May 1962), 124–29.

———. *Land and Water for Recreation: Opportunities, Problems, and Policies.* Chicago: Rand, McNally and Co., Policy Background Series, for Resources for the Future, Inc., 1963.

———. *Land for Americans: Trends, Prospects, and Problems.* Chicago: Rand McNally and Co., Policy Background Series, for Resources for the Future, Inc., 1963.

———. *Uncle Sam's Acres.* New York: Dodd, Mead and Co., 1951.

———, and HELD, R. BURNELL. *The Federal Lands: Their Use and Management.* Baltimore: The Johns Hopkins Press for Resources for the Future, Inc., 1957.

———, HELD, R. BURNELL, and STODDARD, CHARLES H. *Land for the Future.* Baltimore: The Johns Hopkins Press for Resources for the Future, Inc., 1960.

ELY, RICHARD T., and WEHRWEIN, GEORGE S. *Land Economics.* New York: The Macmillan Co., 1940.

FOSTER, JOHN H. "The Process of Land Reallocation among Uses." Governor's Conference on Rural Land Uses in an Urban Environment. Amherst: University of Massachusetts, April 19, 1963, mimeographed.

HALCROW, HAROLD G., ACKERMAN, JOSEPH, HARRIS, MARSHALL, STEWART, CHARLES L., and TIMMONS, JOHN F. *Modern Land Policy.* Urbana: University of Illinois Press, 1960.

HARRISON, ROBERT W. *Alluvial Empire.* Delta Fund in co-operation with ERS-USDA. Little Rock: Pioneer Press, 1961. (*Land Settlement,* by the same author, announced to be published as volume 2, a companion volume to this volume 1.)

Iowa State University, Center for Agricultural and Economic Adjustment. *Dynamics of Land Use—Needed Adjustment.* Ames: Iowa State University Press, 1961.

KRAUSZ, NORMAN C. P., and PINK, FREDERICK G. "Agricultural Assessing Practices: Legislative Action to Control Rural Land Assessments in Areas Subject to Urbanization," *The County Officer,* XXVIII, 4 (April 1963), 151–58.

MANDELKER, DANIEL R. *Green Belts and Urban Growth: English Town and Country Planning.* Madison: University of Wisconsin Press, 1962.

PATTISON, WILLIAM D. *Beginnings of the American Rectangular Land Survey Systems, 1784–1800.* Research Paper 50. Chicago: University of Chicago, Department of Geography, 1957.

PENDLETON, WILLIAM C. *The Value of Highway Accessibility.* Pittsburgh: University of Pittsburgh, 1961, mimeographed.

RENNE, ROLAND R. *Land Economics: Principles, Problems, and Policies in Utilizing Land Resources.* New York: Harper and Bros., 1947.

SALISBURY, JAMES, JR., and SALTER, LEONARD A., JR. "Subsurface Resources and Surface Land Economics," *Journal of Land and Public Utility Economics*, XVII, 3 (August 1941), 271–79; and 4 (November 1941), 385–93.
SIEGEL, SHIRLEY ADELSON. *The Law of Open Space*. New York: Regional Plan Association, 1960.
STOCKER, FREDERICK D. "How Should We Tax Farmland in the Rural-Urban Fringe?" *Proceedings*, 54th Annual Conference on Taxation, sponsored by the National Tax Association, 1961, pp. 464–71.
———. "Recent Developments in Assessment of Farmland for Tax Purposes." Paper prepared for Conference on Inland Empire, Chapter 19, American Right-of-Way Association. Spokane, September 8, 1961, mimeographed.
———. "Some Problems in Assessment of Farmland for Tax Purposes." Paper prepared for Conference of the Washington State Association of Assessors. Spokane, September 12, 1961, mimeographed.
STORIE, RAYMOND EARL. "Real Estate Land Classification in California." Proceedings of the Pacific Scientific Congress, 9 (18), 1957, 37–40.
THORNE, WYNNE (ed.). *Land and Water Use*. Publication 73. Washington: American Association for the Advancement of Science, 1963.
TIMMONS, JOHN F., and MURRAY, WILLIAM G. (eds.). *Land Problems and Policies*. Ames: Iowa State College (now University) Press, 1950.

Non-governmental, Rural (Foreign Countries):

ANTONIETTI, ALESSANDRO, and VANZETTI, CARLO. *Carta della Utilizzazione de Suolo d'Italia*. For Istituto Nazionale dei Economia Agraria, Roma. Feltrinelli Editore. Milano, May 1961.
BEST, ROBIN H. "An Evaluation of British Land-Use Statistics," *The Chartered Surveyor*, XC (June 1958), 660–63. Reprint 119 (New Series). Wye College, University of London.
———. *The Major Land Uses of Great Britain: An Evaluation of the Conflicting Records and Estimates of Land Utilization Since 1900*. Studies in Rural Land Use, Report 4. Wye College, University of London, 1959.
———, and COPPOCK, J. T. *Changing Use of Land in Britain*. London: Faber and Faber, 1962.
DREWES, WOLFRAM U. *The Economic Development of the Western Montana of Central Peru as Related to Transportation: A Comparison of Four Areas of Settlement*. Lima: Peruvian Times, 1958.
KOSTOWSKI, JERZY. *The Aims, Concept and Method of Polish Land Utilization Survey*. Dokumentacya Geograficzna, Zeszyt 3. Instytu Geografii, Polska Akademia Nauk, Warzawa, 1960.
SANDERS, JESSE THOMAS and TIN, U BA. *An Economic Classification of Land in Burma*. Department of Agriculture, Ministry of Agriculture and Forestry, Government of Burma. Rangoon: Thu Dhama Wadi Press, 1952.
STAMP, LAURENCE DUDLEY. *The Land of Britain: Its Use and Misuse*. 3rd ed. London: Longmans, Green and Co., 1962.
——— (ed.). *The Land of Britain: A Report of the Land Utilization Survey of Britain*. London: Geographical Publications, Ltd., 1936.
WIBBERLEY, GERALD PERCY. *Agriculture and Urban Growth: A Study of the Competition for Rural Land*. London: Michael Joseph, 1959.

Non-governmental Publications, Urban:

American Institute of Planners, "Summary of Workshop Proceedings." Conference Workshop 6, Land Use Classification. Washington, November 28, 1961.

———. "Establishing a Standard Land Use Classification System: A Work Program Outline." Arkansas Valley Chapter, Tulsa, Oklahoma, October-November 1961, mimeographed.

———. "Criteria for Development of a Standard Land Use Classification System." Arkansas Valley Chapter, Tulsa, Oklahoma, October-November 1961, mimeographed.

———. "A Proposal for a Standard Land Use Classification System. North Carolina Section, Southeast Chapter, undated.

Automobile Manufacturers Association (Highway Economics Research Committee). *Urban Transportation Issues and Trends.* Material presented to the Subcommittee on Roads, Committee on Public Works, House of Representatives, U.S. Congress, June 26, 1963. Detroit: Automobile Manufacturers Association, 1963.

Bartholomew, Harland. *Urban Land Uses, Amounts of Land Used and Needed for Various Purposes by Typical Cities: an Aid to Scientific Zoning Practice.* Cambridge: Harvard University Press, 1932.

———. *Land Uses in American Cities.* Cambridge: Harvard University Press, 1955.

Bogue, Donald J. *Metropolitan Growth and the Conversion of Land to Non-Agricultural Uses.* Studies in Population Distribution. Oxford, Ohio: Scripps Foundation, 1956.

Boley, Robert E. *Industrial Districts: Principles in Practice.* Technical Bulletin 44. Washington: Urban Land Institute, 1962.

———. *Industrial Districts Restudied: An Analysis of Characteristics.* Technical Bulletin 41. Washington: Urban Land Institute, 1961.

Campbell, Robert Dale, and LeBlanc, Hugh L. *An Information System for Urban Planning.* Urban Planning Data Systems Project. Washington: George Washington University Press, June 1962.

Chapin, Francis Stuart, Jr. *Urban Land Use Planning.* New York: Harper and Co., 1957.

Clawson, Marion. "Suburban Development Districts: A Proposal for Better Urban Growth," *Journal of the American Institute of Planners,* XXVI, 2 (May 1960), 69–83.

———. "Urban Sprawl and Speculation in Suburban Land," *Land Economics,* XXXVIII, 2 (May 1962), 99–111.

Delafons, John. *Land-Use Controls in the United States.* Cambridge: Joint Center for Urban Studies, Massachusetts Institute of Technology and Harvard University, 1962.

Denziger, Burton. "Control of Urban Sprawl, or Securing Open Space: Regulation by Condemnation or by Ordinance," *California Law Review,* L (August 1962), 483–99.

DuBois, Ayers James. *Catalog of Real Estate Appraisal Data Sources.* Washington: Joint Committee on Appraisal and Mortgage Analysis, 1937.

Duncan, Otis Dudley, Scott, William Richard, Lieberson, Stanley, Duncan, Beverly, and Winsborough, Hal H. *Metropolis and Region.* Baltimore: The Johns Hopkins Press for Resources for the Future, Inc., 1960.

Eskew, Garnett Laidlaw. *Of Land and Men: The Birth and Growth of an Idea.* Washington: Urban Land Institute, 1959.

Fagin, Henry, and Weinberg, Robert C. (eds.). *The Suburban Community: Planning and Community Appearance.* Report to Joint Committee on Design Control. New York: Regional Plan Association, 1958.

Fisher, Ernest McKinley. *Urban Real Estate Markets: Characteristics and Financing.* New York: Bureau of Economic Research, 1951.

———, and Fisher, Robert M. *Urban Real Estate.* New York: Holt, 1954.

Gottman, Jean. *Megalopolis: The Urbanized Northeastern Seaboard of the United States.* New York: A Twentieth Century Fund Study, 1961.

GREER, GUY, and HANSON, ALVIN A. *Urban Redevelopment and Housing.* Washington: National Planning Association, 1941.

GUTKIND, ERWIN ANTON. *The Twilight of Cities.* New York: The Free Press of Glencoe, 1962.

HAAR, CHARLES M. *Land-Use Planning: A Casebook on the Use, Misuse and Re-use of Urban Land.* Boston: Little, Brown and Co., 1959.

HARROW, DENNIS. "New Techniques in Shaping Urban Expansion." Planning Advisory Service Information Report 160. Chicago: American Society of Planning Officials, 1963.

Harvard University Law School. "Techniques for Preserving Open Spaces," *Harvard Law Review,* LXXV, 8 (June 1962), 1622–44.

HEARLE, EDWARD F. R., and NIEDERCORN, JOHN H. *The Impact of Urban Renewal on Land-Use.* Memorandum RM-4186-RC. Santa Monica: The RAND Corporation, June 1964.

HERRING, FRANCES W. (ed.). *Regional Parks and Open Space: Selected Conference Papers.* University Extension and the Department of City and Regional Planning on the Berkeley Campus. Berkeley: University of California, 1961.

HIGBEE, EDWARD. *The Squeeze: Cities Without Space.* New York: William Morrow and Co., 1960.

HOOVER, EDGAR MALONE, and VERNON, RAYMOND. *Anatomy of a Metropolis.* Cambridge: Harvard University Press, 1959.

"How to get better land for less, and how to use good land better," *House and Home* (August 1960), entire issue.

HOYT, HOMER. *World Urbanization: Expanding Population in a Shrinking World.* Technical Bulletin 43. Washington: Urban Land Institute, 1962.

———. *The Urban Real Estate Cycle: Performance and Prospects.* Technical Bulletin 38. Washington: Urban Land Institute, 1960.

JACOBS, JANE. *The Death and Life of Great American Cities.* New York: Random House, 1961.

JACOBS, STEPHEN W., and JONES, BARCLAY G. *City Design Through Conservation.* 2 vols. Berkeley: University of California, 1960. (Preliminary draft.)

JAMES, HARLEAN. *Land Planning in the United States for the City, State and Nation.* New York: The Macmillan Co., 1926.

KRASNOWIECKI, JAN Z., and STRONG, ANN LOUISE. "Compensable Regulations: A Means of Controlling Urban Growth through the Retention of Open Space," *Journal of the American Institute of Planners,* XXIX, 2 (May 1963), 87–101.

———, and PAUL, JAMES C. N. "The Preservation of Open Space in Metropolitan Areas," *University of Pennsylvania Law Review,* CX, 2 (December 1961), 179–239. (ANN LOUISE STRONG, member of the Pennsylvania Bar, co-operated with the authors.)

LAIDLAW, CHARLES D. *Readings in Urban Planning Economics.* For use at the Cleveland Electric Illuminating Co. Cleveland, 1955, mimeographed.

LAMONT, I. F. *Land Utilization and Classification in New York, and Its Relation to Roads, Electricity and Reforestation.* Bulletin 372. Ithaca: Cornell University Agricultural Experiment Station, 1937.

"Land Use in an Urban Environment: a General View of Town and Country Planning," *Town Planning Review,* XXXII, 3, 4 (October 1961–January 1962), entire issue.

LANDSBERG, HANS H., FISCHMAN, LEONARD L., and FISHER, JOSEPH L. *Resources in America's Future: Patterns of Requirements and Availabilities, 1960–2000.* Baltimore: The Johns Hopkins Press for Resources for the Future, Inc., 1962.

LESSINGER, JACK. "The Case for Scatteration: Some Reflections on the National Capital Region Plan for the Year 2000," *Journal of the American Institute of Planners,* XXVIII, 3 (August 1962), 159–69.

LOHMANN, KARL BAPTISTE. *Principles of City Planning.* New York: McGraw-Hill, 1931.

LOVELACE, ELDRIDGE, and WEISMANTEL, WILLIAM L. *Density Zoning: Organic Zoning for Planned Residential Developments.* Washington: Urban Land Institute, 1962.

LYNCH, KEVIN. *The Image of the City.* Cambridge: Joint Center for Urban Studies, Technology Press and Harvard University, 1960.

———. *Site Planning.* Cambridge: Joint Center for Urban Studies, Technology Press and Harvard University, 1960.

MARTIN, PRESTON. *Real Estate Principles and Practices.* New York: The Macmillan Co., 1959.

Maryland National Capital Park and Planning Commission. Information Bulletin 2. Washington, 1960.

MCKEEVER, J. ROSS. *Shopping Centers Revisited: Emerging Patterns* (Part 1) and *Practical Experiences* (Part 2). Technical Bulletin 30. Washington: Urban Land Institute, 1957.

MEIER, RICHARD L. *A Communications Theory of Urban Growth.* Cambridge: Joint Center for Urban Studies, Massachusetts Institute of Technology, 1962.

MITCHELL, ROBERT BUCHANAN, and RAPKIN, CHESTER. *Urban Traffic: A Function of Land Use.* New York: Columbia University Press, 1954.

MORTON, JOSEPH EDWARD. *Urban Mortgage Lending: Comparative Markets and Experience.* Princeton: Princeton University Press, 1956.

NELSON, RICHARD L. *The Selection of Retail Locations.* New York: F. W. Dodge Co., 1958.

NORTON, PERRY L. (ed.). *Urban Problems and Techniques.* West Trenton: Chandler-David Publishing Co., 1959.

NIEDERCORN, JOHN H., and HEARLE, EDWARD F. R. *Recent Land Use Trends in Forty-Eight Large American Cities.* Memorandum RM-3664-FF. Santa Monica: The RAND Corporation, June 1963, mimeographed.

OLIEN, C., HALSEY, C., and DONOHUE, G. "Land-Use Intentions and Property Owners in the Rural-Urban Fringe," *Minnesota Farm and Home Science,* XIX, 3 (Spring 1962), 6–7.

PERLOFF, HARVEY S. (ed.). *Planning and the Urban Community.* Pittsburgh: Carnegie Institute of Technology, University of Pittsburgh Press, 1961.

———, DUNN, EDGAR S., JR., LAMPARD, ERIC E., and MUTH, RICHARD F. *Regions, Resources, and Economic Growth.* Baltimore: The Johns Hopkins Press for Resources for the Future, Inc., 1960.

———, and WINGO, LOWDON, JR. "Planning and Development in Metropolitan Affairs," *Journal of the American Institute of Planners,* XXVIII, 2 (May 1962), 67–90.

PICKARD, JEROME PERCIVAL. *Metropolitanization of the United States.* Washington: Urban Land Institute, 1959.

———. *Changing Urban Land Uses as Affected by Taxation.* Washington: Urban Land Institute, 1962.

———, and BALATAM, ARLENE G. *Urban Real Estate Research—1960.* Washington: Urban Land Institute, 1962.

Public Administration Service. *Land Use Classification Manual.* Chicago: The Land Classification Advisory Committee of the Detroit Metropolitan Area, 1962.

RATCLIFF, RICHARD UPDEGRAFF. *Urban Land Economics.* New York: McGraw-Hill, 1949.

RAWSON, MARY. *Property Taxation and Urban Development.* Research Monograph 4. Washington: Urban Land Institute, 1961.

Real Estate Research Corporation. *Recommended Classification of Compatible Business Uses.* Prepared for the Committee on Building and Zoning, City of Chicago, August 25, 1952.

Regional Plan Association. *Metropolis in the Making.* Proceedings of the 25th anniversary of the Association. New York, 1955.

———. *Race for Open Space.* Bulletin 96. New York, 1960.

RODWIN, LLOYD (ed.). *The Future Metropolis.* New York: G. Braziller for the Tamiment Institute, 1961.

SAULNIER, RAYMOND JOSEPH. *Urban Mortgage Lending by Life Insurance Companies.* New York: National Bureau of Economic Research, 1950.

SCHNEIDER, KENNETH R. "Urbanization in the California Desert: Signs of Ultimate Dispersion," *Journal of the American Institute of Planners,* XXVIII, 1 (February 1962), 18–23.

TUCKER, GILBERT MILLIGAN, JR. *The Self-Supporting City,* rev. ed. New York: Robert Schalkenbach Foundation, 1958.

TUNNARD, CHRISTOPHER, and PUSHKAREV, BORIS. *Man-Made America.* New Haven: Yale University Press, 1963.

University of Illinois, College of Fine and Applied Arts, Department of City Planning and Landscape Architecture. *A Procedure for Open Space Planning in an Urban County.* Urbana: University of Illinois, 1962.

UNWIN, SIR RAYMOND. *A Housing Program for the United States: A Report Prepared for the National Association of Housing Officials.* Chicago: Public Administration Service, 1935.

Urban Land Institute. *The Dollars and Cents of Shopping Centers: The Entire Center* (Part 1); *Tenant Characteristics* (Part 2). Washington, 1962.

———. *The Community Builders Handbook.* Executive edition. Washington, 1960.

———. *Home Builders Manual of Land Development,* 2d rev. ed. In co-operation with National Association of Home Builders. Washington, 1958.

———. *New Approaches to Residential Land Development: A Study of Concepts and Innovations.* Washington, 1961.

———. *The New Highways: Challenge to the Metropolis.* Technical Bulletin 31. Washington, 1957.

VERNON, RAYMOND. *The Myth and Reality of Our Urban Problems.* Cambridge: Joint Center for Urban Studies, Massachusetts Institute of Technology and Harvard University, 1962, mimeographed.

WEBBER, MELVIN M. (ed.). *Explorations into Urban Structure.* Philadelphia: University of Pennsylvania Press, 1964.

WEIMER, ARTHUR M., and HOYT, HOMER. *Principles of Real Estate.* New York: The Ronald Press, 1960.

WHYTE, WILLIAM, JR. *Securing Open Space for Urban America: Conservation Easements.* Technical Bulletin 36. Washington: Urban Land Institute, 1959.

WILLHELM, SIDNEY M. *Urban Zoning and Land Use Theory.* New York: Free Press of Glencoe, 1962.

WINGO, LOWDON, JR. *Transportation and Urban Land.* Washington: Resources for the Future, Inc., 1961.

——— (ed.). *Cities and Space: The Future Use of Urban Land.* Baltimore: The Johns Hopkins Press for Resources for the Future, Inc., 1963.

WOOD, ROBERT C. *Metropolis Against Itself.* New York: Committee for Economic Development, 1959.

WOODBURY, COLEMAN (ed.). *The Future of Cities and Urban Redevelopment.* Chicago: University of Chicago Press, 1953.

WURSTER, CATHERINE BAUER. *Housing and the Future of Cities in the San Francisco Bay Area.* Berkeley: Institute of Governmental Studies, University of California, 1963.

ZETTEL, RICHARD M. and CARLL, RICHARD R. *Summary Review of Major Metropolitan Area Transportation Studies in the United States.* Berkeley: Institute of Transportation and Traffic Engineering, 1962.

Non-governmental Publications, Urban (Foreign Countries):

CARVER, HUMPHREY. *Cities in the Suburbs.* Toronto: University of Toronto Press. 1962.

"City Planning in Europe," *Journal of the American Institute of Planners,* XXVIII, 4 (November 1962), 202–92 (several articles).

DREUX, TH. *Le cadastre et l'impot foncier.* Paris: Librairie de renseignement Technique, 1933.

GREBLER, LEO. *Europe's Reborn Cities.* Washington: Urban Land Institute, 1956.

———. "Urban Renewal in European Countries," *Journal of the American Institute of Planners,* XXVIII, 4 (November 1962), 229–38.

HOWARD, EBENEZER. *Garden Cities of Tomorrow.* London: Faber and Faber, 1945. (Originally printed in 1898 under the title, *Tomorrow: A Peaceful Path to Real Reform.* First issued under present title in 1902.)

JAMES, JOHN R. "The Control of Land Use in Britain." Governor's Conference on Rural Land in an Urban Environment. Amherst: University of Massachusetts, 1963, mimeographed.

RODWIN, LLOYD. *The British New Towns Policy: Problems and Implications.* Cambridge: Harvard University Press, 1956.

SELF, PETER. *Cities in Flood.* London: Faber and Faber, 1957.

UNWIN, SIR RAYMOND. *Nothing Gained by Overcrowding.* London: P. S. KING and Son for the Garden Cities and Town Planning Association, 1912.

WINCH, DAVID M. *The Economics of Highway Planning.* Toronto: University of Toronto Press, 1963.

Federal Publications, Rural:

ADAMS, HENRY R. "Land Use Statistics." Washington: U.S. Department of Agriculture, Soil Conservation Service, October 8, 1962.

Advisory Commission on Intergovernmental Relations. *The Role of the States in Strengthening the Property Tax.* Vols. 1 and 2. Washington, 1963.

BEALE, CALVIN L. "Problems of Land-Use Data in Work of the Farm Population Division." Washington: U.S. Department of Agriculture, October 11, 1962.

Geological Surveys prior to 1932:

HASSE, ADELAIDE ROSALIA. *Reports of Explorations Printed in the Documents of the United States Government.* Washington, 1899.

HAYES, CHARLES WILLARD. *The State Geological Surveys of the United States.* Bulletin 465. Washington, 1911.

LEIGHTON, MORRIS MORGAN. *Summary of Information on the State Geological Surveys and the U.S. Geological Survey.* National Research Council, National Academy of Sciences. Bulletin 88. Washington, 1932.

MEISEL, MAX. *A Bibliography of American Natural History: The Pioneer Century, 1769–1865.* 3 vols. Brooklyn: Premier Publishing Co., 1924–29.

MERRILL, GEORGE PERKINS. *Contributions to the History of American State Geological and Natural History Surveys.* Smithsonian Institution. United States National Museum Bulletin 109. Washington, 1920.

SCHMECKEBEIER, LAURENCE FREDERICK. *Catalogue and Index of the Publications of the Hayden, King, Powell and Wheeler Surveys.* Bulletin 222. Washington, 1904.

JOHNSON, HUGH A., CARPENTER, J. RAYMOND, and DILL, HENRY W., JR. *Exurban Development in Selected Areas of the Appalachian Mountains.* Washington: RDED-ERS, U.S. Department of Agriculture, April 1963.

KELLOGG, CHARLES E. *A Method of Rural Land Classification.* Technical Bulletin No. 469. Washington: U.S. Department of Agriculture, 1935.

MARSCHNER, FRANCIS J. *Boundaries and Records in the Territory of Early Settlement from Canada to Florida with Historical Notes on the Cadaster and Its Potential Value in the Area.* Washington: ARS, U.S. Department of Agriculture, 1960.

———. *Land Use and Its Patterns in the United States.* Agriculture Handbook 152. Washington: ARS, U.S. Department of Agriculture, 1959.

National Capital Planning Commission. *Colors and Symbols for Land Use Planning.* Washington: National Capital Regional Planning Council, 1960.

National Research Council, Highway Research Board. *Urban Transportation Planning: Concepts and Application.* Washington: National Academy of Sciences, National Research Council, 1961.

Reports of the National Resources Planning Board and predecessor agencies, 1933–1943 (exclusive of regional and state reports):

Reference List of Publications of National Resources Committee and Its Predecessors: the National Planning Board, the Mississippi Valley Committee, etc. Washington, 1936.

National Planning and Public Works in Relation to Natural Resources and Including Land Use and Water Resources, with Findings and Recommendations. Washington, 1934.

Standards and Specifications for Hydrologic Data. Special Advisory Committee, Water Resources Committee, National Resources Committee. Washington, 1935.

Water Pollution. Water Planning Committee (appended is report of the Special Advisory Committee on Water Pollution). Washington, 1935.

Report on Land Planning to the National Resources Board. Land Planning Committee. Washington, 1934. Eleven supplementary reports, all dated 1935 except I, IV, and XI, as follows:

I. General Conditions and Tendencies Influencing the Nation's Land Requirements, 1936.
II. Agricultural Exports in Relation to Land Policy.
III. Agricultural Land Requirements and Available Resources.
IV. Land Available to Agriculture through Reclamation, 1936.
V. The Problem of Soil Erosion.
VI. Maladjustments in Land Use.
VII. Certain Aspects of Land Problems and Policy.
VIII. Forest Land Resources, Requirements, Problems and Policy.
IX. Planning for Wildlife in the United States.
X. Indian Land Tenure, Economic Status, and Population Trends.
XI. Recreational Use of Land in the United States, 1938.

(Part XI contains also ten appendix units and a large-scale map entitled "Recreational Areas of the United States," dated February 1938.)

Floods in the United States: Magnitude and Frequency. Report prepared in collaboration with the Water Planning Committee of the Natural Resources Board, and its predecessor, the Mississippi Valley Committee. Washington, 1936.

Subject Index of Reports of the National Planning Board, Natural Resources Board, Natural Resources Committee. Stated to be a National Resources Committee publication issued by the National Resources Planning Board. Washington, 1940.

Land Classification in the United States. Report of the Land Committee. Washington, 1941.

National Resources Development Report for 1942. Washington, 1942. (Issued also as H.R. Document 560, 77th Congress, 2d session.)

National Resources Development Report for 1943. Washington, 1943.

Tennessee Valley Authority. *Outdoor Recreation for a Growing Nation: TVA Experience with Man-Made Reservoirs.* Knoxville, 1961.

U.S. Department of Agriculture. *A Century of Service—the First 100 Years of the United States Department of Agriculture.* Washington, 1963.

———. *Agricultural Land Resources: capabilities-uses-conservation needs: a Digest of the National Inventory of Soil and Water Conservation Needs.* Agriculture Information Bulletin 263. Washington, 1962.

———, Conservation Needs Inventory Committee. *Basic Statistics of the National Inventory of Soil and Water Conservation Needs.* Statistical Bulletin 317. Washington: U.S. Government Printing Office, 1962.

———. *The Crop and Livestock Reporting Service of the United States.* Miscellaneous Publication 171. Washington, 1933.

———, Economic Research Service, and U.S. Department of Commerce, Bureau of the Census. *A Graphic Summary of Land Utilization.* Special Report. Washington, 1962.

———, Economic Research Service. "Preferential Assessment of Farmland in the Rural-Urban Fringe of Maryland." (By P. E. House.) Bulletin 8. Washington, June 1961.

———. *Soil Classification: A Comprehensive System. Seventh Approximation.* Washington, 1960.

———, Soil Conservation Service. *Land Capability Classification.* Agriculture Handbook 210. Washington, 1961.

———. Yearbook 1957. *Soil.* Washington: U.S. Government Printing Office, 1957.

———. Yearbook 1958. *Land.* Washington: U.S. Government Printing Office, 1958.

———. Yearbook 1963. *A Place to Live.* Washington: U.S. Government Printing Office, 1963.

U.S. Department of Commerce, Bureau of the Census. *United States Censuses of Population and Housing, 1960: Principal Data-Collecting Forms and Procedures.* Washington, 1961.

U.S. Department of the Interior, Fish and Wildlife Service. *Wetlands of the United States.* Circular 39. Washington, 1956.

Wooten, Hugh H., Gertel, Karl, and Pendleton, William C. *Major Uses of Land and Water in the United States with Special Reference to Agriculture: Summary for 1959.* Agricultural Economics Report 13. Washington: FED-ERS, U.S. Department of Agriculture, 1962.

Federal Publications, Urban:

National Research, Highway Research Board. *Urban Transportation Planning: Concepts and Application.* Washington: National Academy of Sciences—National Research Council, 1961.

National Resources Committee, Reports to or by Urbanism Committee:
Vol. I. *Urban Problems and Techniques.* Washington, 1939 and 1940.
Vol. II. *Urban Planning and Land Problems.* Washington, 1949.

Outdoor Recreation Resources Review Commission. *The Future of Outdoor Recreation in Metropolitan Regions of the United States.* Study Report 21. Washington, 1962. In three volumes:
Vol. I. The National View—Present Condition and Future Prospects of Outdoor Recreation for Residents of the Metropolitan Centers of Atlanta, St. Louis and Chicago.
Vol. II. Outdoor Recreation and the Megalopolis—A Study of Present and Future Needs of the People Living in the New York-New Jersey-Philadelphia Region.
Vol. III. The Impact of the Growth of the Los Angeles Metropolitan Region on

the Demand for Outdoor Recreation Facilities in Southern California—1976 and 2000.

(See also ORRRC Reports 1, 5, 7, 8, 16 and 22.)

United States Congress, House Committee on Banking and Currency. *Urban Mass Transportation Act of 1963.* Hearings on H.R. 3881 (88th Congress, 1st session). Washington, 1963.

———. Report on H.R. 3881. Washington, 1963.

———. Report on S. 6. Washington, 1963.

———, Senate Committee on Commerce. *Urban Mass Transportation, 1963.* Hearings before the Subcommittee on Surface Transportation on S. 807, S. 6 and S. 917 (88th Congress, 1st session). Washington, 1963.

U.S. Department of Commerce, Bureau of the Census. *County and City Data Book, 1962: A Statistical Abstract Supplement.* (87th Congress, 2d session, House Document 465.) Washington, 1962.

———. *1960 Census of Housing.* Vol. III, Series HC (3), City Blocks. Washington, 1960. 421 reports, one report for each city or urban place, generally one report for each city or urban place with a population of 50,000 or more and for 172 additional places that contracted for block statistics.

———. *1960 Census of Population and Housing.* Series PHC (1), Census Tracts. Washington, 1960. 180 reports, one for each of the tracted areas.

———, Office of Area Development. *Future Development of the San Francisco Bay Area, 1960–2020.* Washington, 1959.

U.S. Executive Office of the President. *Standard Industrial Classification Code.* Washington, 1957.

U.S. National Academy of Sciences, National Research Council. *Natural Resources: A Summary Report.* Publication 1000. Washington, 1962.

U.S. Urban Renewal Administration, Housing and Home Finance Agency. *Urban Planning Guide: Policies and Procedures for Federal Assistance under the Urban Planning Program Authorized by Section 701 of the Housing Act of 1954 as Amended.* Washington, 1963, mimeographed.

———. *Urban Planning Assistance Program.* Project Directory. Section 702, Housing Act of 1954. Washington, 1962.

WHYTE, WILLIAM HOLLINGSWORTH. *Open Space Action.* ORRRC Study Report 15. Washington, 1962.

Other Governmental Publications, Urban:

Chicago Area Transportation Study. *Suburban Land Use Survey Manual.* Chicago: Prepared by Robert H. Sharkey, 1958.

———. "The Chicago Area Transportation Study Land Use Inventory: A New Technique and Its Application to Municipal Planning Problems." Chicago, 1959, mimeographed.

CROSSWHITE, WILLIAM M. and VAUGHN, GERALD F. *Land Use in the Rural-Urban Fringe: A Case Study.* (New Castle County, Delaware) Bulletin 340. Agricultural Experiment Station and Division of Urban Affairs. Washington: University of Delaware in co-operation with FED-ERS, U.S. Department of Agriculture, 1962.

Denver City and County Department of Planning. "The Comprehensive Land Use Inventory for Denver, Colorado." Denver, July 13, 1962.

HAMBURG, JOHN R. "Some Typewritten Notes on Land Use Surveys." New York, October 5, 1962.

HARRIS, BRITTON. *Some Problems in the Theory of Intra-Urban Location.* Penn-Jersey Transportation Study. Philadelphia, April 1961, mimeographed.

Los Angeles City Planning Department. "Standard Land Use Classification." Technical Methods Staff, EDP Policy Guidance Committee. Los Angeles, October 1961, mimeographed.

Los Angeles Regional Transportation Study (LARTS). *Instruction Manual, Land Use Summary*. Los Angeles: Division of Highways, Advanced Planning Department, 1960.

———. *Supplement Land Use Summary*. Los Angeles: Division of Highways, Advanced Planning Department, 1962.

Metropolitan Dade County Planning Department. "Existing Land Use Study—Metropolitan Dade County, Florida." Miami, 1961.

Milwaukee Department of City Development, Planning and Programming Division. "Land Use Classification System, 1962." Milwaukee, 1962.

Minneapolis City Planning Commission. "Functional Land Use Classification." Minneapolis, 1961.

———. "Land Use—Code Index of Land Uses." Minneapolis, 1961.

New York State Department of Commerce, Urban Planning Assistance Program. "Planning Consultants' Memorandum 16, Land Use Data and Maps." New York, September 24, 1962.

Penn-Jersey Transportation Study. *Study of Available Land*. Philadelphia, 1962.

Pittsburgh Department of City Planning. *Data Processing and Simulation Techniques*. Pittsburgh, 1962.

———. "Land Use Classification for Pittsburgh's Land Use Survey, 1958–1960." Pittsburgh, 1962, mimeographed.

Pittsburgh Regional Planning Association. "Guide to Methods and Procedures." Six-County Land Use Survey. Pittsburgh, 1962, mimeographed.

Puget Sound Regional Transportation Study. "Land Use Classification." Seattle, 1961.

VAUGHN, GERALD F., and MOORE, EDWARD C. *Idle Land in an Urbanizing Area: The Delaware Experience*. Bulletin 349. Division of Urban Affairs and Agricultural Experiment Station. Washington: University of Delaware in co-operation with RDED-ERS, U.S. Department of Agriculture, July 1963.

Wisconsin State Department of Resource Development. "State Planning Program, State Land Use Analysis Project." Madison, July 24, 1961.

Worcester Planning Department. "The Classification of Land Use." Planning Study 1. Worcester, November 1961, mimeographed.

Other Governmental Publications, Rural and Urban (Foreign Countries):

JACKS, GEORGE V. *Land Classification for Land-Use Planning*. Technical Communication 43. Harpenden, England: Imperial Bureau of Soil Science, 1946.

United Nations, Department of Social Affairs. *Urban Land Problems and Policies*. Housing and Town and Country Planning Bulletin. New York: Columbia University Press, 1953.

———, Economic Commission for Europe. *Urban Renewal Symposium Organized by the Housing Committee of the United Nations Economic Commission for Europe and Held in Geneva, June, 1961*. Report prepared by the Secretariat. Geneva, 1960.

Index

LAND USE INFORMATION:
A Critical Survey of U. S. Statistics
Including Possibilities for Greater Uniformity
by Marion Clawson with Charles L. Stewart

designer: Athena Blackorby
typesetter: Monotype Composition Company, Inc.
typefaces: Bodoni Book and Ultra Bodoni
printer: Universal Lithographers, Inc.
paper: Warren's 1854
binder: Moore & Co., Inc.
cover material: Linetone Bristol Plate Cover